NORWAY

SWEDEN

H

BALTIC
SEA

GERMANY

NETHERLANDS

EUROPE

CROATIA

Ligurian Sea

Adriatic Sea

BLACK
SEA

Corsica

ITALY

Is. Sardinia

Tyrrhenian Sea

Ionian Sea

GREECE

Aegean Sea

TURKEY

Sicily

MALTA

Crete

CYPRUS

MEDITERRANEAN SEA

AFRICA

First published 2003

by **ConchBooks** (formerly Christa Hemmen Verlag),
Mainzer Str. 25, D-55546 Hackenheim, Germany.
e-mail: conchbooks@conchbooks.de
home-page: http://www.conchbooks.de

Bibliographic information published by Die Deutsche Bibliothek
Die Deutsche Bibliothek lists this publication in the Deutsche Nationalbibliografie;
detailed bibliographic data is available in the Internet at http:dnb.ddb.de.

ISBN 3-925919-62-7

Photoworks, Type-setting & Text Editing: Ralf Michael Hennemann
Printing: odd GmbH Grafische Betriebe, D-55543 Bad Kreuznach, Germany
Organisation & Production: **IKAN**-Unterwasserarchiv Frankfurt

Peter Wirtz
&
Helmut Debelius

MEDITERRANEAN AND ATLANTIC INVERTEBRATE GUIDE

Over 1000 photographs
of invertebrate animals
from their natural habitat

ConchBooks

TABLE OF CONTENTS

PICTURE STORIES

INTRODUCTION

Animals range in size from single-celled organisms, less than a tenth of a millimetre long, to 30-m-whales. They are grouped in about 35 so-called "phyla" (Latin, singular: phylum = tribe), that is animals with the same type of basic design (comparable perhaps to groups like bicycles, cars, or trains). The vast majority of these phyla lives in the sea. The multi-celled animals can be divided into three divisions, the Placozoa (tiny plate-like organisms not treated here), the Parazoa (the sponges), and the Eumetazoa (all other phyla). The Eumetazoa clearly consist of two groups, the Coelenterata (sea anemones, jellyfish, and relatives, including the phylum comb jellies) and the Bilateria (all other phyla, showing a clear front and rear end of the body). The relationship of the phyla within the Bilateria is far from clear. While some phyla (such as for instance the Bryozoa, the Phoronida and the Brachiopoda) are obviously related (and indeed are united into a single phylum by some authors), the position of others is still completely enigmatic.

The phylum Chordata contains the subphylum Vertebrata, that is animals with a segmented backbone.

PHOTOS: PETER WIRTZ

As we human beings belong to this tiny group, we have lumped all other groups (the vast majority of the animal kingdom) into the somewhat derogatory term "invertebrates". In German they are even called "Niedere Tiere", which means "Low animals". These lowly creatures should, however, not be underestimated. They show a wealth of stunning capabilities and behaviours long believed to be restricted to vertebrates or even man himself. Here are a few examples.

Many species - like these exceedingly beautiful tunicates from the Cape Verde Islands, for instance - cannot be identified from photographs.

Sponges are the most "primitive" of all multi-cellular animals. As they do not have nerve cells, they were thought to be incapable of sending information from one part of the body to another. However, when a sponge is touched, the filter-feeding cells of its body stop pumping for a short time not only in the area where it has been touched but also in other areas of the body. Canadian scientists have recently shown electrical currents starting at the site of disturbance. Information transfer in nerve cells of "higher" organisms is also accomplished by electrical currents. Even though they do not have eyes, corals can see the moon. The tentacles of the coral polyps are extended only at night. Light-sensitive cells at their tips react to light with the strength of a full moon. Like most birds, the Common Octopus shows what is called "lateral asymmetry in eye use". That is, each individual preferentially uses one eye to look at objects, some individuals preferring to use the left eye, while others mainly use the right eye when regarding, for instance, a shrimp they are going to pounce on. Didemnid sea squirts have evolved an ingenious method for selecting a mate. Sperm enters the body in the water current produced for filter-feeding. Some species can discriminate between incoming sperm cells, either destroying them (especially those from closely related individuals) or allowing them to continue on their way to the eggs inside the sea squirt's body.

Defence against potential predators has lead to astounding adaptations. When smelling that a member of their own species has been broken open by a predator, many sea urchins start to run away with an amazing speed and to form large groups with tightly interlocking spines. The smell of sea stars in the area even causes the Common Mussel to build larger muscles that hold the shell closed: when predators are near, they wisely invest into defence instead of rapid growth!

Because available houses are so rare, many hermit crabs find themselves in houses that are too small to be comfortable. If they encounter a house that is a little bit too large they may have to use it. Thus, there are both crabs with houses too large and crabs with houses too small running around in the same area. Unbelievable as it may sound, many hermit crabs have evolved the behaviour to swap houses. When two animals with ill-fitting houses meet, they enter into a complicated period of what appear to be negotiations and then exchange the shells they occupy.

Here are a few stunning intellectual feats of invertebrates. A Common Octopus that has observed another octopus solving a problem is often able to solve the same problem immediately, without a period of trial and error: it has learned the solution to the problem by observation. A four-month-old Common Octopus in the zoo of Munich, nicknamed Frieda, even learned to open jars of seafood. A zoo attendant said that "All we did was open a jar under water where she could see us". Now Frieda positions her entire body over the lid of the jar and grasps the sides with the suckers on her tentacles; then, with a full body twist, she wrenches the lid off. However, she opens only jars with her favourite snacks of shrimp, crabs and clams, ignoring all others.

The Common Octopus is known to be an intelligent creature but who would have expected intellectual feats of a crab. Males of the Anemone Spider Crab are only about two centimetres long. In the

Never before photographed alive: *Octopus defilippi* at Crete Island, eastern Mediterranean Sea.

Mediterranean Sea, females of this species live close to the stem of a sea anemone, whereas males travel between sea anemones, in the search of females and food. Females of this species become sexually receptive in intervals of about two weeks. When a scientist removed one of the females to an aquarium, the dominant male of that area turned up at her sea anemone the day when the female in the aquarium became sexually receptive. As the female was no longer at her anemone, she cannot have signalled her sexual receptivity by releasing an attractive smell (as do many animals). The male must have been able to predict not only the place but also the time where he would find a sexually receptive female! Apparently the tiny brain of this animal contained a mental map of space and time for the available females in his home range.

Apparently still undescribed: a sea hare (*Aplysia* sp.) from Madeira Island, Atlantic.

This is a guide to the larger marine invertebrates of the Eastern Atlantic (from northern Norway to the Equator) and the Mediterranean Sea. It treats more than 800 common - plus not so common but spectacular - species occurring from the surface down to about 50 m depth. Of many of these species no colour photo has been printed ever before and some of them are still undescribed and hence without a complete scientific name.

To some degree, this book is based on the surveys and fauna lists elaborated by the first author for the Azores, Madeira Islands, the Canary Islands, the Cape Verde Islands, Senegal, Sierra Leone, Cameroon, and São Tomé Island during the last 20 years. Both authors have been exploring many regions of the western and eastern parts of the Mediterranean Sea by SCUBA diving. The "Mediterranean and Atlantic Invertebrate Guide" contains many new records on the distribution of the species. Some western Atlantic species are recorded from the eastern Atlantic for the first time and some species believed to be restricted to the Mediterranean Sea are here recorded from the eastern Atlantic.

A substantial part of this book consists of 25 picture stories which contain information on the fascinating behaviour of marine invertebrate animals, their sensorial abilities and their habitats as well as the influence of Man on the latter. For the species accounts, we have distilled information from several handbooks, such as the "Synopses of the British Fauna" or the "Faune de France", and from many hundreds of scientific publications and publications in the aquarium literature. Throughout the book, we have used as little scientific jargon as possible. In some cases, however, a few technical terms are unavoidable. Large groups were divided into families and the sequence of the families in this book follows (with few exceptions dictated by the layout of the book) the sequence an expert for the group has used in the "European Register of Marine Species" (see Bibliography).

ACKNOWLEDGEMENTS

We could not have written this book without the help of many colleagues who attempted the difficult (and often impossible) task to identify species from underwater photos. Some of these experts even read and corrected the first draft of the chapter on their special group. Many thanks to all of them! They are:
ALAN LOGAN: Brachiopoda. ALAN SOUTHWARD: Balanomorpha. ALEX ROGERS: Echiurida. ANDERS WARÉN: Eulimidae. ANDREW SMITH: Echinoidea. ANGEL VALDEZ: Nudibranchia. ANTÓNIO DOMINGOS ABREU: Mollusca. ANTÓNIO FRIAS MARTINS: Mollusca. ARMIN SVOBODA: Hydrozoa. ARTUR ANKER: Alpheidae. BELLA GALIL: Red Sea immigrants. BERNARD PICTON: Nudibranchia. CARLOS DE LA CUADRA: Bryozoa. CATHERINE McFADDEN: Alcyonaria. CÉDRIC D' UDEKEM D' ACOZ: Decapoda, Amphipoda. CHARLES FRANSEN: Decapoda. CHRISTIAN EMIG: Phoronida. CLAUDE MONNIOT: Ascidia. DANIEL ABED-NAVANDI: thalassinid Decapoda. DENNIS OPRESCO: Antipatharia. DORA JESUS: Holothuroidea. EIJIROH NISHI: Polychaeta. EMILIO ROLAN: Conidae. ENRICO SCHWABE: Polyplacophora. ERLING SVENSEN: animals from Norway. ERWIN KÖHLER: Opisthobranchia. FERDINANDO BOERO: Hydromedusa. FRAN RAMIL: Hydrozoa. FRANCESCO PAGES: "jellyfish". FRANK SWINNEN: Mollusca. FRANZ KRAPP: Pycnogonida. GONÇALO CALADO: Nudibranchia. HALLDIS RINGSVOLD: Asteroidea. HELEN MARTINS: Bivalvia and many others. HELMUTH ZIBROWIUS: coral, polychaetes and many others. JACOBUS DE HARTOG: Cnidaria. JESÚS ORTEA: Nudibranchia. JOSE IGNACIO SAIZ SALINAS: Sipunculida. KARL WITTMANN: Mysidacea. LAURA ENTRAMBASAQUAS MONSELL: Asteroidea. LEEN VAN OFWEGEN: Alcyonaria. LEOPOLDO MORO: Opisthobranchia. LISA ANN GERSHWIN: Ctenophora. LUIS SÁNCHEZ TOCINO: Holothuroidea and Nudibranchia. MICHAEL TÜRKAY: Decapoda. MURINA GALENA-VANTSETTI: Echiurida and Sipunculida. OSCAR OCANA: Actiniaria. PABLO LOPEZ GONZALEZ: Actiniaria and Stolonifera. PAUL HAMILTON: gastropod eye anatomy. PAULO YOUNG: Lepadomorpha. PETER EMSCHERMANN: Kamptozoa. PHYLLIS KNIGHT-JONES: Polychaeta. RAY GIBSON: Nemertini. RICARDO BRUNETTI: Ascidia. ROB VAN SOEST: Porifera and Salpa. SERGIO AVILA: Prosobranchia. STEVEN WEINBERG: Octocorallia. TERRENCE GOSLINER: Opisthobranchia. TRAUDL KRAPP: Amphipoda. VOLKER MISKE: Cephalopoda. VRENI HÄUSER-MANN: Actiniaria. WOLFGANG SEIFARTH: Plathelmintes. XAVIER TOURON: Ascidia.

However, these experts have not seen all the photos and any remaining errors are entirely our own. Your comments and corrections (and records of the species far outside their given ranges) are welcome! Please send them to:
    Dr. Peter Wirtz
    P.O. Box 103
    P - 9125 Canico, Madeira   or per e-mail to
    Portugal   biomar@dragoeiro.uma.pt.

Part of this book was written, and many of the photos were taken while Peter Wirtz was an invited scientist at the Department of Oceanography and Fisheries of the University of the Azores. Many thanks to Ricardo Serrão Santos, Helen Martins, and all the people at the "DOP" for their support!
This book is a contribution from the Centro de Ciências Marinhas (CCMAR) of the University of the Algarve.

Golden Sponge *Aplysina aerophoba*, Madeira >>>

TRULY ACID

Sponges are the oldest living multi-cellular organisms. Fossils show, that they existed as long ago as 550 million years. At a closer glance, however, they are not as simple and "primitive" as one might think.

Sponges do not have muscle or nerve cells. Tiny flagellated cells, the so-called choanocytes, produce a permanent water current running through the body of the sponge. When the sponge is touched, the choanocytes on this spot stop their activity for a few seconds. In some species of sponges, the choanocytes react not only at the stimulated spot but also on other parts of the body. How does the information about the disturbance reach other parts of the

No nerves but quite excitable: the sponge *Aplysina aerophoba*.

body in an animal that has no nerve cells?

Sally Leys and George Mackie from the university of Victoria in Canada were able to measure tiny electrical currents starting at the site of disturbance. Electrical currents also accomplish the information transfer in the nerve cells of higher organisms. Thus, the method of information transfer by electrical currents appears to be older than the invention of nerve cells.

Boring sponges like *Cliona celata* and *Cliona viridis*, which are common in the Mediterranean Sea, can dissolve limestone with acid and in this way slowly bore into the rock. The visible part of these sponges is only "the tip of the iceberg"; the major part of the body of the sponge is inside the rock! This process can go as far as to completely dissolve a limestone boulder, with the sponge finally replacing the rock.

Limestone is comparatively easy to dissolve. Quartz is

The yellow sponge *Cliona celata* is completely hidden inside a rock (which is covered by a red bryozoan or moss animal): only the inhalant and exhalant openings of the sponge are visible.

much more difficult to etch. The only organisms known to be able to dissolve quartz are some species of lichen. Recently, however, Giorgio Bavestrello and his colleagues from the University of Genoa have found a species of sponge that also can dissolve quartz – the kidney sponge *Chondrosia reniformis*, which is common in the eastern Atlantic and the Mediterranean Sea. To etch quartz, the kidney sponge apparently uses ascorbic acid (which is nothing else than vitamin C!). The sponge's ability to etch quartz could be blocked with ascorbatoxydase, an enzyme that oxidises ascorbic acid.

The Kidney Sponge *Chondrosia reniformis* can even dissolve quartz.

Elephant's-hide Sponge
GEODIIDAE

S: to 40 cm. D: Orkney Islands to Spain. G: massive, with symbiotic microalgae (purple-grey), in dark places without (white). Locally common, current exposed rocks, 1-300 m. Below: *Oscarella* sp (Plakinidae), Mediterranean, Azores to Canaries; brown, blue.

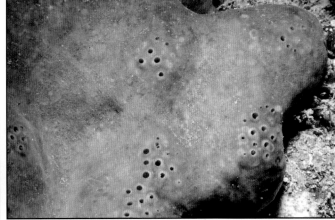

Pachymatisma johnstonia   Isle of Man

Green Boring Sponge
CLIONIDAE

S: to 50 cm. D: Mediterranean, NW-Spain and Azores to Canaries. G: both species slowly dissolve limestone rock by means of acid and occupy the space excavated. Easily told apart by their colour. Below: Yellow Boring Sponge *C. celata*, to 40 cm.

Cliona viridis   Faial Island, Azores

Red Encrusting Sponge
SPIRASTRELLIDAE

Size: colonies usually up to 5 cm in diameter, rarely larger. Distribution: Mediterranean Sea. General: this encrusting species can be locally common. It is very similar to *Crambe crambe* (p. 13). The best way to tell them apart is to touch them: the surface of *Crambe crambe* feels smooth and soft, whereas that of *Spirastrella cunctatrix* feels rough. The crust of this sponge is quite thin, a few millimetres thick at most. *Spirastrella cunctatrix* prefers dark places, such as caves, dark overhangs.

Spirastrella cunctatrix   Crete Island, Greece

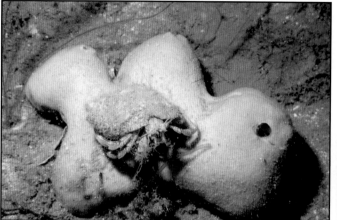

Suberites domuncula   **North Sea**

Hermit Crab Sponge
SUBERITIDAE

S: to 20 cm. D: W-coast of Britain and Ireland south into Mediterranean. G: orange to white, globular or elongated colonies with 1 or few large exhalent openings. Below (North Sea): *S. carnosus* usually has a single large exhalent opening. Contracts to 1/4 size when prodded!

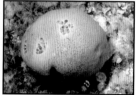

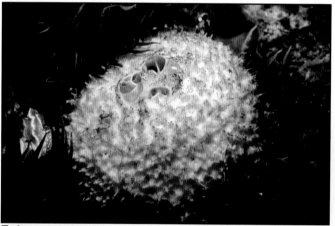

Tethya aurantium   **Bay of Setúbal, Portugal**

Sea Orange
TETHYIDAE

S: to 4 cm. D: Mediterranean and north to west coasts of British Isles. G: form typical, yellow, orange, locally common, 5-900 m. Below: *Polymastia robusta* (Polymastiidae), form typical, also orange, Arctic southwards along the European and North American Atl. coasts, 5-2000 m.

Chondrosia reniformis   **Madeira**

Kidney Sponge
CHONDRILLIDAE

S: up to 5 cm high, up to 10 cm wide. D: Mediterranean; in the E-Atlantic south to at last the Canary Islands. G: both, common and Latin name *(reni-formis* = kidney-shaped) allude to the elongated shape of most colonies. The grey-brown colonies of this species may, however, also have other forms. *Cliona* sponges (see previous page) can dissolve limestone, using acid; *Ch. reniformis* can even dissolve quartz. It then uses the etched particles to incorporate them into its body tissue (see the story "Truly Acid").

Yellow Horn Sponge
AXINELLIDAE

S: up to 40 cm high. D: from Ireland to Madeira; W-Mediterranean. G: this erect, yellow-orange sponge usually grows on upward facing rocks below 20 m, down to about 100 m. Below: *A. verrucosa,* very similar, differing only in fine-structure, to 10 cm, 10-70 m, Mediterranean Sea, French Atlantic coast.

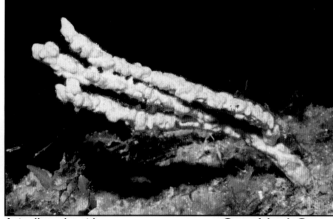

Axinella polypoides   Crete Island, Greece

Brush Sponge
HALICHONDRIIDAE

S: to 4 cm high. D: Med.; Scotland to Madeira, Cape Verdes. G: unmistakable, base often covered by sand or gravel, protrusions white to golden. Below: Breadcrumb Sponge *Halichondria panicea,* very common in 5-500 m in NE-Atlantic.

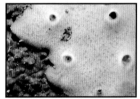

Ciocalypta penicillus   Faial Island, Azores

Common Sponge
CRAMBEIDAE

S: to 1 m², often only a few cm². D: Med.; Azores to Canaries. G: shallow, most common sponge in temperate Atlantic. Forms crusts, often on shells of living *A. noae* (p. 230) and *S. gaederopus* (p. 235). Below: *Iophon hyndmani* (Iophonidae), soft, encrusting, often yellow. Norway into Med.

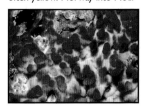

Crambe crambe   Faial Island, Azores

Crater Sponge
HYMEDESMIIDAE

S: several cm². D: Med.; Scotland to Madeira. G: pink, encrusting, unmistakable (numerous small craters on surface). 5-15 m. <u>Below</u>: *Esperiopsis fucorum* (Mycalidae), soft, encrusting, variable, often tasselled, 5-100 m, 15 cm, Faroes and Norway into Med.

Hemimycale columella   Madeira

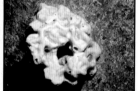

Stony Sponge
PETROSIIDAE

S: colonies to 1+ m², usually smaller. D: Med., temperate E-Atlantic. G: locally common, solid, hard lumps up to 10 cm high, down to about 50 m depth. Purple-brown due to photosynthetic cyano-bacteria. In caves white (below). Preferred food of *Discodoris atromaculata* (p. 221).

Petrosia ficiformis   Madeira

Pink Cylinder Sponge
CHALINIDAE

S: tubes up to 10 cm high, 2 cm wide. D: Med., temperate E-Atlantic. G: pink to purple, soft, encrusting, tends to form tubes. 10-40 m. <u>Below</u>: *H. fistulosa* also forms tubes but is much lighter, less soft, more crumbly in texture. 5-50 m, Britain into Med.

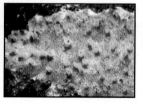

Haliclona mediterranea   Costa del Sol, Spain

Greek Bathing Sponge
SPONGIIDAE

S: up to 35 cm. D: Mediterranean. G: massive, rounded, sold commercially as bathing sponge. Exhalent openings on top of small chimneys. On rocky bottoms, down to 40 m. Once common, now comparatively rare, due to over-collecting.

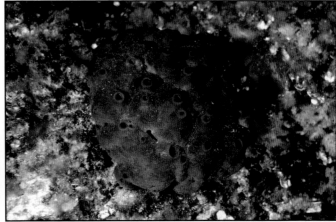

Spongia officinalis   Corsica, France

Rough Horn Sponge
DYSIDEIDAE
S: up to 25 cm. D: Med. and Galicia, NW-Spain. G: very common in W-Mediterranean, often on vertical cliffs, 1-100 m. Pink to violet, with many shallow cone-shaped elevations. Below: *Ircinia fasciculata* (Irciniidae; Lanzarote), locally common, 70 cm, Med., Galicia to Canary Islands.

Dysidea avara   Crete Island, Greece

Leathery Horn Sponge
IRCINIIDAE
S: up to more than 50 cm (but usually less). D: Mediterranean; from Galicia to West Africa. G: massive, red-brown to black. Exhalent openings sometimes with raised transparent rim. 5-400 m. Below: *S. foetidus,* similar but has smaller openings without raised rims. Mediterr., locally common.

Sarcotragus muscarum   Crete Island, Greece

Aplysina aerophoba **Croatia, Adriatic Sea**

Golden Sponge
APLYSINIDAE

S: tubes up to 4 cm high and 2.5 cm in diameter; colonies can be more than 1 m in diameter. D: Mediterranean; in the E-Atlantic from Spain and the Azores south to at least the Canary Islands. G: this unmistakable species can be quite common on rocky shores, from 0.5-20 m depth. The name *aerophoba* comes from the Greek and literally means "afraid of the air": the sponge turns blue-black when exposed to air, staining one's fingers. The Golden Sponge Snail *Tylodina perversa* (p. 195) feeds on this sponge and deposits its eggs on it.

Clathrina clathrus **Banyuls, French Mediterranean**

Network Sponge
CLATHRINIDAE

S: 10 cm. D: Med.; British Isles to Canaries. G: soft, forms an irregular mass of yellow or white branching and re-uniting tubes. Hangs from rock in dark places, 5-50 m. Below: *C. coriacea*, 3 cm, white cushions of tightly knit trelliswork of 1 mm wide tubes. E-Atlantic, Arctic to South Africa.

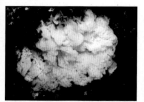

Small Calcareous Cup Sponge   SYCETTIDAE

S: up to 3, max 9 cm. D: Arctic to Gibraltar. G: young roundish, later elongated. Tubular body with fringe of spicules. Often in groups, 5-40 m. *S. raphanus*, more globular, smaller, Med. Below: *Clathrina cerebrum*, white, yellow or red mass of interwoven tubes. Med., France to Madeira (photo).

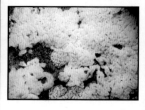

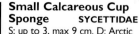

Sycon ciliatum **Faial Island, Azores**

Sponges also thrive in lightless caves, Croatia >>>

Root-arm Medusa
CLADONEMATIDAE

S: medusa 7 mm. D: French Atlantic; Med. G: in hydrozoans, a
sessile polyp stage and a free
swimming medusa alternate: the
medusa produces sex cells, from
which polyps grow, which build
small medusae. This one can
crawl with its tentacles. <u>Below</u>:
polyps, one producing a medusa.

Cladonema radiatum   **Netherlands, North Sea**

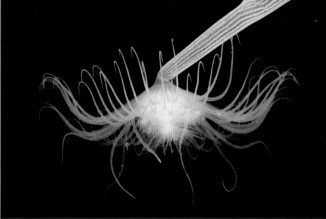

Corymorpha nutans   **Croatia, Adriatic Sea**

Solitary Bell Hydroid
CORYMORPHIDAE

S: up to 10 cm high. D: from N-
Norway to the Mediterranean;
Red Sea. G: most hydroids form
colonies. This one is a solitary
species and a giant one on top
of it. It lives on silty or sandy or
gravely bottoms to about 100 m
depth and is quite common in
the Black Sea. The head, on top
of a long upright stalk and with
a whorl of c. 32 large tentacles,
is usually bent forward or even
downward (photo turned 90 °).
Observations at Rovinj (Adriatic
Sea) have shown that, despite its
large size, the polyp stage lives
only a few months, producing
medusae throughout this time.

Halocordyle disticha   **Madeira**

Sea-nettle
PENNARIIDAE

Size: up to 20 cm high.
Distribution: a circum-global
species in (sub)tropical waters
including the southern
Mediterranean Sea.
General: the small white bushes of this species sting fiercely,
thus its common name "Sea-
nettle". It lives from the water-
line down to at least 40 m
depth. The nudibranchs *Flabellina affinis* (see page 208) and
Phydania lynceus feed on the
polyps of this species.

PORPITIDAE

S: 2 cm. D: warm waters of all oceans. G: float of chitinous air-filled rings, edge with tentacles capturing plankton. Below: By-the-wind Sailor, *Velella velella*. Stiff jelly-like oval disk (4-8 cm) with distinctive sail. Drifts on surface, temperate waters of all oceans. Both contain symbiotic algae.

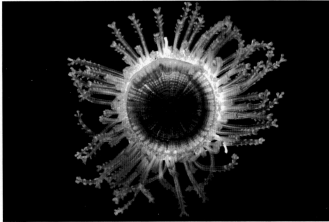

Porpita porpita   Tenerife, Canary Islands

SPHAEROCORYNIDAE

S: up to 8 mm high. D: Madeira; W-Atlantic: Caribbean to Bermudas; Red Sea; Indo-Pacific. G: author PW found this sp in Madeira, on the sponge *Petrosia ficiformis* (p. 14), in 5-10 m. First record of the species in E-Atlantic. It is, however, unlikely that it only occurs at Madeira in the E-Atlantic. Due to its small size, it has probably been overlooked in places like the Canary or Cape Verde Islands or in the Gulf of Guinea. Most so-called "amphi-atlantic" spp (i.e. occurring on both sides of the Atlantic) have their centre of distribution in the tropics.

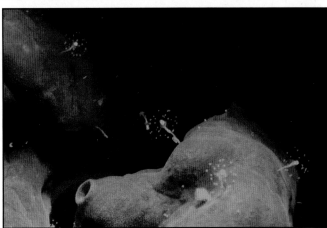

Sphaerocoryne bedoti   Madeira

Oaten Pipes Hydroid
TUBULARIIDAE

S: 15, max 40 cm. D: S-Norway, North Sea. G: in clumps of unbranched stems, 5-280 m. Each stem bears a pink polyp with a fringe of white tentacles. Below: Flower-head, *T. crocea*, similar, warm waters, all oceans, 0-30 m. E-Atl.: northern limit at Madeira.

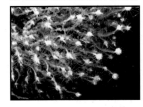

Tubularia indivisa   Isle of Man

Golden Sea Fern
AGLAOPHENIIDAE
(this page)

S: 15 cm. D: Ireland to Senegal; W-Med. G: unmistakable, with typical feather shape of all family members. The feathers of the colony, which end in a triangular tip, stand in parallel. No medusa. Prefers moderately protected areas, 10-40 m. <u>Below</u>: *Aglaophenia* "sea ferns," viz *A. pluma,* very common in NE-Atlantic and Med., and, below it, *A. octodonta.*

Gymnangium montagui   **Southwestern Ireland**

Stinging Bush Hydroid

Size: bushes up to 40 cm high. Distribution: all around the globe in tropical waters. General: this strongly stinging species forms large bushes, from 2 m depth down to at least 35 m. Like many other tropical species, it apparently reaches its northern limit in the eastern Atlantic at Madeira. A number of crustacean species lives on it but they are difficult to detect because they are transparent, e.g. *Pseudoprotella phasma* (p. 113).

<u>Below</u>: *A. tubulifera* prefers dark places and greater depths and can only rarely be found as shallow as 40 m, from Great Britain to the Cape Verde Islands.

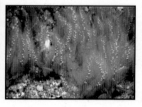

Macrorhynchia philippina   **Madeira**

Herring-bone Hydroid
HALECIIDAE

S: 25 cm. D: Med.; Norway to South Africa. G: stiff, feather-shaped, 10-1300 m. *Doto* spp (p. 201) eat the polyps. <u>Below</u>: *Antenella secundaria* (Halopteriidae) forms thin, yellow-green threads between an *Obelia* hydroid. Cosmopolitan in warm seas, 5-60 m.

Halecium halecinum   North Sea

Ribbon Hydrozoan
PLUMULARIIDAE

S: up to 20 cm high. D: Iceland and Norway to West Africa; W-Med. G: the rather strong central stem of this species divides irregularly. Prefers dark places, greater depths, rarely shallower than 20 m. <u>Below</u>: Sea Beard, *N. antennina,* clusters of up to 50 stiff, unbranched stems, 25 cm.

Nemertesia ramosa   Faial Island, Azores

Clarke's Hydrozoan
PLUMULARIIDAE

S: 10 cm. D: both sides of tropical Atlantic. G: unmistakable, black, very common in shallow water (Cape Verdes) and usually harbours many caprellid amphipods (p. 113). Mildly stings soft skin. <u>Below</u>: *Eudendrium racemosum* (Eudendriidae), common in Med. and NE-Atlantic, 5-200 m.

Nematophorus clarkei   Cape Verde Islands

Hermit Crab Hydroid
HYDRACTINIDAE

S: polyps 8-13 mm high. D: Arctic to Morocco. G: 1-30 m., in white to pink mats on rocks and the shell of hermit crabs, here *Pagurus bernhardus*. Predators (crabs, octopus) are repelled by the stings. The hermit protects the hydrozoans against sea stars and *H. carunculata* (see "Fire!"). Lower small photo: close-up. Upper: an undescribed *Podocoryne* species.

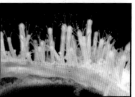

Hydractina echinata   **Baltic Sea**

Branching Fire Coral
FIRE CORALS, MILLEPORIDAE

S: up to 45 cm high. D: Cape Verde Islands, Gulf of Guinea; tropical W-Atlantic. G: not a true coral, the polyps that build the hard calcareous skeleton are formed quite differently. Looking closely, one can see them like a small pelt over the hard surface (small photo). These polyps sting fiercely (name). The polyps produce tiny medusae. Many different growth forms, from cylindrical branches to flat slabs to encrusting areas over rock and other structures. Only genus member in E-Atlantic, if it is hard and greenish-yellow and burns like hell it is the one. Shallow to 20 m. See photo of *C. tubularis* (p. 138) for an encrusting form.

Millepora alcicornis   **Cape Verde Islands**

Olindias-Medusa
OLINDIASIDAE

Size: about 2.5 cm in diameter.
Distribution: north-eastern
Atlantic
General: another beautiful little hydromedusa. This one has
60 to 80 rather long tentacles.
The four radiary channels are
clearly visible. Below them, the
gonads form yellow, folded
bands from the centre to the
margin of the bell. It is typical
for the species that it clings to
vegetation, trailing the tentacles into the water.

While *Gonionemus vertens*
lives only in the Atlantic, a
similar species, *G. vindobonensis*,
can be found in the Mediter-

Gonionemus vertens   Norway

Green Polyp
CAMPANULARIIDAE

S: up to I cm. D: cosmopolitan.
Madeira: first record. G: one of
the most common hydrozoans
in the NE-Atlantic. On plants
(photo: on the sea grass *Cymodocea nodosa*), 5-30 m. Below
(Norway): *Obelia geniculata*,
stems with typical zig-zag appearance. See also next section.

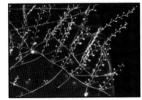

Clytia hemisphaerica   Madeira

Bell Hydroid
CAMPANULARIIDAE

S: 3 cm. D: Norway into Med.
G: On the flat fronds of large
brown algae *(Fucus)*, very common, abundant. The stems (small
photo above) grow from a network of root-like "stolons". Up
to 20 polyps per stem. Below:
the tiny medusae of this species.

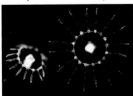

Obelia geniculata   Southwestern Ireland

AURELIA

The fragile nature of the adults and the small size and hidden lifestyle of their several developmental stages, make jellyfish difficult subjects for observation in the field. In order to photograph details of their life cycle and to realise long-term observations, Robert Brons, a well-known Dutch expert for breeding marine animals of all kinds, used a very simple method to culture the polyp stages and medusae.

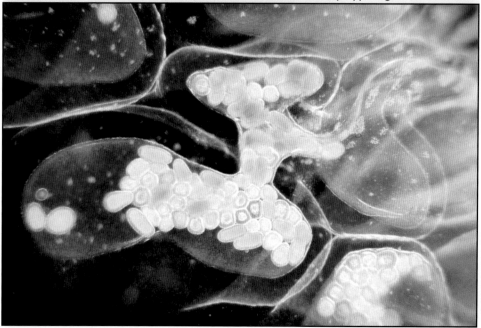

Brood-pouches of *Aurelia aurita,* filled with "planula" larvae.

Here we will discuss "a simplified but effective husbandry" of the Moon Jellyfish *Aurelia aurita*. This species is not only found in the area covered by this book but also in most tropical waters. This jellyfish species is spectacular, easy to obtain and not too difficult to maintain in captivity.

Aurelia is the easiest to collect in temperate climates such as in the North Sea and therefore it is required that we set up a cool water tank (maximum temperature 12°C) for the polyps as well as the jellyfish. For my own photographic purposes, I limited my experiments to the winter months and simply kept the tank in an unheated room. However, if the animals have to be maintained into the summer, water refrigeration is obviously required.

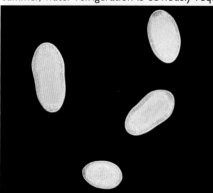

"Planula" larvae of *Aurelia aurita.*

The culture tank for the polyps can be kept very simple: 100 litres volume is quite sufficient, a medium circulation is required and lighting and filtration are not necessary: periodic partial water changes are sufficient. The polyps can be collected from the sea in two ways. First by gathering "live rocks", oyster shells etc. at low tide. We must, however, make sure it is material that has been under water all the time. These substrates are brought into the aquarium and after feeding *Artemia* nauplii we will usually find the white polyps of *Aurelia* after a couple of days along with a rich collection of other organisms. This method has the advantage that it can be done during the winter, so that the tank does not have to be cooled. Disadvantage is that we obtain a mix of many marine organisms, which can, however, also be seen as an advantage to the broadly interested marine naturalist.

The second method involves catching several live adult *Aurelia* in the sea, hold them firmly by their umbrellas, and shake them vigorously inside a bucket of seawater. We repeat this procedure with several individuals. What we are actually doing is collecting "planula" larvae from adult female *Aurelia*. This species is a "brooder": oocytes (egg cells) are fertilised while in specialised brood pouches of the female and develop there to "planula" larvae. Females can be recognised by the brownish coloration of the oral tentacles, which is the colour of the filled brood pouches.

At home the bucket with collected larvae is emptied into the aquarium, where eventually the "planula" larvae will settle down and develop into polyps. Obviously, some rocks should be provided as substrate for settle-

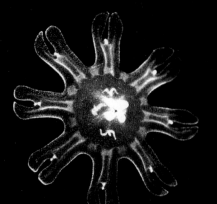

Release of a free swimming "ephyra" from the strobilating polyp at the left in the group.

One-day-old "ephyra".

ment: This method has the advantage that we are more certain we will have *Aurelia* polyps and that we will have "a clean culture" without many other organisms. The disadvantage is that the best chance of finding ripe jellyfish females is in the spring or summer, so that the aquarium has to be cooled.

The water temperature should preferably stay below 12°C and to stimulate the polyps to produce jelly-fishes, even colder temperatures of 4-5°C. are required. After feeding *Artemia*, the polyps grow fast and develop into colonies. By lowering the temperature to about 4°C for a couple of days we simulate winter conditions. Then the temperature is

A 21-day-old medusa.

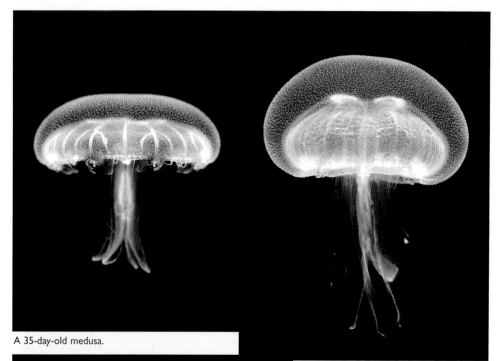

A 35-day-old medusa.

A 50-day-old medusa.

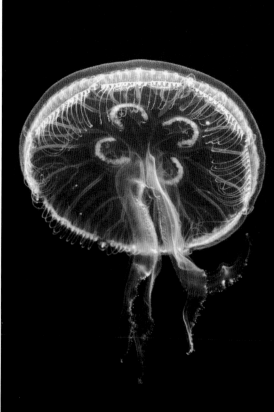

Transparent beauty: an almost adult Moon Jellyfish *Aurelia aurita*.

raised to about 8°C. Usually within several days changes in certain polyps can be observed: they divide up into a stack of thin little disks in a process called strobilation. Every disk becomes a young jellyfish called "ephyra". As soon as these are seen swimming free, they are collected from the polyp tank by siphoning and brought into a separate small aquarium of about 50 litres that is aerated through an open tube. The polyps are easy to maintain during longer periods and the strobilation procedure may be repeated, so that new material can be made available, should the jellyfish culture not succeed at first trial.

Now the "ephyrae" are offered *Artemia* nauplii, which remains the food source of choice throughout their development. Although still lacking tentacles, they are able to feed as soon as they are released from the polyp. Through daily feedings the "ephyrae" grow steadily and from rather flat creatures, they gradually develop the characteristic umbrella shape, grow tentacles and attain the typical jellyfish swimming mode.

Maintaining these rarely encountered invertebrates at home is an adventure and a challenge for the interested and creative aquarist. That it can be a low-cost enterprise is all the more reason to pursue the study of this highly fascinating animal group.

Moon Jelly *Aurelia aurita*, Aegean Sea, Greece >>>

Sea Nettle, Compass Jelly   PELAGIIDAE

S: up to 20 cm in diameter. D: Atlantic and Mediterranean.
G: bell with 16 V-shaped marks clearly visible in the small photo (Helgoland), less so in the large photo (young animal). The tentacles may be up to 2 m long. The large veils originating from the mouth also capture prey. The species is a sex-changer: juvenile animals first become males and only later in live turn female. Contact with this jellyfish causes a severely burning sensation. The poison injected by the stinging cells on the tentacles and veil is a complex mixture of toxic proteins. See _Pelagia noctiluca_ for the **treatment of stings** by all jellyfish.

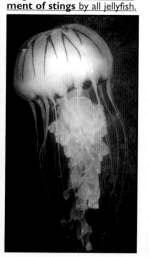

Chrysaora hysoscella   **Netherlands, North Sea**

Moon Jelly
ULMARIIDAE

S: up to 30, max 45 cm in diameter. D: All oceans (70°N-70°S).
G: bell flat, with numerous tentacles (10 cm). Four horseshoe- or ring-shaped white to pink reproductive organs distinctive. Females with brood pouches. First planktonic larva: planula; the 2nd (ephyra, see the story "Aurelia"), is causing great damage to salmon farmers: the tiny larvae sting the fish in the gills and may cause suffocation. However, the stinging cells do not penetrate human skin. Captures most of its plankton prey on body surface, transported to the mouth by ciliated cells.

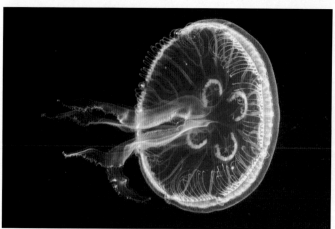

Aurelia aurita   **Netherlands, North Sea**

Luminescent Jelly
PELAGIIDAE
S: bell to 0.6, tentacles to 4 m.
D: Med., Atl. G: very common
in temperate waters, seasonally
very abundant. Strongly luminescent, visible only at night and
when disturbed. Often accompanied by juvenile jacks (family Carangidae; <u>small photo</u>: *Trachurus
picturatus*) which seek protection
but are not immune. Amphipods
can live on the bell (<u>large photo</u>).
<u>Severely stinging</u>, **treatment:** if
tentacle remnants adhere to the
skin throw sand on them and
scrape them off carefully without
rubbing them in. Do NOT apply
acid liquids (vinegar, lemon juice)
as this causes the discharge of
stings. Wash with sea- or freshwater. Apply skin ointment (anti-
histamines, cortico-steroids have
no beneficial effects). It will continue to hurt (up to several days,
in the case of *Pelagia*). The damage is done and you now have
to sit it out. Medical treatment
becomes necessary only if there
are reactions such as nausea or
circulatory problems. Healing of
skin slow, dark scars may result.

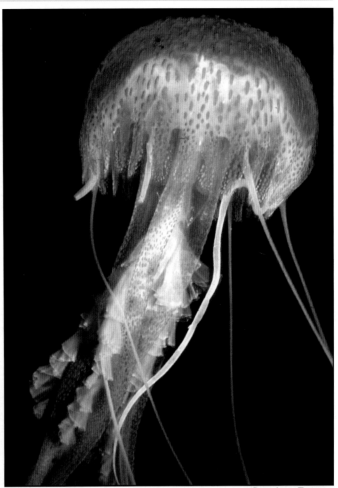

Pelagia noctiluca   Corsica, France

Atlantic Cauliflower Jelly
S: up to 50 cm in diameter. D:
estuary of the river Tejo, near
Lisbon, and from there southwards along the African coast.
G: name derived from the old
Latin name of the river Tejo,
Tagus. Common in its estuary
and along the Portuguese coast
south of Lisbon. Closely related to *R. pulmo* (next page).
The 8 arms are fused to form
a massive cauliflower-like structure. Water is pumped through
it and plankton captured there.
Incapable of eating prey larger
than a few mm. As in *R. pulmo*,
the "jelly" forming the bell and
the arms is much more solid
than in other jellyfish.

Catostylus tagi   Bay of Setúbal, Portugal

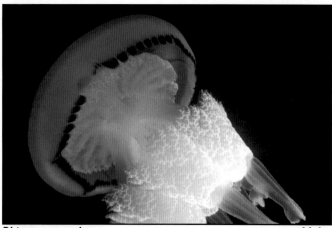

Rhizostoma pulmo   **Malta**

Lung Jelly
RHIZOSTOMATIDAE
S: up to 60 (max. 100) cm diameter. D: Med., Atl. G: largest jelly in Med. No tentacles, eight strong arms project from mouth, united in the upper region, forming a cauliflower-like structure in the middle. Bell milky white to yellow or pink, rim often blue. Feeds on plankton. Stinging cells do not penetrate human skin. Frequently accompanied by juvenile fish *(Trachurus, Boops, Seriola)*. According to some, they feed on items captured by the jellyfish or even on the jelly itself, according to others, they pick parasites off it. Probably both is true. *R. octopus* (N-Atlantic) is a synonym.

Cyanea capillata   **Lofoten Islands, Norway**

Giant Lion's Mane
CYANEIDAE
S: largest jellyfish of the world! May grow to 2.3 m diameter in continuous arctic daylight. D: circumpolar; in N-Atlantic south to Gulf of Biscay. G: fairly common in N-Europe. About 100 thin, hair-like tentacles (name), up to 30 m long! Severely stinging. Lower edge of bell divided into 8 lobes. Milky-yellow to brown. Feeds on any animal it can capture, incl. other jellies. Its ephyra larva is causing great damage to Norwegian and Scottish salmon farmers (see *A. aurita*). Its thin tentacles easily break apart and then can flow into the fish cages and damage the salmon.

Cyanea lamarcki   **Outer Hebrides, Scotland**

Dwarf Lion's Mane
CYANEIDAE
S: up to 30 cm in diameter. D: northern Atlantic (south to the Gulf of Biscay); N-Pacific. G: this species is very similar to the Giant Lion's Mane, *C. capillata*. It does, however, not grow to such a large size. It has a purple-blue umbrella instead of a yellow-brown one. If you should come into close contact with it as a swimmer you may be grateful about another difference between the two species: the sting of *C. lamarcki* is nowhere near as painful as that of *C. capillata*. Like its larger sister, *C. lamarcki* feeds on any animal it can capture.

Fried Egg Jelly
CEPHEIDAE

S: to 15, max 25 cm in diameter. D: Med.; temperate E-Atlantic; Red Sea. G: unmistakable due to colour, peculiar shape. Most colourful European jelly. Seasonally in great numbers (E-Med.); then a nuisance to swimmers, even though its sting is very mild. No tentacles like in the related *R. pulmo* and *C. tagi*. The oral arms divide many times and end with a conspicuous tip that often is blue (below, close-up). Symbiotic unicellular algae live in the oral arms and the products of their photosynthetic activity benefit the jellyfish, which otherwise is a plankton feeder. Often accompanied by juvenile fish (*Trachurus*, Carangidae) seeking protection.

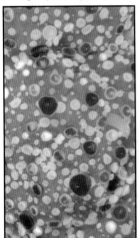

Cotylorhiza tuberculata
Ionian Sea

Crown Polyp

S: up to 7 cm long. D: Spitsbergen and Greenland to Great Britain. G: a strange creature! Most people would not suspect that the order Stauromedusae belongs to the jellyfish. Imagine a jellyfish that attaches itself to the bottom with the top of its bell; then draw out the bell to a long stalk and divide the edge of the bell into several arms and there you have it: a stauromedusa. The bell of *L. quadricornis* has 4 sides, 2 small arms arise at each corner which each bear 100+ small tentacles. From shallow water down to 80 m depth. Captures small animals, for instance small snails crawling by.

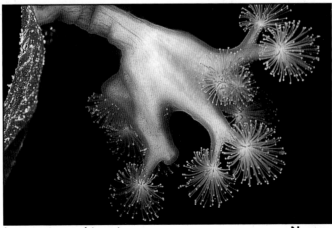

Lucernaria quadricornis
Norway

Portuguese Man-of-war

S: 30 cm (gas float), 50 m (tentacles). D: Atlantic; occasionally in W-Med. Also Indo-Pacific (as *P. utriculus*). G: Siphonophora are floating colonies of polyps with quite different shapes and functions. Some polyps catch prey, some build the float, some build other body structures. *Physalia* is the only siphonophore with a gas float that drifts on the surface of the sea. The bluish float is the source of many tentacles that can trail up to 50 m (!) behind the float. While some fish, e.g. *Schedophilus medusophagus* (photo), associate with the Portuguese Man-of-war, swimmers and divers should keep a large distance. The sting of the tentacles is so painful that it has caused heart attacks in some people. The normal function of the poison is to stun and kill the prey, fish or pelagic crustaceans. Below (Cape Verdes): some animals trapped in a tide pool.

Main predators are loggerhead turtles *(Caretta caretta)* and the small opisthobranch *Glaucus atlanticus* (p. 209).

Physalia physalis   **Faial Island, Azores**

Pearl-chain Jelly

S: to 30 m. D: Med.; E-Atlantic: Norway to South Africa; Indian and Pacific Ocean. G: the long colonies of this species have a tendency to break up into smaller sections (2-8 m). They are drifting in the open sea, usually in the upper 100 m, also down to 800 m. When disturbed the colony can contract considerably. It consists of a mixture of individuals providing buoyancy, catching prey, feeding, and reproducing. An opportunistic predator snagging any prey it can get (salp, jellyfish, krill, other crustaceans, fish). Stings strongly, penetrates the skin in the palm of a hand.

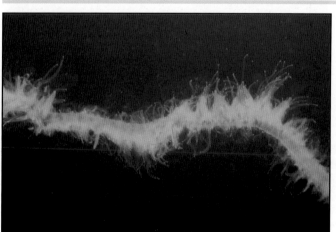

Apolemia uvaria   **Faial Island, Azores**

Bell Siphonophore

S: up to 5 cm. D: temperate and tropical waters of all oceans, incl. Mediterranean. G: two bells form upper part of body (large photo). From them trails a very long, thin stem with numerous polyps extending a "fishing line" into the water (small photo). This deadly curtain catches small pelagic animals.

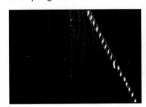

Diphyes dispar   **Gran Canaria, Canary Islands**

Bubble Jelly

S: up to 5 cm high. D: worldwide in all seas, except polar waters. G: the composite structure of siphonophores is very evident in this species. A small "pneumatophore" at the top keeps the animal in an upright position. The large reddish "palpons" protect the reproductive elements in the centre of the colony. Small tentacles (contracted in the animal photographed) trail behind to capture plankton.

The small photo shows a young individual of the Red-spotted Siphonophore, *Forskalia edwardsi* from the Azores. There are four closely reated species in this genus which cannot be identified from photos. The cone-shaped upper part of the animal, the so-called nectophore, can grow to a length of at least 0.5 m. The many red-speckled tentacles trailing from the end can be more than 1 m long. Contact with these will cause an intense but short-lived sting. *F. edwardsi* lives in all oceans, is especially common in the Mediterranean.

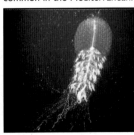

Physophora hydrostatica   **Madeira**

Red Sea Finger
ALCYONIIDAE

S: 30 cm. D: W-Scotland south to Portugal and Azores. G: each polyp of a soft coral (order Octocorallia) has 8 feathered arms. Slender, on rocky bottoms from a few metres down. Can withdraw polyps and slowly contract into small solid lump. Crimson in shallow water, deeper pale pink.

Alcyonium glomeratum   **São Jorge Island, Azores**

Dead Man's Fingers

S: 20 cm. D: Norway, Iceland south to Bay of Biscay. G: pale, can cover large areas of current swept rocky substrate (left). 3-50 m. Polyps often withdrawn (for weeks in cases!), may then be confused with a sponge. Eggs, sperm released into the water (compare *A. coralloides* below!).

Alcyonium digitatum   **Norway**

Coral-like Sea Finger

S: on sea fans to 30+ cm high. D: Brittany (France) to whole Med. G: thinly encrusting (2 mm thick) on sea fans (large photo), also in lumps on its own, up to 5 cm high (small photo). Dark red to yellow to white, polyps yellow or white. Eggs fertilized inside female, larvae released later on.

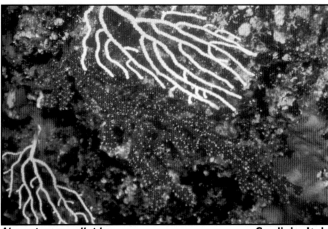

Alcyonium coralloides   **Sardinia, Italy**

Grey Sea Finger
S: 10 cm. D: Mediterranean Sea; continental coast of Portugal. G: growth form: numerous slender fingers that project from rocky substrate. The photo is the first record outside the Med. The <u>small photo</u> shows *Alcyonium acaule*, common in Med., colour variable, normally dark red with lighter polyps, up to 15 cm.

Paralcyonium spinulosum   **Bay of Setúbal, Portugal**

Stoloniferous Coral
CORNULARIIDAE
S: 1 cm. D: NE-Atl., W-Med. G: Stolonifera are small Octocorallia forming colonies by extending narrow projections (stolons) on the substrate from which more solitary polyps grow. *C. crassa* can be locally common in slightly dark places from 5 m down.

Clavularia crassa   **Costa del Sol, Spain**

Azorean Coral
S: 1 cm. D: Azores only. G: author PW found this species at the Azores and sent it to an expert who described it in a new genus. It grows on current swept rocky walls as well as on tubes of the large polychaete *Sabella spallanzanii* (p. 92) in more sheltered areas. <u>Below</u>: undetermined species, photo from Madeira.

Azoria bayeri   **Terceira Island, Azores**

Giant Sea Pen, Sea Whip

S: up to 2 m. D: both sides of N-Atl.; Med. G: on muddy bottoms in (20) 40-2600+ m. Characterised by a quadrangular stem. Polyps 3 mm wide.

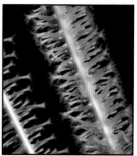

Funiculina quadrangularis   North Sea

Round Sea Pen

S: 60 cm. D: Med.; E-Atl.: Bay of Biscay to S-Africa. G: polyps (photo) to 5 cm; animal on preceding p. On mud to gravel below 15 m. Can retract into substrate or withdraw its body and let the currents roll it away. Below: Slender Sea Pen *Virgularia mirabilis*, 20+ cm. Med., Norway-Canar., 15-400 m.

Veretillum cynomorium   Madeira

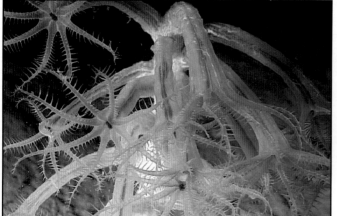

Star Coral

Size: up to 75 cm.
Distribution: this species is found on both sides of the northern Atlantic and also ranges into the western Mediterranean Sea.
General: the polyps of the Star Coral are among the largest cnidarian polyps known. Normally, this unmistakable species lives between 150 to 3500 m depth. The photo was taken at the exceptional depth of 50 m. See also the story "Glass Coral" on pages 73-77.

Kophobelemnon stelliferum   Sognefjord, Norway

Precious or Red Coral
CORALLIIDAE

S: usually 5-20, max to 100 cm. D: Med. G: Easy to recognize by their solid red axes with white polyps (2-4 mm). Prefers dark places. Found shallow (in caves) but usually deeper than 40 m, down to at least 280 m.

The Red Coral is an exception among the Gorgonaria because its red skeletal elements ("sclerites") are fused with calcium carbonate to form a solid mass. This hard skeleton is the cause of its near extinction: it was used since pre-christian times to make jewellery. Main harvesting areas were Corsica, Sardinia, Tunisia. Grows very slowly, at a rate of only 2-8 mm per year. Imagine the age of a colony 1 m high!

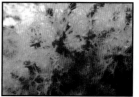

Corallium rubrum   **Ligurian Sea, Italy**

White Sea Fan
PLEXAURIDAE

S: up to 70 cm high. D: Med. G: the skeleton of most sea fans consists of skeletal elements (calcareous "sclerites") fused together by a horn-like substance. The relative amounts of hard sclerites and horny matrix can vary and thus result in skeletons more or less flexible. Most sea fans are branched in one plane, forming large fan-like structures that face with their broad side into the current. The numerous small polyps on the branches capture plankton. Sea fans serve as host for many shrimps (e.g. *Pseudocoutierea wirtzi*, p. 131) and gastropods (e.g. *Pseudosimnia carnea*, p. 173).

E. singularis appears to prefer horizontal, rocky substrates that may have a sediment cover, in 5-60 m. Its few branches arise already fairly low down the stem. Growth rate 1.5-4.5 cm per year, a 50-cm-colony is several decades old. Female colonies eject large amounts of "planula" larvae (2.5 mm) in June and July. The brown polyps contain symbiotic unicellular algae.

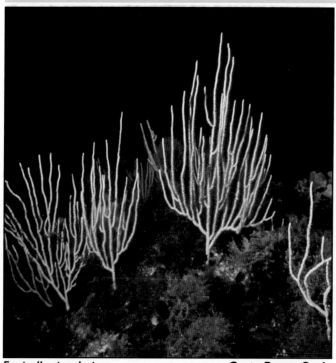

Eunicella singularis   **Costa Brava, Spain**

Common Sea Fan

PLEXAURIDAE

S: 35 (80) cm. D: E-Atl.: S-Ireland to Gulf of Guinea; W-Med. G: common, 10-200 m, white to yellow. Polyps in distinct conical humps. Grows 1 cm p.a., it takes many years to replace a branch carelessly broken off! <u>Below</u>: Yellow Sea Fan *E. cavolinii*, 40 cm.

Eunicella verrucosa   **Bay of Setúbal, Portugal**

Orange Sea Fan

Size: up to 60 cm high.
Distribution: French Atlantic coast to Morocco; western Mediterranean Sea.
General: despite its popular name "Orange Sea Fan" this species is extremely variable in colour, as the three photos show (which were all taken in an area of a few 100 metres). It can be recognized by the numerous thin branches in the terminal area. It grows much faster than *E. verrucosa*, 2-5 cm per year in 10-250 m depth.

The spawn of the nudibranch *Tritonia nilsodhneri* can frequently be found on this sea fan (also on *Eunicella verrucosa*). The nudibranch itself is perfectly camouflaged and difficult to find.

Leptogorgia sarmentosa   **Bay of Setúbal, Portugal**

Leptogorgia gainii   **Cape Verde Islands**

Grey Sea Fan

S: 60 cm. D: trop. E-Atlantic: Mauritania to Angola. G: very common at the Cape Verdes (20+ m). It is inhabited by several species of shrimps, such as *Balssia gasti* (p. 126) and *Pseudocoutierea wirtzi* (p. 131). *L. capverdensis* (below) lives in the same depth range. Its branches fuse into a network.

Lophogorgia ruberrima   **Tenerife, Canary Islands**

Scarlet Sea Fan
GORGONIIDAE

S: up to 50 cm high. D: Canary Islands to São Tomé. G: bright red (name). 10-180+ m. At the Canary Islands locally common (in 20 m), often with *L. vimnalis* (below): to 70 cm, bright yellow, rarely brown, Spanish Atlantic coast to the Gulf of Guinea and SW-Med. (Morocco, Algeria).

Paramuricea clavata   **Ibiza, Spain**

Purple Sea Fan
PARAMURICEIDAE

S: 100 cm. D: Med., Atl. coast of Portugal. G: common, in dark places, 10-100 m. Purple (branch tips may be yellow), rarely yellow. Photo: catshark egg in centre. Below: Northern Sea Fan *Swiftia pallida*, 15 cm, steep cliffs below 10 m. White, pale grey. Branches not as fan in a single plane. See also p. 39.

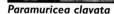

HIDDEN CALENDARS

The growth rings of old trees allow the reconstruction of climate data from as far back as 4000 years. A corresponding analysis can probably be made by studying the growth rings in the skeletons of coral. Peter Wirtz explains some facts from the young science of ageing marine invertebrates.

The black coral species *Antipathella wollastoni* from the Azores.

The skeleton of stony coral (Order Madreporaria) contains a biological record of past temperatures. Sea surface temperatures have been reconstructed from coral growth rates back to 1740 for Australian waters and runoff from an Australian river (probably a good measure of rainfall) has even been reconstructed back to 1640 using coral fluorescence. This time span, however, appears to be the limit of the method in stony coral. Other types of coral offer the potential of looking much deeper into the past.

Most of the approximately 150 species of black coral (Order Antipatharia) look like large bushes. Frequently they are pink or white or green in colour. It is the black skeleton that gave the name to the group. The skeleton of large tropical species is sometimes used to produce jewellery and the old Greek made amulets from the Mediterranean species that were supposed to ward off evil: "anti-pathes" literally means "against harm". Distinct growth rings have recently been detected in the skeletons of subtropical species.

Encrusting anemones (Order Zoantharia) normally do not have a skeleton. Species of the genus *Gerardia* are an exception. They build a horny skeleton and the colonies thus can grow to a height of up to 2 metres. The American research submersible "Alvin" collected such bushes from 620 m depth. Cross sections of the skeleton revealed rings of five to ten micrometer widths. If these rings really are annual growth rings – which is likely because

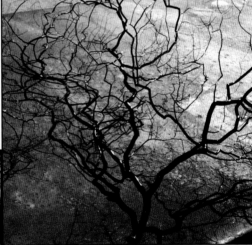

It is the black skeleton that gave the name to Black Coral.

of the annual variation in food supply to the deep sea – these bushes of *Gerardia* anemones are some of the oldest marine organisms on earth: the number of rings indicates individual ages of 1300 to 2700 years!

The reconstruction of past climates using the growth rings of coral is in its beginning phase but might well lead to interesting results in the near future.

The encrusting anemone *Gerardia savaglia* photographed at the island of Madeira.

GLOBAL WARMING

There is no doubt that we are living in a period of global warming. The only doubt that exists is to what degree mankind is accelerating the process. The effects of global warming can already be seen in the marine environment.

Increasing in abundance in the northern Mediterranean: the green alga *Dasycladus vermicularis*.

The Mediterranean Sea shows a great range of temperatures. The northwestern part is the cold region and contains many north Atlantic species that cannot be found in the eastern part. The southeastern part is the warm region and contains many species that cannot be found in the western Mediterranean. In recent years, more and more southern species are appearing in the north.

The red sea star *Ophidiaster ophidianus* was recorded at the northern coast of Corsica for the first time in 1990; the long-spined sea urchin *Centrostephanus longispinus* followed in 1991. Warm-water species previously rare in the Gulf of Lion, such as the alga *Dasycladus vermicularis*, the black sea urchin *Arbacia lixula* and the Rainbow Wrasse *Thalassoma pavo* have increased in frequency more than tenfold. Some of these warm-water species were probably carried by currents into colder water as larvae or as juveniles and previously managed to survive there but not to reproduce – forming so-called "pseudopopulations". The Rainbow Wrasse is now regularly reproducing in the Ligurian Sea (north of Corsica), where it has never managed to breed before. The circum-tropical hydrozoan *Halocordyle disticha* was previously known only from the southern shores of the Mediterranean Sea. It has now been recorded as far north as Genoa, Italy.

A similar northward march of southern species can be found all along the shores of the eastern Atlantic. At Madeira Island, the tropical sea hare *Aplysia dactylomela* has appeared and increased enormously in abundance. The tropical alga *Stypopodium zonale*, not recorded in a survey of the marine plants of Madeira in 1974, is now one of the most common species! Peter Wirtz was surprised to see the sea anemone *Alicia mirabilis* when diving at Cascais on the Portuguese mainland coast in 2001. This is the northernmost

The circumtropical hydrozoan *Halocordyle disticha* can now even be found in the northern Mediterranean Sea as far north as Genoa, Italy.

The tropical sea hare *Aplysia dacty-lomela* is now common at Madeira.

record for the species. When asked about it, the owner of the local diving centre said that this (large and conspicuous) sea anemone had appeared "two years ago" and had not been present before.

Warm-water fish species such as the Tarpon *Tarpon atlanticus* and the Almaco Jack *Seriola rivoliana* have now been recorded as far north as the French Atlantic coast. At the same time, northern species are retreating from the south. However, the gradual disappearance of a species is much more difficult to record than

ROBERTO RINALDI

The sea anemone *Alicia mirabilis* can now be found as far north as Cascais, Portugal.

the sudden appearance of a species previously unrecorded in the area.

In May 1998 the Feather Star Shrimp *Hippolyte prideauxiana* was found in Loch Carron, northwest Scotland, several hundred kilometres further north than previously recorded. The question here is: can this be attributed to warmer seawater temperatures, or is this little shrimp so well camouflaged in the arms of its host that it is only rarely spotted?

The Feather Star Shrimp *Hippolyte prideauxiana* from western Scotland, its new northern limit of distribution.

SUE SCOTT

45

Actinia equina   **Malta**

Actinia equina   **Faial Island, Azores**

Beadlet Anemone
ACTINIDAE (both pages)
S: up to 7 cm tall and up to 6 cm in diameter but usually half that size. D: Mediterranean Sea; in the eastern Atlantic from the White Sea to the Cape Verde Islands. G: this is one of the most common species of sea anemones. It lives in shallow water, often falling dry during low water, down to 8 m depth. As the two large photos show, it may be either red or green in colour, also straw-coloured or pale. Each individual has a row of bright blue "beads" directly below the tentacles, hence the common name of the species. There is often a blue ring around the base of the foot. A life-bearing species: females brood embryos and release small sea anemones.

A ball-shaped ciliate parasite, *Foetingeria actiniarium,* can be seen inside the tentacles of some of the green individuals. This is one of the few single-celled species that are visible to the naked eye (see "Giant Single Cells" on pp. 282-283).

<u>Small photo below:</u> closed specimen, hence also called "Sea Tomatoe".

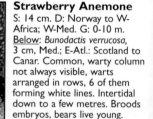

Actinia fragacea   **Guernsey, Channel Islands**

Strawberry Anemone
S: 14 cm. D: Norway to W-Africa; W-Med. G: 0-10 m.
<u>Below:</u> *Bunodactis verrucosa,* 3 cm, Med.; E-Atl.: Scotland to Canar. Common, warty column not always visible, warts arranged in rows, 6 of them forming white lines. Intertidal down to a few metres. Broods embryos, bears live young.

Snakelocks Anemone

S: 13 cm wide. D: Med.; Shetland Isles to Canaries. G: very common! Synonym *A. sulcata.* Several colour morphs that may actually be different species. Up to 200 tentacles per animal. The greenish colour is due to symbiotic unicellular algae. In contrast to most sea anemones, this species cannot withdraw its tentacles. <u>Upper small photo</u>: the Anemone Goby *Gobius bucchichi* often (but not always) associates with this species. <u>Lower small photo</u>: Sargassum Anemone *Anemonia melanaster,* to 4 cm, E-Atl. Usually on rocks in shallow water. Star-shaped pattern on oral disk distinctive.

Anemonia viridis   **Aegean Sea, Greece**

Anemonia viridis   **Galway, Ireland**

S: 5 (10) cm tall. D: Mediterranean Sea; E-Atl.: Isle of Man to Equatorial Guinea, incl. Azores, Madeira, Canaries. G: shallow, often in tide pools. Easily identified by species-typical colour pattern (<u>below</u>) if column is visible. Tentacles are greenish-brown due to unicellular symbiotic algae and pale white in dark places (caves).

Anthopleura ballii   **Faial Island, Azores**

Condylactis aurantiaca   **Croatia, Adriatic Sea**

Golden Anemone
ACTINIDAE (this page)
S: up to 28 cm tentacle span. D: Med. G: often confused with the similarly-coloured *Cribrinopsis crassa* but the latter has much thicker, shorter tentacles (see below) and usually lives on rocky bottom. Column of *C. aurantiaca* usually buried in sand or gravel, the foot not being attached to a hard object. Colour depends on density of its symbiotic unicellular algae; in shallow water with high algal densities the anemone can be dark green, in deeper (to 80 m), darker places it is much lighter. Several *Periclimenes* shrimps, most often *P. scriptus* (p. 129) associate with this anemone.

Thick-armed Anemone

S: body to 7, tentacles to 5 cm. D: W-Med., Adriatic Sea. G: often confused with *Condylactis aurantiaca* (see above). 5-100 m, usually in cracks in the rock. If this anemone projects from soft bottom (rarely), its foot is attached to a rock or a piece of shell. <u>Photo below</u>: Provence, France.

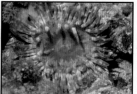

Cribrinopsis crassa   **Malta**

Dahlia Anemone

S: up to 10 cm in diameter. D: from the Arctic to the Bay of Biscay. G: common, the short column is usually hidden in sand or gravel or covered with sand or gravel and fragments of shell. Has up to 160 tentacles. Colour variable (see photos). Intertidal down to about 100 m depth.

Urticina felina   **Galway, Ireland**

Trumpet Anemone
AIPTASIIDAE (this page)

Size: tentacle spread up to
15 cm wide.
Distribution: Mediterranean
Sea; in the eastern Atlantic
from southern England to the
Gulf of Guinea.
General: the brown or green
colour of this common species
is due to symbiotic unicellular
algae harboured in its tissues.
It lives on rock from shallow
water down to about 20 m
depth. The Trumpet Anemone
buds small pieces of tissue
from its pedal disk that crawl
away and rapidly grow into
new anemones, genetically
identical to its parent. Such
clones frequently form small
groups or even dense carpets
on the rock.

Aiptasia mutabilis   Malta

Aiptasia mutabilis is one of
the preferred prey species of
the nudibranch *Spurilla neapolitana* (page 203).

Below: the typical pattern
on the tentacles of Mediterranean specimens.

Aiptasia mutabilis   Faial Island, Azores

S: diameter of column up to
1 cm. D: Mediterranean Sea; E-
Atl.: Portugal to St. Helena; W-
Atl. G: like *A. mutabilis*, reproduces asexually by pedal laceration, forming carpets of
clones; on rocks, shallow to
about 5 m. Below (Madeira):
Aiptasiogeton hyalinus, Mediterranean, S-England to Canaries,
below stones, in cracks.

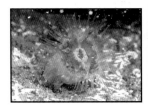

Aiptasia diaphana   El Hierro, Canary Islands

Alicia mirabilis   **Sicily, Italy**

Alicia mirabilis   **Faial Island, Azores**

Berried Anemone
ALICIIDAE

S: stem up to 40 cm high.
D: western Mediterranean;
Portugal to Canaries; Florida,
Bahamas. G: one of the most
painfully stinging sea anemones
of the world. Do not touch it!
It expands only at night. In the
morning, it first swallows its
tentacles and then contracts.
The berry-like bubbles along
the stalk (lower small photo),
being armed with batteries of
powerful stinging cells, then
form the outside of a cauliflower-like creature, seldom recognized as a sea anemone (upper
small photo). Very mobile, can
move about freely.

Author PW has recently
seen this species at Cascais,
Portugal. Apparently, *A. mirabilis*
has expanded its range northward during the last few years
(see "Global Warming").

Aureliania heterocera   **North Sea**

Imperial Anemone
AURELIANIIDAE

Size: up to 7 cm wide and up
to 7 cm high.
Distribution: from western Ireland and south-west England
into the western Mediter-
ranean Sea.
General: this is an uncommon
species. It lives on rock or
shells or buried in mud, sand,
or gravel, from shallow water
to about 600 m depth. It has
up to 150 tentacles in four circles, each ending in a small
knob of variable shape. Colour
red or yellow, often speckled
with grey or white.

DIADUMENIDAE

S: up to 7 cm long. D: from Norway to the Atlantic coast of France. G: the deep orange mouth of this species contrasts with the light orange body. There are up to 200 slender tentacles. This sea anemone frequently reproduces by pedal laceration: a small piece of the pedal disc crawls way and forms a new anemone. It therefore frequently occurs in groups. On stones and mussels, sometimes growing through sponges, from shallow water down to about 40 m depth. The species tolerates brackish water, has penetrated far into the Baltic Sea.

Diadumene cincta   Norway

GONACTINIIDAE

Size: body (without tentacles) up to 2 cm high, tentacle span up to 7 cm.
Distribution: from northern Norway to the North Sea and the Kattegat.
General: has up to 200 long tentacles. From 15-500 m, has been found associated with *Lophelia* reefs (p. 69). One of its main food items appear to be polychaete worms. This is a surprisingly lively species of sea anemone that, upon stimulation, can wave its tentacles and bend its column.

Protanthea simplex   North Sea

HALCAMPIDAE

Size: up to 7 cm long.
Distribution: all coast of Britain and north-western France.
General: the elongated column of this species is buried in mud, sand, or gravel, from shallow water down to about 100 m depth. There are 12 tentacles with brown bands on a creamy background. This may be the same species as *H. duodecemcirrata* of northern Europe and the Atlantic coast of North America. The genus needs revision.

Halcampa chrysanthellum   Isle of Man

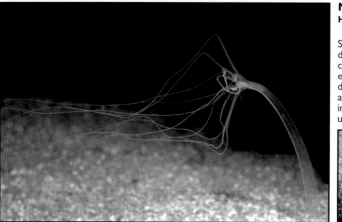

Night-tail
HALCAMPOIDIDAE

S: up to 8 cm high. D: Med.; Madeira. G: generic systematics unclear. Several undescribed spp, exact distribution unknown. By day buried in sand, only expands at night, trailing its long tentacles in the current. <u>Below</u> (Crete): undescribed *H.* sp, spans 10 cm.

Halcampoides mediterranea   **Madeira**

HALOCLAVIDAE

Size: up to 12 cm long. Distribution: W-Mediterranean; in the E-Atlantic from southern Norway to the Canary Islands. General: this strange animal lives buried in sand or gravel, often below large stones, from shallow water down to about 600 m depth. Only the tentacles (two rings of 10) stick out of the substrate. The form of the tentacles, with a constriction near the tip, is species-typical. When touched, *A. mazeli* quickly withdraws into the sand.

Anemonactis mazeli   **Costa del Sol, Spain**

HALOCLAVIDAE

S: 30 cm. D: North Sea to Med. G: body entirely buried in sand, only the 12 tentacles are extended, level with bottom. Without sucker-like disk for attaching to a hard surface but just with rounded end (can dig into the seabed). Tentacle colour distinctive. 5-50 m. Larva: hydromedusa parasite.

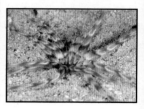

Peachia cylindrica   **Malta**

Hermit Crab Anemone

HORMATHIIDAE (this page)
S: up to 10 cm tall and 5 cm wide. D: western Mediterranean Sea and Adriatic Sea; in the eastern Atlantic from southern Norway to the Cape Verde Islands, including Madeira and the Canary Islands but apparently not the Azores. G: despite the name *"parasitica"*, the presence of the sea anemone is of benefit to the hermit crab: when it carries one or several anemones on its shell it is less likely to be attacked by an octopus! *Dardanus calidus* (page 138) and *Dardanus arrosor* are the two hermit crabs thus favoured. *C. parasitica* has been recorded from 10 to about 200 m depth. Usually more than one anemone is attached to a shell and there may be up to eight anemones on the same shell.

Below: the very similar *Anthothoe affinis,* pedal disk up to 3 cm wide, Azores, Madeira, Canary Islands. At Madeira and the Canaries, *A. affinis* and *C. parasitica* may occur together on the same shell occupied by a *Dardanus calidus*.

Calliactis parasitica   Sardinia, Italy

Cloak Anemone

S: 10 cm. D: W-Med. and Adriatic Sea; Norway to Canaries. G: almost always associated with *Pagurus prideaux* (p. 139), rarely with other hermit crabs. Completely envelops the shell inhabited by the hermit. When feeling molested, the anemone emits numerous bright pink threads of stinging cells called acontia.

When feeding, the hermit often puts pieces of food into the mouth of the sea anemone. A few minutes to a few hours later, however, the crab may pull the food out of the stomach of the sea anemone and eat it!

Adamsia carciniopados   Corsica, France

Telmatactis cricoides   **Madeira**

Club-tipped Anemone
ISOPHELLIDAE

S: up to 32 cm tentacle span. D: E-Med.; E-Atl.: Madeira to Cape Verdes; W-Atl. G: this is one of the largest sea anemones in the temperate E-Atlantic and Med. It can easily be recognized by the club-shaped thickening of the tips of the tentacles. Animals at Madeira and the Canary Islands are about twice as large as in the rest of the distribution area but a detailed study could not find any other differences. The Club-tipped Anemone is very variable in colour pattern, as the photos on this page show. 205 animals recorded by author PW at Madeira and the Canary Islands had 25 different colour patterns. The frequency of these colour patterns was not correlated to water depth. The species lives on rocky bottoms, from 5 to at least 40 m depth. Many decapod crustaceans associate with this sea anemone. The most common associate at Madeira and the Canary Islands is the shrimp *Thor amboinensis* (p. 120). The lower large photo shows several *Stenorhynchus lanceolatus* (p. 148) clustering around a large *T. cricoides*. First small photo: *T. forskalii* can be seen projecting from cracks in rocky substrate, especially in dark places and at night, also on sand. Med. and from the area of Biarritz, France, to the Cape Verde Islands.

Telmatactis cricoides   **Cyprus**

Telmatactis cricoides   **Tenerife, Canary Islands**

TRAPPED

It was much warmer than today, 120,000 years ago. Elephants, lions and hyaenas roamed all over Europe and tropical species were common every-where in the Mediterranean Sea. But then the ice came.

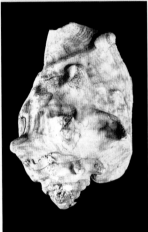

The fossil conch *Strombus bubonius.*

The cooling of the climate during the last ice age wiped out many tropical species that lived in the Mediterranean Sea. During the peak of the last glaciation, about 18,000 years ago, winter temperatures in the western Mediterranean Sea were probably as low as 5°C.

The proof that tropical species really lived in the Mediterranean before the last glaciation is the fossil record. Big snails with strong shells are, of course, especially likely to be preserved as fossils. Well preserved shells of the Bubonian Conch *Strombus bubonius* can be found all around the Mediterranean Sea and along the coasts of the Atlantic as far north as Portugal. The species, however, no longer lives there. Today it can only be found along the coasts of West Africa, from Gabon to the Cape Verde Islands and Senegal.

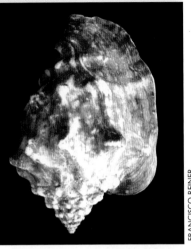

Shell of a contemporary *Strombus bubonius* from the Cape Verde Islands.

FRANCISCO REINER

Other tropical species were only partly wiped out by the cold. They disappeared from the western Mediterranean but managed to survive in the much warmer eastern Mediterranean. The result is a most curious distribution pattern: these species can now be found on subtropical-tropical shores of west Africa and in the eastern Mediterranean Sea but not (no longer!) in the area in between. An example is the ghost crab *Ocypode cursor*, today living in two separate populations, in the southeastern Mediterranean and from Mauritania to Namibia. Before the last ice age, it must have also lived in the area in between. And, indeed, there is a fossil record from Mallorca for the species.

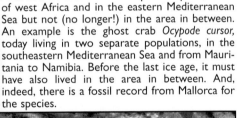

The ghost crab *Ocypode cursor.*

We have no fossil records for the sea anemone *Telmatactis cricoides,* but this species, too, has the typical distribution pattern of animals "trapped in the eastern Mediterranean". In the eastern Atlantic, it is known from St. Helena Island to Madeira.

Global warming has already caused the expansion of warm-water species of the southeastern Mediterranean Sea into the cold northwestern part. If this trend continues the Atlantic and the Mediterranean populations of some of these species might even re-unite!

The Club-tipped Anemone *Telmatactis cricoides.*

PETER WIRTZ

Plumose Anemone
METRIDIIDAE

Size: up to 50 cm high.
Distribution: from the Arctic
to the Bay of Biscay.
General: this beautiful
anemone has up to 200 short
tentacles, which give it its typical fluffy appearance. It is the
largest sea anemone in the
eastern Atlantic. There are
two colour forms, a common
pink one and a less common
pale one that does not grow
to such a large size as the pink
form. The species lives on
hard bottoms from the low
water line down to about
100 m depth.

Metridium senile   **Gulmarsfjorden, Sweden**

SAGARTIIDAE

S: up to 3 cm high. D: southern
Ireland and western Britain to
the Canary Islands. G: flower-
like, with up to 100 long, pure
white tentacles. Can be locally
common, forming colonies of
thousands of individuals, 5-50 m.
The mouth area is often yellow-
orange (small photo, Cascais).

Actinothoe sphyrodeta   **Galway, Ireland**

Daisy Anemone
SAGARTIIDAE (this page)

S: disk 12 cm. D: Scotland into Mediterranean including Azores. Hidden in ground. Margin with 500 small tentacles. There are two forms: the one in shallow water (<u>below</u>, Azores) is viviparous: female broods baby anemones, released via mouth. <u>Right</u>: larger form, to 50 m.

Cereus pedunculatus   **Adriatic Sea**

S: tentacle span up to 6 cm. D: Iceland and Norway into Mediterranean Sea. G: very variable. Many different colour patterns have been called different names. The <u>small photo below</u> from the North Sea shows the variety called *"rosea"*, with pink to red tentacles and a white oral disk. Intertidal down to about 50 m.

Sagartia elegans   **Oosterschelde, Netherlands**

S: up to 12 cm tall. D: Mediterranean Sea; E-Atl.: S-Norway to Portugal. G: locally common, tentacles usually have longitudinal stripes. On shallow hard bottoms, attached to stones or shells in sand, mud. <u>Below</u> (Helgoland): *S. laceratus*, locally common, 3 cm, Norway to French Atl. coast, 10-100 m.

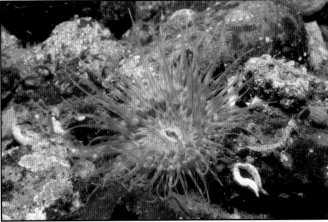

Sagartiogeton undatus   **Galway, Ireland**

Following pages: *Cerianthus membranaceus*, Sicily, Italy   **57**

Mediterranean Tube Anemone
CERIANTHIDAE
S: up to 35 cm high. D: Mediterranean Sea only. G: the body of tube anemones secretes a cloth-like material which consists of a network of used stinging cells. They have two rings of tentacles. The outer tentacles of this sp may reach 20 cm in length. Food captured by the outer tentacles is handed over to the inner ones which then put it into the mouth. Up to 150 tentacles, 1-40 m, colour very variable. In the aquarium, one specimen has reached an age of 50+ years. *Phoronis australis* (p. 253) can sometimes be found on its tube. Settles on various substrates: on sand (preceding pages), on hard bottoms, at the entrances of caves (left). Upper small photo: dark form (Ibiza); lower: living in groups (Sicily).

Cerianthus membranaceus　　　Croatia, Adriatic Sea

Lesser Tube Anemone
S: 15 cm. D: Greenland to English Channel. G: locally common, colour variable. Up to 80 tentacles (brown, white, green, banded). On mud, sand, gravel, low water line to 300 m. Photo below from the Netherlands.

Cerianthus lloydii　　　Western Scotland

Banded Tube Anemone
CERIANTHIDAE

S: 12 cm. D: Azores to Cape Verde Islands; W-Atl. G: banded outer tentacles distinctive, extended only at night. Regionally very common on rock, gravel, sand, 5-20+ m. <u>Below</u>: *Isarachnanthus cruzei* (Canaries), similar, to 20 cm; tubes very thin, without any symbionts.

Isarachnanthus maderensis   Cape Verde Islands

Dwarf Tube Anemone

S: to 8 cm. D: western Mediterranean Sea; rather common near Naples and in a cave near Marseilles. G: on sand, among sea grass, in caves with sponges, 1-20 m. Easily recognised by the brown rings on the tentacles, but also uniformly brownish. Has a high potential for asexual reproduction.

Arachnactis oligopodus   Sardinia, Italy

Dohrn's Tube Anemone

S: 50 cm. D: Mediterranean, Can. G: closely resembles *Cerianthus membranaceus* in size, also variable in colour. It may harbour *Phoronis australis* (p. 253) in the tube. The crab *Stenorhynchus lanceolatus* likes to shelter between its long tentacles. <u>Below</u>: *P. multiplicatus*, 50 cm, Ireland, Skagerrak, Kattegat, Trondheimsfjord (Norway).

Pachycerianthus dohrni   Adriatic Sea, Italy

Following page: *Pachycerianthus dohrni,* El Hierro, Canary Islands

Yellow Encrusting Anemone

S: polyps to 20 mm. D: Med.; N-Ireland, SW-Britain to Mauritania, Azores, Madeira, Canaries. G: easy to recognize by intense yellow colour. Often orange around the mouth. Polyps have up to 34 tentacles. From shallow water down to c. 100 m, in shallow water only in dark places.

Parazoanthus axinellae   Costa Brava, Spain

Canarian Sea Mat

S: disk diameter of expanded polyps up to 3 cm. D: Canary Islands, Madeira, Porto Santo. G: this species was thought to be restricted to the Canary Islands until author PW found it at Madeira and Porto Santo Islands. It lives from the intertidal (where it can even fall dry at low tide) down to at least 43 m depth. The species usually occurs in dense carpets of genetically identical animals.

Encrusting anemones grow in colonies of many small polyps that overgrow solid structures (rocks, sponges, dead black coral). Sea anemones (Actiniaria) have a different internal structure.

Protopalythoa canariense   Porto Santo Island, Madeira

S: polyps to 20 mm. D: Britain, Ireland south to the Portuguese Atlantic coast. G: grey-brown, polyps with 24-32 transparent tentacles with conspicuous white tips. 5-100 m. <u>Below</u>: *Isaurus tuberculatus*, tropics; Cape Verdes (1st record by author PW); Can., there brown, in tide pools, 5 cm.

Epizoanthus couchi   Bay of Setúbal, Portugal

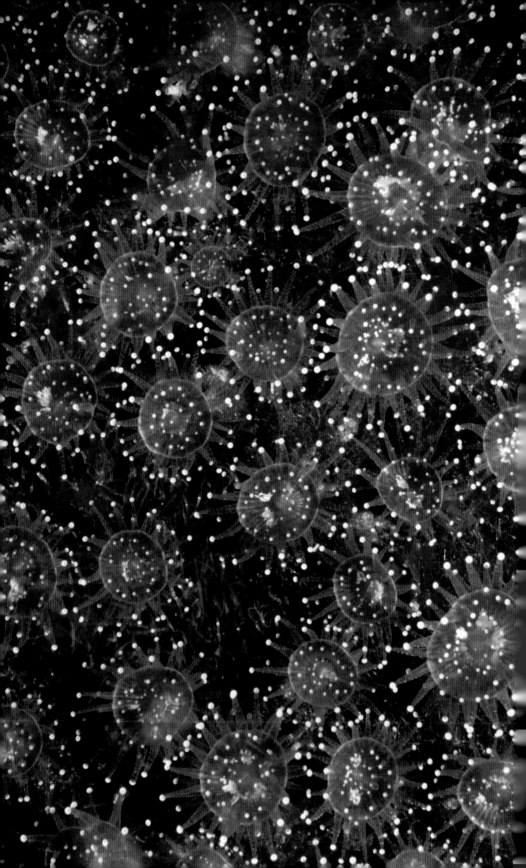

Orange Ball Coral Anemone

CORALLIMORPHIDAE

S: up to 6 cm. D: Canary, Cape Verde Islands; W-Atl.: Caribbean. G: are the strange Coral Anemones closer to the true anemones or to coral? Currently, they are placed in an own order because, although they have more affinities with coral, they lack a hard calcareous skeleton. This species is closed during the day (small photo), opening its treble ring of ball-tipped tentacles only at night. In the E-Atl., it was known only from the Canaries, until author PW recently found it also at the Cape Verdes. Like many other amphi-atlantic spp it probably crossed the Atlantic via the Equatorial counter current.

Pseudocorynactis caribbeorum   **Tenerife, Canary Islands**

Jewel Anemone

S: 1 cm. D: Mediterranean Sea; E-Atl.: Shetland Islands to Canary Islands. G: the riot of colours on a cliff face covered with Jewel Anemones is unsurpassed. The species reproduces either sexually (producing eggs and sperm cells) or asexually. In the latter case, the animal splits evenly down the middle forming an exact mirror image of itself. Clones of genetically identical animals form patches and compete with each other for space. They prefer vertical rock faces with plenty of water movement and can commonly be encountered directly below the water line but they have also been found down to 100 m. The mouth is in a raised cone in the centre and surrounded by three circlets of up to 100 tentacles.

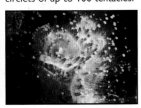

Corynactis viridis   **Faial Island, Azores**

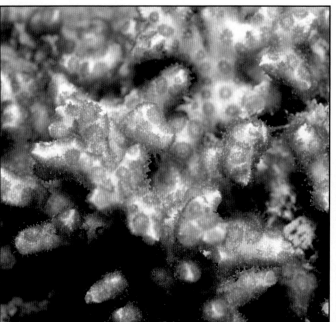

Green Reef Coral
POCILLOPORIDAE

S: branches to 20, polyp 2 mm. D: Madeira to Cape Verdes. G: most corals in our area are "solitary" (a single polyp and its calcareous skeleton. This one, however, consists of a colony formed by many small polyps. Green due to symbiotic unicellular algae (zooxanthellae), in caves without these, white. Form variable. Upper small photo: *M. pharensis.* Med., both sides of Atlant.

Madracis asperula   Madeira

Porous Coral
PORITIDAE

S: colony 60 cm, polyp 1.5 mm. D: Cape Verdes; trop. W-Atl. G: colonies flat, encrusting in shallow waters, large, ball-shaped in deeper, calmer waters. W-Atl.: in 1-50 m; Cape Verdes: to 20 m only. Lower small photo: a more yellowish colony. Upper: Lesser Starlet Coral, *Siderastrea radians* (Siderastreidae), incrusting plates to 30 cm wide, light pinkish-grey to dark brown. CV.

Porites astreoides   Cape Verde Islands

Pillow Coral
FAVIIDAE (this page)
S: colony to 60 cm. D: Med.; Algarve? G: with zooxanthellae. 5-70 m. Under good conditions (moving water, plenty of light) it grows 10% p.a., as fast as tropical spp. Some large colonies in NW-Italy: 3.5 m long, 60 cm high; only reef-building ("hermatypic") coral of Med. <u>Below</u>: in Aegean Sea.

Cladocora caespitosa   **Ligurian Sea, Italy**

Golfball Coral

S: colony diameter 2-6 cm. D: Cape Verde Islands; W-Atl. G: semicircular or ball-shaped colonies unmistakable. Large polyps slightly raised above colony surface. Very shallow down to c. 20 m, highest densities in 1-3 m. Colour variable from light yellow to dark brown (see photos).

Favia fragum   **Cape Verde Islands**

Great Star Coral
S: colony 60-240, polyps 1.2 cm. D: Gulf of Guinea islands; tropical W-Atlantic. G: colony massive, hump-shaped, unmistakable. In the Caribbean: shallow to about 90 m. Polyps closed during the day, opened at night (<u>small photo</u>, Carib.). Light-sensitive, spawning in the nights after a full moon.

Montastrea cavernosa   **São Tomé Island**

Round Cup Coral
CARYOPHYLLIIDAE
(this page)

S: up to 1.5 cm in diameter. D: Med.; English Channel to Morocco, Azores, Madeira, Canaries. G: does not contain zooxanthellae, prefers dark places (caves) from 1 m down. May grow in very high densities. Females brood eggs. White, pink, brown.

Caryophyllia inornata   **Faial Island, Azores**

Oval Cup Coral

S: 3 cm. D: Med.; Norway to Angola. G: prefers shady places, oval shape typical. Polyp base small, circular. 5-300 m. Tissue nearly transparent, calcareous skeleton can be seen. Females brood eggs. Below: *Polycyathus muellerae*. Med., Portugal to Gulf of Guinea, in dark places, 5+ m.

Caryophyllia smithii   **Faial Island, Azores**

S: up to 3 cm high. D: Iberian Peninsula to Gulf of Guinea. G: the species avoids the light. In shallow water, it lives in caves. 5-120+ m. Its tissue is so transparent that the coral appears to consist of only the skeleton. With parasitic barnacle, p. 105. Below: another form of *Polycyathus muellerae*, to 5 mm wide, 7 mm high.

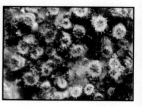

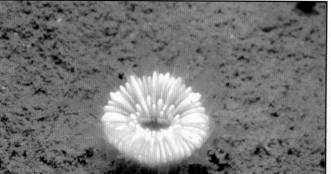

Paracyathus pulchellus   **Madeira**

Glass Coral
CARYOPHYLLIIDAE

S: branches up to 1 cm in diameter. D: world-wide, including the Mediterranean Sea. G: there are coral reefs in the cold northern Atlantic! *Lophelia pertusa* forms great reefs in 150-400 m depth (exceptionally already in 60 m) along the coasts of Norway, the Faroe Islands and western Scotland. Reefs apparently occur where there is a strong flow of plankton-rich waters. Some of these reefs are more than 100 m high and more than 10 km long. A common size is about 200 m in diameter and several metres high. Only the outer margin consists of living coral. At a growth rate of 4-6 mm per year, a 1.5 m high reef would be 250-350 years old. Larger reefs were estimated to be about 10,000 years old. A great number of animals is associated with these reefs, other cnidarians such as Gorgonaria, polychaetes, crustaceans, ophiuroids, fishes and many others. These reefs are increasingly threatened by deep-sea trawling. See also the story "Glass Coral".

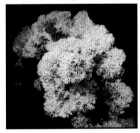

Lophelia pertusa   **Trondheimsfjord, Norway**

Dark Colonial Coral
DENDROPHYLLIIDAE

S: colony up to 10 cm in diameter, polyps up to 20 mm high. D: Med.; Portuguese Atlantic coast to Senegal, incl. Madeira, Canary Islands. G: six large septal walls characterize the polyps; there are six smaller ones between them. The living tissue may be completely transparent (thus showing the calcareous skeleton very well) or reddish brown (completely hiding the calcareous skeleton). Typical for dark places like overhanging walls or the entrance area of caves, from 5 m downwards. Closely related to *P. americana* from the tropical western Atlantic.

Phyllangia mouchezii   **Cyprus**

Orange Star Coral
DENDROPHYLLIIDAE
(both pages)
S: polyp Ø to 8 mm. D: S-Med. (incl. S-Spain, S-Italy); E-Atl.: just N and S of Strait of Gibraltar. G: massive colonies, yellow, orange, 2-30 m. No symbiotic algae, prefers dark places, under favourable conditions, large areas are covered (see also "Trapped").

Astroides calycularis   **Sicily, Italy**

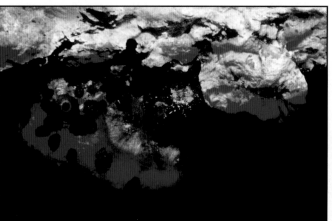

European Star Coral
S: up to 15 mm Ø. D: Mediterranean. G: common; figure-8 shape of skeleton (adults; young round). Up to 140/m². 5-50+ m. Simultaneous hermaphrodite, broods eggs in body. Below (Madeira): Golden Star Coral *B. regia*, Med., Ireland to Can. Shallow; round, golden, orange, Ø to 10 mm.

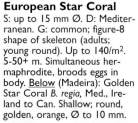

Balanophyllia europaea   **Crete Island, Greece**

Size: up to 1.5 cm in diameter. Distribution: only known from the Cape Verde Islands. General: despite its commonness in the Cape Verdes and its conspicuous colour, this species has still not been described. Author PW encountered it from 5-10 m depth, frequently on the upper edge of a vertical wall.

Balanophyllia n. sp.   **Cape Verde Islands**

Golden Cup Coral

Size: colonies up to 30 cm in diameter, polyps up to 2 cm long.
Distribution: Cape Verde Islands to Gulf of Guinea; tropical western Atlantic and Indo-Pacific.
General: the systematic of this genus is unclear and needs revision. The Golden Cup Coral avoids intense sunlight and appears to preferentially grow on overhanging rock faces, down to a depth of at least 20 m. Polyps open at night to capture plankton.

The small photo shows a Golden Cup Coral feeding on a polychaete that had bumped against it, blinded by the diving light of author PW.

The parasitic barnacle *Megatrema anglicum* (p. 105) may grow on this species and the Fireworm *Hermodice caruncula-ta* (p. 98) feeds on it.

Tubastraea aurea — São Tomé Island

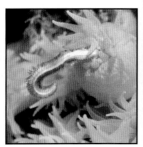

Tubastraea aurea — Cape Verde Islands

Yellow Cup Coral

S: up to 8 cm high, Ø to 14 mm. D: Med.; S- Britain to the Canary Islands. G: the polyps of *L. pruvoti* can grow so close together that one might mistake it for a colonial species. It lives from 10 m down to considerable depth, in shallow water mainly in caves and other dark areas. It is frequently infested by the parasitic barnacle *Megatrema anglicum* (p. 105). In the Canary Islands, it is only known from Lanzarote. The base of the polyp frequently is no longer covered by living tissue and overgrown by other animals or plants.

Leptopsammia pruvoti — Lanzarote, Canary Islands

Tree Coral
DENDROPHYLLIIDAE
Size: colony up to 1.5 m long.
Distribution: Mediterranean
Sea; in the E-Atlantic from
Portugal to the Gulf of Guinea.
General: this impressive coral
usually lives below 30 m, down
to several hundred metres
depth. Small colonies can occa-
sionally be found in caves in
shallower water.

The upper small photo
shows *Dendrophyllia laboreli*,
which forms small colonies (up
to 14 polyps) in open light
from 12 m downwards, from
southern Morocco to the Gulf
of Guinea; it is quite common
in the Canary Islands.

Lower small photo: *Dendrophyllia cornigera*, a species that
forms colonies up to 15 cm
high in the Mediterranean Sea
and in the E-Atl from the Bre-
tagne to the Cape Verdes.

Dendrophyllia ramea   **Lanzarote, Canary Islands**

OCULINIDAE
S: colonies up to 2 m in diameter. D: see text. G: this SW-Atl.
sp was first recorded in the
Mediterranean Sea – near the
harbour of Savona in the Gulf of
Genoa – in 1966 (photo). It
now occupies hundreds of kilometres of coastline in Italy, SE-
Spain, Lebanon, Egypt and Israel.
See also "Long Distance" and
"Gelatinous Invasion". In addition to sexual reproduction, this
coral also reproduces asexually:
a polyp rises on an elongated
calcareous stalk which breaks of
and the polyps then settles else-
where and forms a new colony
by budding. Spawning occurs
during full moon in September.

Oculina patagonica   **Gulf of Genoa, Italy**

GLASS CORAL

We all instinctively relate coral reefs with the tropics. Nevertheless, coral reefs can also be found in sub-arctic and even arctic waters. In Norway, for example, large reefs have been found with a stunning variety of species. Unlike tropical corals, the reef building Glass Coral *Lophelia pertusa* thrives best in cold water between 4-8°C. But even in Norway the right conditions for this coral are only found at great depth. Together with an experienced team of Norwegian divers, the UW-cinematographer Florian Graner has managed to find some of the most attractive animals in this book!

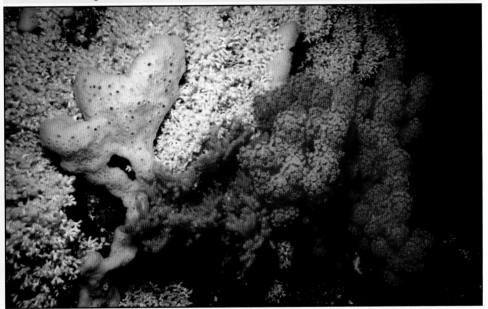

The Norwegian coldwater reefs are very intense in colour, almost like their tropic relatives: on the white-beige Glass Coral *Lophelia pertusa* grow (f.l.t.r.) the sponge *Mycale lingua*; orange: *Paramuricea placomus*; red: *Paragorgia arborea*.

Lophelia reefs have a world-wide distribution. Although the largest known reefs have been found in Norway, this coldwater coral extends its range into the Mediterranean Sea and grows on the continental shelf of the eastern Atlantic boundary, as well as in the Indian and Pacific Oceans. They are commonly found at great depth ranging from 150-2000 m and always on locations where cold nutrient rich currents provide them with plenty of food. In contrast to their tropical relatives, Glass Corals rely entirely on catching their own prey. Tropical corals rely on symbiotic dinoflagellates which are sheltered in the coral tissue and provide a bulk of the energy by means of photosynthesis. As a consequence *Lophelia* corals have much larger coral polyps which are capable of catching the necessary amount of plankton. These measure 10-20 mm at the base and have a crown with up to 60 nearly transparent tentacles which are equipped with stinging cells typical for all cnidarians. The colonies are usually of a white to beige colour, sometimes with a pink touch, but orange coloured varieties also exist and may grow right next to the beige counterparts. The size of the reefs varies. The largest known *Lophelia* reef has been found recently by the Norwegian oil company Statoil during the installation of a gas pipeline northeast of the Frøyabank. The so-called Sula reef is 13 km in length, up to 35 m high and 750 m wide. Off the southern part of the Lofoten Islands Statoil has discovered some 165 individual reefs. Today *Lophelia* reefs in Norway are known and mapped from the Oslofjord in the North Sea extending north and passing the Arctic circle into the Barents Sea. Amazingly, these reefs were known to naturalists long before the modern age of the oil industry. A Norwegian bishop mentioned Glass Corals in 1752, and his colleague Johan C. Gunnerus described the species in a treatise published in 1768 that included very good drawings of a smaller coral variety *Madrepora pertusa*. The bishop had received samples from Røberg in Trondheimsfjord. In this fjord, we found a reef suitable for diving and, equipped with an echo-sounder, sea charts and coordinates, produced our first photographs and videos in the year 2000.

My good Norwegian friends Rudolf and Erling Svensen discovered a *Lophelia* reef in 1997 in only 50 m depth and were thus the first divers to see live specimens of these coldwater corals. In 1998, Rudolf and I returned to this reef in Beitstadfjord, which is located north of the Skarnsund bridge, to film this reef. All we found was broken pieces. The reef had been destroyed by bottom trawls. In March 2000 we surveyed the central part of the adjacent Trondheimsfjord with the

In order to be able to catch passing prey *Lophelia* coral polyps are large and have up to 60 nearly transparent tentacles equipped with stinging cells.

help of the Leksvik diving club. We finally found another reef and the reef head was only 36 m deep! The reef starts at 44 m depth and is approximately 35 m long. At 42 m depth a beautiful red variety of the soft coral *Paragorgia arborea* found a spot on the reef rising some 70-80 cm in height. Like the typ-

Also in 40+ m depth thrives the brilliantly red soft coral *Paragorgia arborea* which likes to grow on the Glass Coral.

ically orange coloured soft coral *Paramuricea placomus* right next to it, it is commonly associated with *Lophelia* reefs. *Paramuricea* soft corals live around the entire reef, providing the reef with a colourful tropical touch in only 4°C of ambient temperature!

Why this reef endures at this location soon became clear to us. Diving on this reef is generally only possible 30 minutes before high and low tide. Very strong tidal currents are typical for some of Norway's fjords, as for example at Saltfjord off Bodø, where tidal currents can reach up to 28 knots, the strongest tidal current in the world.

Similar to the reef building Glass Coral *Lophelia* the soft coral *Paragorgia* has unusually large polyps for catching prey.

"I am totally amazed..." The underwater lights of the UW-photographer catch the incredible reef community comprised of Glass Corals, a variety of soft corals and up to 860 associated species, most of them invertebrates.

During our first dive, the mooring line descended vertically for 50 minutes before low tide. Delighted with the prospect of extra time on the reef, we decided to dive down to it immediately. In Trondheimsfjord the water is very clear, but of a strangely dark colour so that even on sunny and plankton-deprived winter days it is pitch black at 20 m depth. At 32 m our mooring line suddenly angled off nearly horizontally, disappearing in the darkness of the deep fjord, a clear indication for the wicket current that awaited us there. Pulling ourselves along the rope we just about managed to drop down onto the reef. We had to seek shelter from the current in the lee of the reef. At 45 m depth the soft corals trembled in the current before us. Beside us the current passed by at 4-5 knots. Such currents are precisely what keeps the reef alive. They transport the necessary nutriment to feed the coral polyps. Similar conditions must exist on the continental shelf, where nutrient rich deep water currents are forced upwards.

Cold water coral reefs are – like their tropical counterparts – a shelter for a whole arsenal of animals. Up to 860 species are known today to live in *Lophelia* reefs and it is likely more species will be discovered in due time. Some of the Norwegian reefs are very old. With the help of complicated chemical processes, calcium carbonate dissolved in the sea water is fixed by the coral polyps as aragonite (a crystal form of calcium carbonate) and incorporated into the skeletal structure of the reef building coral. *Lophelia* corals grow on average 7 mm per year (4-25 mm). That is not a lot, but compares favourably with similar reef building corals in the tropics, which have the benefit of photosynthetic symbionts but live in nutrient poor waters. When a *Lophelia* branch reaches 5 cm it splits and forms tree-like side branches. The living parts of the corals are always on the outskirts and have direct contact with the currents. Touching branches will fuse and thereby provide a stronger skeletal structure. When the corals reach about 2 m, the overall structure becomes too heavy and will collapse. The broken parts generally die, forming the base for new coral growth. In this way the reef expands. But it is hard to guess just how old a reef of 13 km in length and 35 m in height might be. The carbon-14

A medusa star *Gorgonocephalus caputmedusae* has made its home on this soft coral *Paramuricea placomus*.

method makes it possible to accurately measure the age of these reefs. The oldest reefs around Norway are 8500 years old and started developing immediately after the ice cover of the last ice age retreated.

To dive on *Lophelia* reefs is an incredible experience, but also a challenge. The reefs are difficult to find and can only be reached safely by experienced teams due to long decompression requirements, the use of mixed gases like Trimix and HelOx, and the harsh currents in cold water conditions (2-7°C). The reefs are also vulnerable, a bit like fine china. Here very careful and preventive diving coupled with a good deal of respect for this marvellous ecosystem is a prerequisite for divers. The protection of *Lophelia* reefs has meanwhile entered the arena of national and international regulations. The first country to react was Norway. On March 11, 1999, the Sula reef and the Haltenpipe reef were officially protected and excluded from commercial fishing activities.

Let us hope the measurements taken and their enforcement are efficient enough to protect this habitat. In the ongoing battle to catch the last fish, bigger equipment is constantly designed capable of going deeper and scraping the sea floor more efficiently. Today a single bottom trawl can destroy a large *Lophelia* reef in a matter of a few hours.

Never before has the fragile beauty of the Glass Corals in its natural environment been revealed in this perfection.

Left: Glass Coral reefs definitely are a challenge to divers because they are situated in cold, hardly accessible depths. But the effort is more than compensated by the almost supernatural beauty of the corals.
Right: the polyps of the Star Coral *Kophobelemnon stelliferum* are among the largest cnidarian polyps known and their large silvery tentacles gave rise to the latin and hence some of the common names attributed to this species: Latin *stella* = star. They may be as tall as 75 cm!

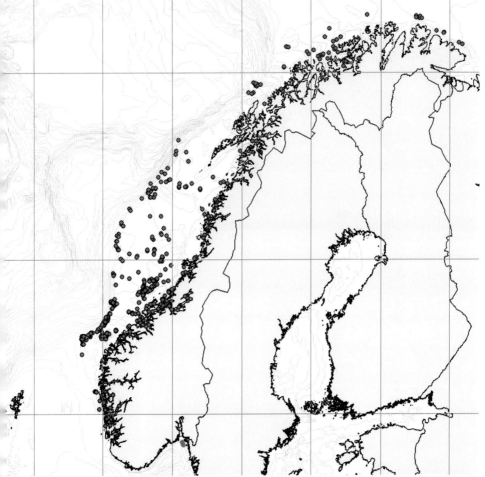

Distribution of Glass Coral reefs (blue symbols) off the coast of Norway as presently known. Map courtesy of Institute of Marine Research, Bergen, Norway.

Wollaston's Black Coral

S: up to 1.5 m high. D: Azores, Madeira, Canary Islands.
G: while Black Coral in the Med. can only rarely bee found above 80 m, veritable "forests" of it may be encountered already from 30 m downward at the Atlantic Islands. Despite the name, bushes can be white, pink, grey, green or reddish brown. It is the skeleton that is black and (in larger, tropical species) used to make jewellery. Its horn-like substance is strengthened by a chitinous component.

The Greek used to make amulets from Black Coral and this explains the scientific name: *Anti-pathes* literally means "against disease".

Bushes of Black Coral are home to many different animals, transparent shrimps, such as *Periclimenes wirtzi* (p. 129) and *Balssia gasti* (p. 126), the ascothoracid *Synagoga* (p. 107), mussels like *Pteria hirundo* (p. 234) and the goose barnacle *Oxynaspis celata* (p. 106).

Antipathella wollastoni   Faial Island, Azores

Subpinnate Black Coral

S: 1 m. D: Med. to Cape Verdes.
G: branches grey to pink, often hanging, softer than *A. wollastoni*. *Tanacetipathes spinescens* (below) is shorter (50 cm), stout, bristly. Both very common at CV. Symbionts see above. Fish (photo: *Sargocentron hastatus)* are better protected between its branches.

Antipathella subpinnata   Cape Verde Islands

Wirtz' Black Coral

S: to 20 cm. D: found by author PW, only known from caves at Madeira. 9-20 m. In the same caves lives *T. cavernicola* (below), to 20 cm, which differs in details, one is: branches of the more brownish *T. wirtzi* are brittle, break easily, those of the more greyish *T. cavernicola* are flexible and difficult to break.

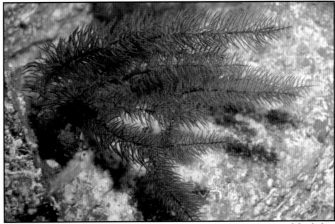

Tanacetipathes wirtzi   Madeira

Whip Coral
ANTIPATHIDAE

S: to 2 m. D: Madeira, Caribbean? G: *S. setacea* only rarely can be seen in water as "shallow" as 40 m. Deeper down, in about 100 m depth, it forms huge fields, as photos and films taken from remotely operated vehicles (ROVs) have shown. Its tropical relative, *S. lutkeni* (small photos below), already occurs in 15 m but also becomes more common deeper down. The shrimp *Pseudocoutierea wirtzi* (p. 131) can sometimes be found on it. *S. lutkeni* lives at the Cape Verde Islands and at São Tomé (E-Atl.), and from the Caribbean to Bermuda (W-Atl.). The systematic of whip corals is confused; the last revision of the group is from 1914 (!) and the E- and W-Atl. forms are probably different species in reality.

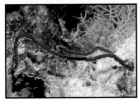

Stichopathes setacea   Madeira

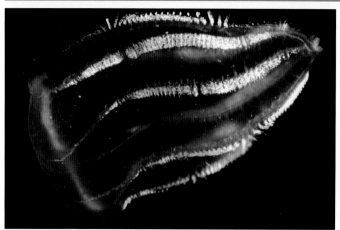

Beroe ovata **Gran Canaria, Canary Islands**

Sea Mitre

S: 6 cm. D: all warm seas; Med. G: comb jellies often mistaken for jellyfish. They are, however, built differently: 8 rows of cilia provide propulsion, their beating action appearing as an iridescent light moving along comb rows. *Beroe* spp (below *B. forskali)* are predators on other comb jellies.

S: 16 cm. D: Atl., Med. G: all genus members without tentacles. Eats anything it can get into its large mouth, mainly other comb jellies (below a *Pleurobrachia pileus).* Bioluminescent. Most comb jellies are hermaphrodites (not so *Ocyropsis,* bottom). Eaten by the Ocean sunfish *Mola mola.*

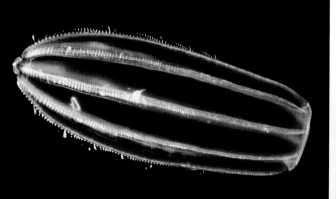

Beroe cucumis **Netherlands, North Sea**

Venus' Girdle

S: 1.5 m. D: world-wide in warm waters; Med. G: long, ribbon-shaped, can swim with wriggling movement, bioluminescent. 4 of 8 comb rows reduced, catches plankton with whole body surface. *Velamen parallelum* (20 cm) similar. Below: Winged Comb Jelly *(Ocyropsis* sp) with eggs.

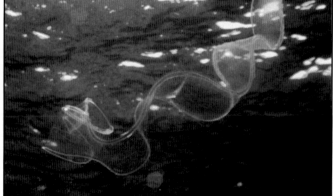

Cestus veneris **Sardinia, Italy**

Sea Gooseberry

Size: 3 cm (body without tentacles).
Distribution: North-eastern
Atlantic, Mediterranean Sea.
General: the firm body is an
oval shape. The two long
feathery tentacles, which can
be completely retracted and
have small side branches, may
trail up to 20 cm behind the
body. The tentacles are used
to catch prey. They are covered with cells that produce a
glue and hold fast to any small
object the tentacles might
brush against. Large numbers
of this species may occasionally
be found cast ashore (see the
small photo below) or in tide
pools, especially in summer,
when the species reaches its
highest densities.

Pleurobrachia pileus   **Netherlands, North Sea**

S: up to 20 cm. D: world-wide
in warm waters; Med. G: many
warty protuberances on the
body, which can be expanded
and contracted. Large oral
lobes, 1/3 of body length,
expanded (below) or folded
against body. Large animals are
brown-pink. Near the shore,
they are rapidly torn apart by
wave action and by fish.

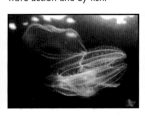

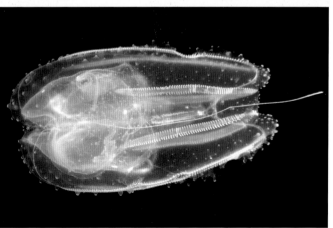

Leucothea multicornis   **Ionian Sea, Greece**

SAILORS OF THE OPEN SEA

The Azores are situated halfway between Europe and America. Therefore, the harbour of the city of Horta, on Faial Island, is a favourite stop-over for yachts crossing the Atlantic. Among biologists, Horta Harbour is famous for a second feature: several times each year, currents transport creatures of the open sea right into the harbour. Not long ago, four living Blanket Octopuses (*Tremoctopus violaceus*) were swimming there in only 3 m of depth and Peter Wirtz was able to take unique photos of these little-known animals.

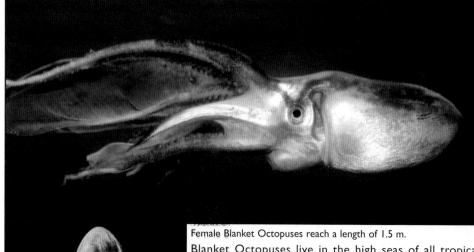

Female Blanket Octopuses reach a length of 1.5 m.

Blanket Octopuses live in the high seas of all tropical and subtropical oceans, ranging from close to the surface to several hundred metres in depth. Like all species in the cephalopod order Octopoda, they have eight arms. The four upper arms of females are elongated and connected with each other by a membrane like a large sail. Thus the Portuguese name "polvo de véu" (sail octopus) and the English name "Blanket Octopus". The German name "Löcherkrake" (holes octopus) refers to two elliptical holes in the sail, the function of which is entirely unknown.

In order to hand over to the female a well-wrapped packet of sperm, the male uses a special arm that breaks off from its body and makes its own way into the body of the female. It is unknown how the solitary fragment of an arm finds its way. A living male arm taken out of the body of a female was observed to crawl around like a worm. Females have been found containing several male arms. After mating, males − having given their all − probably die.

Among the octopuses, the female usually guards her eggs, which are deposited on the bottom. This is impossible for a species living in the open ocean. The female Blanket Octopus lays about 130.000 eggs onto its sail and carries them with her until the larvae hatch.

The function of the two holes in the membrane is still unclear.

All four animals encountered in Horta Harbour were females. With arms extended, females are up to 1.5 m long. The animals are violet in colour above, with small iridescent gold and purple spots, and creamy white below.

The main prey of the species appear to be fish. When attacked by a predator, a sailfish for example, females can sacrifice parts of the blanket and even parts of the arms, which break off at pre-formed breaking points, like the tail of a lizard.

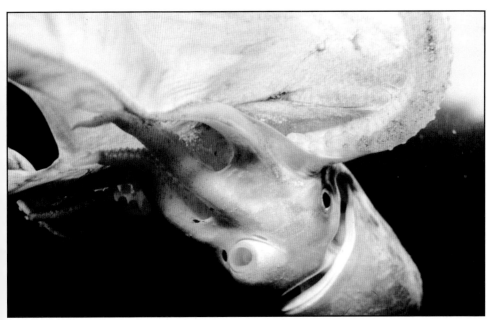

A sail-like membrane connects the upper four arms of the female Blanket Octopus.

As if a sparrow were to attempt to mate with an airplane — that fairly well describes the kamikaze sex life of the male Blanket Octopus. Males of this species are less than three centimetres long, which is about the size of the female's eye! They weigh about a quarter of a gram. The species thus displays one of the most extreme cases of sexual dimorphism known, with females about five hundred times larger than males. Or, in other words: females outweigh males by up to 40.000 times! Males do not have a sail-like membrane between the arms (and thus also no holes in the membrane).

Males and young females show a most extraordinary behaviour: they carry fragments of the tentacles of the highly poisonous jellyfish *Physalia physalis* in the four upper arms and use them to defend themselves. They thus represent one of the few examples of "tool-use" among invertebrate animals. The first scientist to detect this behaviour was badly stung while handling a small female.

While doing "black-water dives" (night dives suspended below a boat over deep water) off the northern Great Barrier Reef, David Paul managed to take the first ever photo of a living male Blanket Octopus. Until then, the male was only known from dead individuals collected in trawls and plankton nets. The animal had slowly but steadily approached the dive lights which had been fixed underneath the boat at a depth of about 8 m.

DAVID PAUL

The first ever photo of a living male Blanket Octopus, taken off the Great Barrier Reef.

83

Large Horned Flatworm

PSEUDOCEROTIDAE (this page)
S: 4 cm. D: Med.; temperate E-Atl. G: marine flatworms are often mistaken for nudibranchs, but their "tentacles" are simple folds of the anterior margin. They can move along much faster than sea slugs, are much thinner and tend to break up if handled. No gills, respiration by diffusion through body surface. *P. maximum* very common in Med., temp. E-Atl. Colour variable.

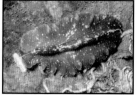

Pseudoceros maximum   Madeira

Magnificent Flatworm

Size: up to 7 cm.
Distribution: Madeira and Canary Islands.
General: despite its large size and its magnificent brilliant colours, this species is still undescribed!

Many species of the family Pseudocerotidae are thought to feed on colonial ascidians, sponges, and bryozoans. For feeding, the highly ruffled pharynx protrudes and can be expanded into the individual zooids of colonial ascidians. While discharging protein-dissolving secretions, the muscular pharynx is used like a pestle to mash the prey's tissue. Partially digested tissue is then drawn into the gut.

Pseudoceros sp   Madeira

Pink Flatworm

Size: up to 2 cm.
Distribution: Mediterranean Sea and temperate eastern Atlantic.
General: this is one of the most common flatworm species of the Mediterranean Sea. Its colour patterns makes it unmistakable. The <u>small photo</u> from Porto Santo Island (near Madeira) shows *Prostheceraeus giesbrechtii*. It is still not clear if this really is a separate species or only a colour morph of *roseus* (in which case *Prostheceraeus giesbrechtii* would be the correct name for both of them because *giesbrechtii* was described before *roseus*). They live from shallow water down to about 40 m depth.

In general, polyclads are simultaneous hermaphroditic, having male and female reproductive organs at the same time. They copulate to engage in mutual cross-fertilization. In a process called "hypodermic insemination", the penis is stabbed into almost any part of the body of the other animal and remains there for several minutes. During that time, spermatozoa are injected into; they then make their own way to the female reproductive organs.

Prostheceraeus roseus   **Mediterranean coast of Israel**

The <u>small photo below</u> shows *Planoceros graffi*, which grows up to 3 cm long. It lives in the Mediterranean Sea and temperate eastern Atlantic. Unfortunately, most flatworms cannot be identified from photos but only in the laboratory!

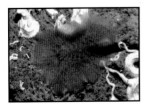

Prostheceraeus roseus   **Crete Island, Greece**

Candy-striped Flatworm
S: 5 cm. D: Norway to Med. G: ivory-coloured, with variable number of thin, black lines; hides by day, emerges at night, eats tunicates. Polyclads are active predators/scavengers, feeding on various sessile invertebrates. A few are herbivores, specializing on green algae, benthic diatoms.

Prostheceraeus vittatus   **Norway**

Moseley's Flatworm

S: 3 cm. D: Med., temp. E-Atl. G: feeds on tunicates (below). Colour closely resembles that of *Chromodoris* spp (p. 217). Many tropical flatworms mimic unpalatable nudibranchs. Any fish that has learned that certain nudibranchs taste bad will also avoid the similarly coloured flatworm.

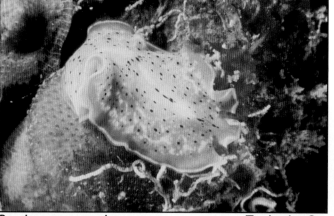

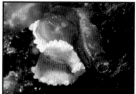

Prostheceraeus moseley   **Tyrrhenian Sea**

S: 3 cm. D: Med., temp. E-Atl. G: only European *Eurylepta*. Pseudotentacles form long "horns". A tropical relative, *E. leoparda*, drills through mantle of a solitary ascidian, sucks complete content of tunicate within several hours. Below (Azores): probably (!) a species of the genus *Notoplana*.

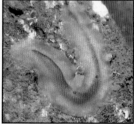

Eurylepta cornuta   **Faial Island, Azores**

S: 5 cm. D: Med., temp. E-Atl. G: polyclads are very thin, delicate creatures. *T. brocchi* hides during the day and comes out to feed at night. During locomotion, the edges of the body are moved in a wave (large photo). Colour light brown to black, often with white cross on the back. 5-80 m.

Thysanozoon brocchii   **Faial Island, Azores**

S: up to 6 cm long. D: Mediterranean Sea. G: found on rocky substrates in 2-25 m depth. Many flatworm species, especially those in the tropics, are brilliantly coloured. They have, however, very poor eye sight and it is very unlikely that they can sense much more than light and dark and passing shadows. Thus, their brilliant colour patterns probably have evolved entirely for defence against predators, mainly fish, which have excellent eye sight. As fish feeding experiments revealed, polyclads were spat out whereas other prey was consumed. Polyclads contain strong toxins such as tetrodotoxin.

Yungia aurantiaca   **Tyrrhenian Sea**

EURYLEPTIDAE
S: up to 2 cm long. D: Sicily, Mediterranean Sea. G: both photos show species of the family Euryleptidae, probably genus *Eurylepta*. Small photo taken by author PW, at night in 1 m depth in a large tide pool on the island of Faial, Azores. More cannot be said about these animals on the basis of only these two photos.

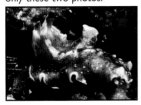

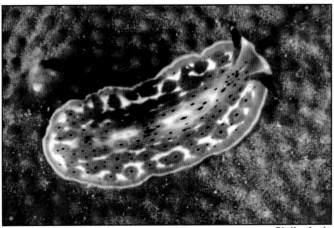

Eurylepta sp   **Sicily, Italy**

S: 80 cm. D: from Norway into the Mediterranean Sea. G: ribbon worms are long, soft-bodied, unsegmented worms with a "sticky" surface. Most are capable to elongate their bodies to quite amazing sizes. *Linneus longissimus* (Europe) reaches 30 m! Ribbon worms have a protrusible proboscis. Its chief function is the capture of living prey, around which it coils and which it then draws to the mouth. In many species, the proboscis bears small calcareous little knifes. *T. superbus* lives on sand and gravel in 5-50 m. Most ribbon worm species, however, cannot be identified from photos.

Tubulanus superbus   North Sea

S: up to more than 1 m. D: all over the world in temperate to tropical latitudes. G: recognized by 5-12 light brown stripes on the back. Soft, thin, long, body only 5 mm wide. One of the most common species of ribbon worms in Med. and temp. Atl., where it is found in seagrass meadows or below stones in 2-15+ m. Active at night.

Baseodiscus delineatus   Madeira

S: 9 cm. D: Greenland and Norway to N-France. G: the bright red colour and the flattened shape are typical. From the low water line down to 500+ m, on sand or gravel. Quite common in Norwegian fjords, especially in winter. Below (Azores): *Drepanophorus spectabilis* also lives in the Med. and reaches a length of 5 cm.

Nipponnemertes pulcher   Norway

Size: up to 40 cm long.
Distribution: Mediterranean Sea.
General: this species used to be called *Linneus geniculatus*. It has a slightly flattened body and a spatula-shaped head. The red-green or brown-green body bears numerous thin white bands. This is one of the most common species of ribbon worms in the Mediterranean Sea, where it can be found below stones, already in shallow water. Like most ribbon worms, it is active only at night.

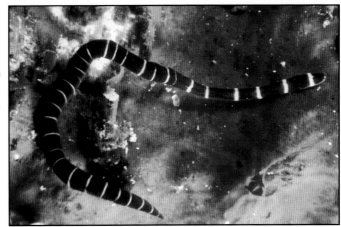

Notospermus geniculatus   Sardinia, Italy

Peanut Worm

S: up to 35 cm. D: world-wide in temperate to tropical waters, including Med. G: the body of sipunculids feels quite solid. A long proboscis can be everted from the frontal end. Most lead a secretive live, buried in soft sediments and feeding mainly on detritus, or hiding below stones and in cracks in the rock. There are only about 160 species of peanut worms in the world, 33 in the Med. *S. nudus* lives about 0.5 m deep in sand, shallow down to a few 100 m. Rectangular sculpturing of the surface distinctive. Eaten in Asia.

Sipunculus nudus   Faial Island, Azores

S: 5 cm (12 cm with proboscis everted). D: Mediterranean Sea, temperate eastern Atlantic. G: from shallow water down to c. 100 m depth, can be locally quite common. <u>Below</u> (Azores): the similarly sized *P. stephensoni*, E-Atlantic, Mediterranean. The appearance of these 2 species is typical of a large number of sipunculids living below stones and in rock cracks.

Phascolosoma granulatum   Madeira

Bonellia
BONELLIIDAE
S: female 1.5 m, males 3 mm .
D: Med.; Norway to Canaries.
G: walnut-sized body of the
female hidden in rock crevices;
proboscis may reach a length
of 1.5 m. It is extended only at
night. The two lobes at the end
(small photo) collect organic
particles from the bottom.

Bonellia viridis   **Tenerife, Canary Islands**

Green Rock Echiuran

S: up to 8 cm (body) and 6 cm
(proboscis). D: Madeira, Canaries, W-Africa; also W-Atl. and
Indo-Pacific. G: hidden below
stones. As in all echiurans, there
is a greatly extendable proboscis
at the front of the plump body.
The brain of the animal is in the
proboscis. Its ventral surface
forms a shallow channel along
which detritus is brought to the
mouth (it cannot be retracted
into the body as in sipunculids,
see above). Males and females of
this species are similar in size.
The green colour is typical of
most echiurans. It is due to a
toxic pigment called "Bonellin".

Ochetostoma baronii   **Madeira**

Azorean Echiuran

S: 20 cm. D: only known from
the Azores. G: described quite
recently. Lives buried in sand, a
large mound indicates its presence (below). Such mounds may
form large fields on sandy bottoms in sheltered bays from 3 to
at least 15 m depth. About 160
echiuran species are known.

Ochetostoma azorica   **Faial Island, Azores**

Plankton means a lot of food for tube worms, Italian Adriatic >>>

Spiral Tube Worm
SABELLIDAE (both pages)
S: body up to 15 cm, crown up to 7 cm long. D: Med.; E-Atl.: Roscoff, France, to Canaries, Azores (absent from Madeira). G: the sedentary bristle worms are a conglomerate of species that have turned to a sessile way of live. Because the sedentary habit evolved repeatedly within the free-moving bristle worms, some of the families of "Sedentaria" are in fact not closely related to each other. Sabellidae live in membranous tubes, often reinforced by the inclusion of mud particles and have a feathery, filter-feeding crown that can be quickly withdrawn into the tube when danger threatens. Many have acute sight (see the story "Invertebrate Vision").

The body of the spiral tube worm is hidden in a long tube. It has up to 200 segments. This sp was transported by man to Brazil, Java, and Australia – most likely via its long-lived larval stage, in the ballast water of ships (see "Long Distance"). Colour of crown variable. The long tubes serve as base for many species.

Sabella spallanzanii   **Mediterranean coast of Israel**

S: crown Ø up to 10 cm.
D: W-Africa, Cape Verdes.
G: difficult to photograph because, on sensing nearby movement, the animals quickly withdraw their crowns into the parchment-like tube. Often in clumps of many animals, 1-35 m. <u>Below:</u> Peacock Worm, *Sabella pavonina,* common in Mediterranean Sea and eastern Atlantic.

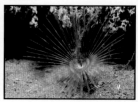

Bispira guinensis   **Cape Verde Islands**

Double-fanned Worm
S: body to 10+, crown to 3+ cm long. D: E-Atl.: Norway to the Canaries; Med. G: there are several closely related spp in this genus, which cannot be told apart by photos. *B. volutacornis* is probably the most common of them. Small photo from Madeira.

Bispira volutacornis   **Bay of Setúbal, Portugal**

Big-eyed Tube Worm
S: body to 5.6 cm, crown to 3.5 cm long. D: E-Atl.: English Channel to SA; Med. G: *Megalomma* literally means "big eye": the 2 dark compound eyes on the tentacles certainly can see images (see also "Invertebrate Vision"). On sand, 2-90+ m. Below (Lanzarote): *Bispira viola,* also found in Mediterranean.

Megalomma vesiculosum   **Cape Verde Islands**

S: up to 20 cm long; diameter of crown about 3 cm. D: Mediterranean Sea; SW-England to Canary Islands. G: the funnel-shaped crown is always directly above the substrate. In muddy sand and mud, in sheltered places such as harbours. Colour of crown can vary from a uniform white to yellow to brown to purple.

Myxicola infundibulum   **Faial Island, Azores**

Devil Worm
HONEYCOMB TUBEWORMS, SABELLARIIDAE (this page)
S: up to 10 cm long. D:Madeira, Canary Islands, Cape Verde Islands, Sao Tomé. G: another species difficult to photograph. The animal withdraws its two filter feeding "devil's horns" on the slightest disturbance. The tube it inhabits is cemented with small stones and shell fragments and can reach a length of 30 cm, often ending below a big stone. Named after author PW, who detected it first at Madeira, then in the Canary Islands and in the Cape Verde Islands and recently at São Tomé Island (new record).

Below (Costa del Sol, Spain): the related species *Lygdamis murata*. Med., NE-Atlantic.

Lygdamis wirtzi   Madeira

Ross Worm
S: body 3 cm long. D: Mediterranean Sea, NE-Atlantic. G: the sand-encrusted tubes of *Sabellaria* spp form massive structures on the shoreline or in shallow water. These may contain 15,000-60,000 individuals per m². The tube openings of some species give the front of the colony a honeycomb appearance. The sabellariid reef at the St. Luvie inlet, Florida, is 9 km long, 1 km wide! *S. spinulosa* specimens collected by author PW after taking this photo were identified by an expert for the family. The very similar and common *S. alveolata* (N-Europe) reaches an age of 10 years, other species 3-5 years. Below: a colony of *Idanthyrsus luciae*, a Cape Verde Islands endemic.

Sabellaria spinulosa   Adriatic Sea, Italy

Lugworm
ARENICOLIDAE

Size: up to 35 cm, usually 10-12 cm long.
Distribution: from the Arctic to the Mediterranean Sea.
General: the Lugworm lives in clean or muddy sand flats on mid-shore, where it occupies a U-shaped burrow. Densities of up to 150 animals per square metre have been recorded. All the diver is likely to see are the heaps of worm-like casts ejected from the rear end of the burrow. The front end is marked by a shallow depression nearby, much more difficult to detect.

Arenicola marina   **Mediterranean Coast of France**

Sand Mason
TEREBELLIDAE

S: 30 cm. D: Arctic to South Africa; Med. G: forms a tube of cemented sand grains, bits of shell, small stones. End of tube divided into numerous small branches, which project above sediment. Feeding tentacles grasp along branches for organic particles. <u>Below</u>: *Polycirrus* sp.

Lanice conchilega   **Ireland**

Medusa Worm
TEREBELLIDAE

S: 15 cm. D: all oceans. G: body hidden in sandy tube, itself below stone or in sand. From it project numerous, long, mobile feeding tentacles. Small organic particles are transported along these to mouth. Tentacles to 50+ cm. <u>Below</u>: body without tube. White spots characteristic.

Eupolymnia nebulosa   **Faial Island, Azores**

Serpula vermicularis   **Crete Island, Greece**

Red Tubicolous Worm
SERPULIDAE (this page)

Size: up to 7 cm long.
Distribution: found in all oceans of the world.
General: the round, calcareous "operculum" next to the crown of the worm is typical for the species. It is used to tightly close the tube when the worm is withdrawn. The tentacle crown may be yellow or various shades of red. The species lives from shallow water down to more than 800 m depth.

The second large photo is a close-up of a reef-like colony of this species which was about 3-4 m long and consisted of thousands of individuals.

The small photo below from the Isle of Man shows the Post Horn Worm *Spirorbis spirorbis*. Its tube (up to 3.5 mm in diameter) is coiled clockwise. (The similar Norwegian species *Circeis spirillum* is coiled counter-clockwise.) This small species typically grows on fronds of seaweed, and is distributed from the coasts of Norway to the English Channel.

Serpula vermicularis   **Galway, Ireland**

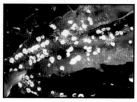

S: animal to 10, tube to 20+ cm.
D: in all oceans of the world.
G: lives in a large white, calcareous tube. U-shaped crown white, yellow or red. In shallow water the sp prefers dark places.
Below: *Pomatoceros triqueter,* to 2.5 cm, very common worldwide. Tube triangular in crosscut but the elevated distal ends can be circular. Tentacle crown white, yellow, red or brown.

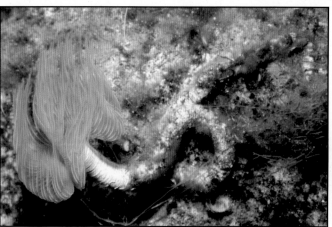

Protula tubularia   **Crete Island, Greece**

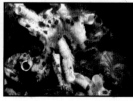

Filigree Tube Worm
SERPULIDAE

S: 4 mm; colony Ø to 20+ cm. D: all oceans. G: white tubes of many individuals form a complex network. One tentacle on each side of worm with tiny, cup-shaped "operculum", used for sealing tube. Simultan. hermaphrodite. See also similar *S. dysteri* below.

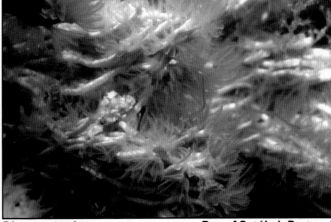

Filograna implexa   **Bay of Setúbal, Portugal**

Tusk Worm
SERPULIDAE

S: 2.5 cm. D: Norway to Canar. G: hard, tusk-shaped tube (may be confused with scaphopods, p. 239) has 2 layers, outer thick, glassy, inner thin, opaque. Crown small. Sand, mud, 10-1000+ m, up to 500 per m². *Salmacina dysteri* (below, North Sea) similar to *Filograna implexa* but no opercula.

Ditrupa arietina   **Madeira**

Periscope Tube Worm
ONUPHIDAE

S: max 50 cm. D: Med., temp. E-Atl. G: tubes in sand, mud, 5+ m. By day, only antennae project, at night, animal partly emerges. Grabs any organic object, pulls it into tube. The 2 large mandibles gave a surprising bite to author PW when he dug up a specimen.

Diopatra neapolitana   **Tenerife, Canary Islands**

FIRE!

The Fire Worm *Hermodice carunculata* reaches a length of 30 cm and can grow to the thickness of a finger. It lives on many different kinds of bottoms, in the warmer parts of the Mediterranean Sea and on both sides of the subtropical and tropical Atlantic. Peter Wirtz tells us about this beauty which actually is a beast...

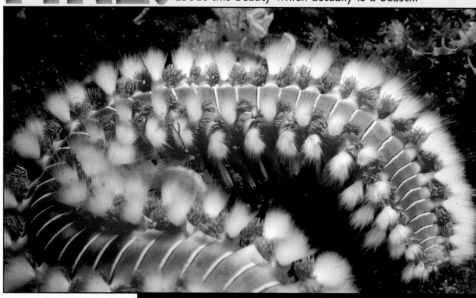

When feeling threatened, the Fire Worm spreads its bristles.

This is an impressive species for several reasons. Each of the up to 125 segments bears two tufts of white bristles. When the Fire Worm feels threatened it can spread the bristles. Do not touch this worm! The bristles easily penetrate the skin, where they break off and cause an intense burning sensation that can last for weeks.

Any carrion, here a dead fish, on the bottom of the sea will soon be covered in Fire Worms.

Therefore the name Fire Worm! You can try to remove some of the bristles with cello tape but you will not be able to remove all of them...

As the photos show, the colour of the worm can vary from red to greenish, with golden rings between the

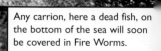

Fire Worm feeding on dead irregular sea urchin.

segments. In addition to the two tufts of bristles, each segment bears a pair of red, branched gills. The large pleated and branched red appendage on the head of the worm is called a caruncle. The function of this structure is still not known with certainty but it is most likely to be a chemosensory organ, that is it probably serves for smelling.

Fire Worms prey on many different invertebrates and belong to the few animals that even eat sea anemones! The Caribbean shrimp *Periclimenes*

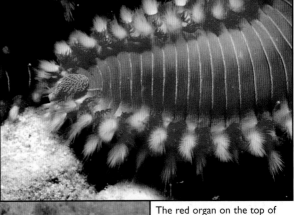

The red organ on the top of the head, called a caruncle, probably serves for smelling.

Smelling something interesting?

yucatanicus is said to defend its sea anemone against approaching Fire Worms, thus re-paying the protection it receives from the anemone against its own predators. Fire Worms also prey on coral, such as *Tubastrea*.

In addition to preying on invertebrates, Fire Worms are scavengers. Any dead animal on the bottom of the sea, from jelly fish to true fish, will attract them from far away. Soon, the corpse is entirely covered by a mass of Fire Worms...

Fire Worm feeding on *Tubastraea* coral at the Cape Verde Islands.

Fire Worms even eat sea anemones, in this case an *Anemonia viridis*.

S: up to 5 cm. D: Med. G: the bristles arising from the legs ("parapodia") are well visible in the photos. Body has up to 31 segments. Below stones during daytime, in 5+ m, on muddy or sandy bottoms or between algae, emerges only at night.

Gyptis rosea   **Costa del Sol, Spain**

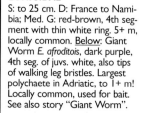

EUNICIDAE
S: to 25 cm. D: France to Namibia; Med. G: red-brown, 4th segment with thin white ring. 5+ m, locally common. Below: Giant Worm *E. afroditois*, dark purple, 4th seg. of juvs. white, also tips of walking leg bristles. Largest polychaete in Adriatic, to 1+ m! Locally common, used for bait. See also story "Giant Worm".

Eunice torquata   **Costa del Sol, Spain**

AMPHINOMIDAE
S: 15 cm. D: all (sub)tropical seas, Med. G: uniformly pink with thick white erectile bristles. Locally common, usually in clumps of several individuals. A predator and scavenger.

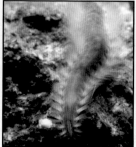

Eurythoe complanata   **Canary Islands**

Leopard Worm
HESIONIDAE
S: 7 cm. D: France to Angola; Mediterranean. G: numerous white rings on reddish body are typical. Below stones during the daytime, in 5+ m. The small photo shows the same species from the Cape Verdes, where it has stronger colours.

Hesione splendida   Faial Island, Azores

EUNICIDAE

S: 6 cm. D: North Sea to Angola; Med.; W-Atl., E-Pac. G: front projects from transparent, stiff tube, worm pulls tube after it in the manner of a caddis fly larva. On mud, sand, 30-1700+ m. Below: *Phyllodoce madeirensis*, circum(sub)tropical, Med. 15 cm. Crawls amazingly fast, can swim.

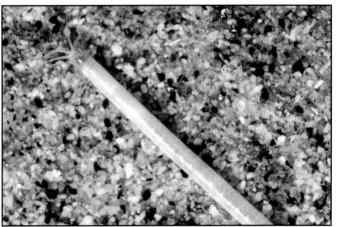

Hyalinoecia tubicola   Tuscany, Italy

Sea Mouse
APHRODITIDAE
S: up to 20 cm. D: E-Atl.: Norway to Canary Islands; Med. G: easy to identify because of its characteristic, oval body shape, the many small, pelt-like bristles on its back and the large iridescent bristles on its side. The pelt hides a row of fairly large scales, which the animal occasionally slightly lifts to ventilate the gills. On the lower side, the approximately 40 body segments can be seen; the appearance of the belly has been liked to "a deeply ridged shoe sole". In mud, sand, ploughs through it in search of prey (worms, small bivalves). Shallow down to several 100 m.

Aphrodita aculeata   North Sea

Sea Star Worm
POLYNOIDAE

S: up to 4 cm. D: Med.; in the eastern Atlantic at the Canary Islands but apparently absent from Madeira (even though its main host is common there). G: as the Latin name *"astericola"* says, this species lives with sea stars, mostly *Astropecten aranciacus* (p. 274), but also other *Astropecten* spp and *Luidia* (p. 276). It is usually found in the groove on the lower side of the arms of the sea star. However, this sp can even enter the mouth and the stomach of the sea star! The animal in the photo is just entering the mouth of the sea star. Reportedly, *A. astericola* can spend up to one hour inside the stomach without being damaged by its digestive juices. It feeds by stealing particles gathered by the sea star.

The body of *A. astericola* consists of up to more than 100 segments. Its back is covered by about 45 transparent plates with a dark margin. The fleshy-pink body of the worm is visible through them.

Acholoe astericola   **Lanzarote, Canary Islands**

ICHTHYOBDELLIDAE

S: up to 3 cm. D: Iceland and N-Norway south to Scotland. G: most leeches live in freshwater and on land. There are, however, several marine species, all parasites sucking blood. Leeches are segmented worms, like the polychaetes, but have no bristles. They crawl in a typical "looping" movement. Some leeches also swim quite well. A sucker at the rear and at the front is characteristic for leeches. Blood taken from fish can be stored inside branches of the gut for a long time. All leeches are hermaphrodites: every animal is male as well as female – but not necessarily at the same time. In some species, individuals are male first and copulate with as many other males as possible. Later, they turn female and use some of the sperm received and stored in the body to fertilize the eggs. Photo: northern sp on Bull Rout *(Myoxocephalus scorpius)*. They hold on with their strong rear sucker.

Calliobdella nodulifera   **Norway**

MY SHELL IS MY CASTLE

Shrimps are highly vulnerable and therefore the preferred prey of many marine fish. Hermit crabs have found a good way to protect their bodies from predators, as is well known, but a group of shrimps have come up with an equally practical solution. They live inside of bivalve molluscs whose hard shells provide them with a perfect sanctuary.

Penshells of the genus *Pinna* are quite common in the Mediterranean and Eastern Atlantic. Practically every Spiny Penshell *Pinna rudis* (below) at the Azores or Madeira is inhabited by a pair of shrimps *Pontonia pinnophylax* (left). If one looks down into the open slit of the penshell one will usually detect the thick upward-turned posterior of the female shrimp. The small male is more difficult to find. The presence of the shrimps appears to offer no benefits to the bivalve. On the contrary, the shrimps steal some of the particles filtered out of the water by the bivalve.

Another bivalve species frequently inhabited by shrimps of the genus *Pontonia* is the Rock Oyster *Spondylus senegalensis* (below right). Pairs or single shrimps of *Pontonia manningi* (below) live in it. The shells of the Rock Oyster are among the thickest shells of bivalves and thus these shrimps live behind very strong castle walls.

HELMUT DEBELIUS

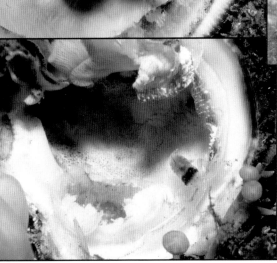

Bivalves are sedentary filterers that always populate places where currents transport sufficient plankton for their nourishment. In exotic places such as the Cape Verde Islands, other *Pontonia* shrimps can still be detected in bivalves. The photo at the left shows a *Pontonia* in a *Pseudochama radians* at a depth of 10 m off the island of São Tiago. Undescribed when the photo was taken, the species has in the meantime received the name *Pontonia pilosa*. This is a much smaller bivalve species than the big Rock Oysters (compare the thumb of the photographer in the left of the photo), and thus the shrimp is also much smaller.

Carthagian Barnacle

BALANIDAE (this page)

S: up to 2 cm in Ø. D: world-wide in temperate waters, incl. Med. G: barnacles were not recognized as crustaceans for a long time. Charles Darwin showed that they have a crustacean larva. The larva settles and builds a conical house around itself. The appendages, which appear out of the top and keep up a constant grasping movement, correspond to the legs of other crustaceans. Arrangement of the walls of the house (plates) and its doors is species-typical.

Common on North American coasts. It was suspected to have been introduced into the Mediterranean Sea by ships (see the story "Long Distance") but shells excavated by archaeologists at the Carthaginian naval base near Tunis prove that the species has been in the Med. for over 2000 years. For its size, *B. amphitrite* has rather thin plates.

<u>Below</u> *B. balanus* (Isle of Man). Arctic Norway to S-Britain. One of the most common species in Britain, from the lower intertidal down to several 100 m. Can be recognized by the irregular, crenellate edge of the shell.

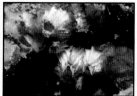

Balanus amphitrite   **Adriatic Sea**

Pyramid Barnacle

S: c. 1 cm Ø. D: in all oceans in (sub)tropical waters, including the Mediterranean Sea. G: 1-40 m, can completely cover rocks. Plates with many small, slightly red longitudinal lines. <u>Below</u> (Roscoff, France): *B. crenatus*, N-Norway to Bay of Biscay, lower intertidal to a few metres depth, on large algae, e.g. *Fucus serratus*.

Balanus trigonus   **Madeira**

Kite-shaped Barnacle
CHTHAMALIDAE

S: 6-10 mm in Ø. D: Scotland to W-Africa, including the eastern-most Canary Islands but absent from Madeira and Azores; Med. G: very common in the interti-dal. Rather similar to *C. stellatus* (below), which lives in the same area. Opening of *montagui* kite-shaped, of *stellatus* oval-circular.

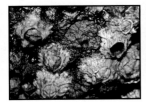

Chthamalus montagui   Gulf of Genoa, Italy

Giant Barnacle

S: 4 cm high. D: Azores, Madei-ra. G: harvested, eaten (Azores, see "Appetising"). Common just below water line on exposed shores but now overexploited locally. To 10+ m. Empty shells are used as housing by many ani-mals, such as the Red Blennies *(Parablennius ruber)* in the photo.

Megabalanus azoricus   Terceira Island, Azores

Turtle Barnacle
BALANIDAE

S: 2 cm. D: world-wide on sea turtles in (sub)tropical waters; Med. G: unmistakable, opening always faces into the current around a swimming sea turtle. Below (Madeira): Coral Barnacle *Megatrema anglicum*, on solitary coral, *Paracyathus pulchellus*: small bump on coral stalk or oral disc.

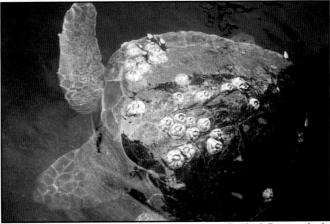

Chelonibia testudinarium   Gulf of Genoa, Italy

Common Goose
Barnacle   LEPADIDAE

S: body up to 5 cm, stalk usually
10-20, max 75 cm. D: cosmopolitan in warmer seas. G: five
large smooth calcareous plates
typical. Attached to floating
objects such as driftwood,
buoys or the hull of ships by its
dark wrinkly stalk. Sea turtles
may also be covered by them.
In medieval times, people
thought that ducks hatch from
these animals – thus the Latin
"*anatifera*". Simultaneous hermaphrodite: animals cross-fertilize
by means of a very long penis.
Two weeks later, well-developed
larvae are released. Below: the
cirri grasping for plankton.

Lepas anatifera   **Faial Island, Azores**

Rock Goose Barnacle
SCALPELLIDAE

S: 8 cm. D: SW-Cornwall to
Morocco; SW-Med. G: in large
colonies on rocky, wave-bat-
tered shores, intertidal down
to a few metres, once very
common but now almost disappeared (collected for human
consumption), still common
only in areas difficult to reach
by man. Boiled in salt water,
the fleshy content of the stalk
is considered a delicacy in
Spain and Portugal. Ovaries inside stalk. *Oxynaspis celata*
(below) grows on black coral
such as *Anthipathella wollastoni*
or *Tanacetipathes spinescens* (p.
78) in 7-1400+ m, in temperate and tropical waters world-
wide. Only 1.5 cm long.

Mitella pollicipes   **Brittany, France**

RHIZOCEPHALANS

Parasitic Barnacle

S: 2 cm. D: Mediterranean Sea, English Channel, North Sea, Baltic Sea. G: Rhizocephala are parasitic on other crustaceans, mostly decapods. *S. carcini* infects crabs of the family Portunidae and Pirimelidae, the Green Crab *Carcinus maenas* being the most common host. The larva is of the same type as in other cirripeds. Female larvae attach to the leg of a crab and bore into it. Then the cells of the larva migrate into the body of the crab and the empty larval skin falls of. The story, seemingly out of a horror movie, continues in the following way. The cells of the parasite multiply and form a root-like tissue through the body of the victim. After about seven months, the parasite opens a hole, usually on the belly of the crab and a sac-like structure grows from it. This sac contains the ovaries and has a small opening. A male larva can enter through the opening and start life as a minute parasitic male inside the body of the female. New larvae are released through the hole in the external sac.

Sacculina carcini   North Sea

ASCOTHORACIDS

SYNAGOGIDAE

Size: 4 mm.
Distribution: Azores, Cape Verde Islands.
General: the approximately 70 species of ascothoracids were formerly included in the cirripeds. Many species are endoparasites (parasites living in the body) of black coral, gorgonarians, brittle stars, and sea stars. Others are ectoparasites (parasites living on the body) of black coral, zoanthids, and crinoids. The members of the genus *Synagoga* are the only species in this group that do not live attached to a host or even inside a host. Previously, this genus was known only from the Mediterranean Sea. The species shown in the photo is an undescribed species that author PW found on the black coral *Antipathella wollastoni* and *Antipathella subpinnata* (page 78) in the eastern Atlantic.

Synagoga nov sp   Faial Island, Azores

GELATINOUS INVASION

Fifteen years ago, three species of jellyfish were living in the Black Sea: the Sea Gooseberry *Pleurobrachia pileus,* the Moon Jellyfish *Aurelia aurita,* and *Rhizostoma pulmo.* Then, at the end of the 1980s, the western Atlantic comb jelly *Mnemiopsis leidyi* appeared and a whole ecosystem began to change dramatically.

Mnemiopsis leidyi, a voracious newcomer to the Black Sea.

FLORIAN GRANER

Nobody knows how *Mnemiopsis* managed to move from the western Atlantic to the Black Sea; perhaps in the ballast water of ships. The warm water, relatively low salinity and high zooplankton levels of the Black Sea apparently were ideal for the newcomer: it started to multiply explosively. In 1989, biomass levels were up to 2 kg wet weight per cubic meter of water, totalling close to one billion tons of *Mnemiopsis* for the entire sea!

The species is a voracious predator, feeding on many small animals including fish larvae and fish eggs. Simultaneous with the enormous increase in the quantity of *Mnemiopsis,* the amount of zooplankton declined and the Turkish anchovy fishery collapsed. From 1989 on, the numbers of *Mnemiopsis* in the Black Sea began to decline, probably because the comb jellies had eaten almost all there was to eat. In 1995 they were at 460 g per cubic meter. Low levels of glycogen in the body suggested that they were close to starving. Zooplankton levels (including fish eggs and larvae) remained very low.

In October 1997, yet another new jellyfish appeared in the Black Sea. This time it was the common Atlantic and Mediterranean Sea Mitre *Beroe ovata.* This species is also a predator. However, it feeds on much larger organisms than *Mnemiopsis.* In fact, it started to feed on *Mnemiopsis!*

Mnemiopsis numbers declined even more and in the middle of 2001 they had reached their lowest level after the peak development, an average of only 12 g per cubic meter of water. Zooplankton levels (including fish eggs and larvae), however, remain very low...

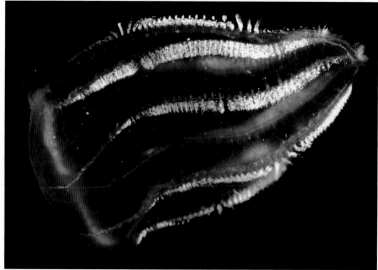

LEOPOLDO MORO

Unbelievable as it may seem, the story is about to repeat itself. Because of a channel connecting the rivers Danube and Volga, it is possible to get, by ship, from the Black Sea to the Caspian Sea. In the middle of the 1990s, *Mnemiopsis* was transported to the Caspian Sea! There it is currently multiplying explosively. Zooplankton levels and fishery have entered into a steep decline...

The Sea Mitre *Beroe ovata* eats *Mnemiopsis leidyi.*

Fish Fleas
CALIGIDAE (this page)

Size: up to 2 cm (with egg sacs).
Distribution: that of the host species.
General: there are many different species of fish fleas of the genus *Caligus*. It is impossible to identify them from photos. Some species are very catholic in their choice of host; *Caligus elongatus*, for instance, has been recorded from more than 80 different species of fish in the northern Atlantic. Other species are specialists; *Caligus labracis*, for instance, apparently only lives on the Ballan Wrasse *Labrus bergylta* and on the Cuckoo Wrasse *Labrus mixtus*.

   Caligus are not firmly attached to the skin of the fish. They are able to hop, quite rapidly, to a different place when disturbed, by the hand of a diver for instance. They feed on the mucus of the fish and are probably not harmful to their hosts (in contrast to parasitic isopods like *Nerocila* or *Anilocra*; see page 111).

   Females carry the eggs as two packets attached on either side of the tail.

   The photos show fish fleas on a large grouper, *Epinephelus marginatus* (top photo) and on a Conger Eel, *Conger conger* (lower photo).

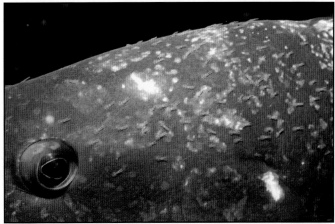

***Caligus* species**   **Madeira**

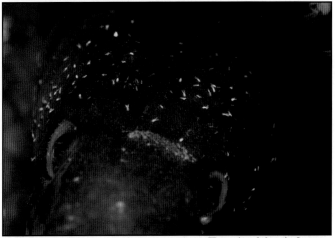

***Caligus* species**   **Terceira Island, Azores**

Nordmann's Fish Flea

Size: up to 3 cm.
Distribution: that of the host species.
General: the species of the genus *Lepeophtheirus* are rather similar to those of the genus *Caligus*. *Lepeophtheirus salmonis* is a pest in salmon aquaculture because at high infestation rates they do weaken and damage the fish. The species *Lepeophtheirus nordmanni* that lives on Ocean sunfish *Mola mola*, shown in the photo, is brightly pink.

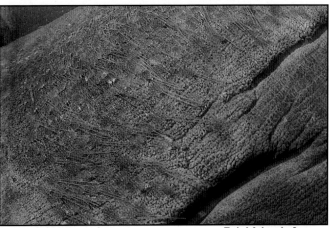

Lepeophtheirus nordmanni   **Faial Island, Azores**

Baltic Slater
IDOTEIDAE

S: 3 cm. D: Norway to Med., Black Sea. NW-Atl. G: 3-pointed abdomen typical, colour variable. Dorso-ventrally flattened body typical for most isopods. <u>Below</u>: *Ligia italica*, very common in Med. It lives directly at the water line and apparently feels comfortable inside and outside of the water.

Idotea baltica   **Baltic Sea**

CYMOTHOIDAE

S: 2 cm. D: Med. G: sometimes has two yellowish longitudinal body bands. A common fish parasite in shallow water in Med., its mouthparts bore deeply into the victim's tissue, small fish may be killed. <u>Below</u>: the fish parasite *N. armata* on a Bigeye, *Heteropriacantus cruentatus*, at Madeira.

Nerocila bivittata   **Crete Island, Greece**

GNATHIIDAE

S: 8 mm. G: larval stage (praniza) of gnathiid isopods sucks blood from fish. The rare photo shows such a larva sucking on a sleeping wrasse. Males with huge mandibles. In crevices, sediments and empty mollusc or barnacle shells during the day. <u>Below</u>: *Anilocra capensis*, similar to *Nerocila*.

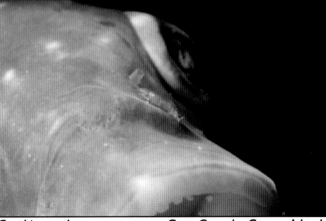

Gnathia species   **Gran Canaria, Canary Islands**

Stenopleustes latipes   **Sognefjord, Norway**

Hydroid Amphipod

GAMMARIDEA (this page)
Size: up to 1.2 cm.
Distribution: in the NE-Atlantic, from the Arctic Ocean and Greenland to the Azores.
General: this species has the laterally compressed body shape typical for gammarid amphipods. There are many hundreds of amphipod species in Europe, most less than 1 cm in length and impossible to identify without the help of a microscope. Almost all European amphipods are rather drab coloured, grey to brown (like the gammarid in the small photo on the bottom of this page). *Stenopleustes latipes* is an exception. The lovely red colour of the species is, however, not visible where it lives: at a depth of 60 m (rarely 30 m) to 1400 m. With its strong legs *("latipes"* literally means "broad legs") it climbs in bushes of the hydroid genus *Eudendrium* (p. 21). On such bushes, *S. latipes* frequently live in large numbers of adult and young animals.

Fat Gammarid

S: 7 mm (in the Atlantic rarely to 12 mm). D: from N-Norway into the Med. G: this plump species *("obesus"* means "fat") lives mainly on sandy or muddy bottoms and on kelp and has been found from 10-300 m. The small photo shows an unidentified gammarid from Sweden. There are about 20 species that look very similar to this one! Some are up to 3 cm long. They can be found between plants in shallow water. Other, similar species live in rotting seaweed at the shoreline.

Iphimedia obesa   **Trondheimsfjord, Norway**

Sea Star
Skeleton Shrimp

CAPRELLIDAE (this page)
S: 1 cm. D: Azores. G: skeleton (or ghost) shrimps are slender animals, standing upright with claws held in praying mantis like fashion. Claw of males with poisonous spine, used to fight rival males. Skeleton shrimps seasonally occur in enormous numbers on seaweed and are the main prey of many fishes. Frequently associated with other animals such as sponges or hydroids (see below). Author PW found this sp on sea stars/cucumbers at the Azores, below 20 m. Shown on *Ophidiaster ophidianus* (p. 276); also on *A. wollastoni* (p. 78).

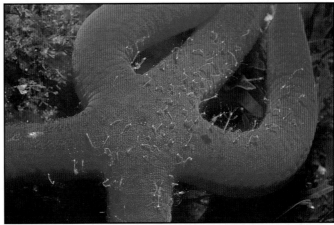

Caprella stella   Faial Island, Azores

S: 3 cm. D: Norway to France, W-Baltic Sea. Also cold W-Atl., Alaska. G: very common, often in large numbers on the sponge *Halichondria panicea* (p. 13). Shallow down to several 100 m. Below (Cape Verdes): *Phtisica marina* on the hydroid *Nematophorus clarkei* (p. 21); often associated with cnidarians. In Mediterranean on the tips of the tentacles of *Anemonia viridis* (p. 47).

Caprella linearis   Spitsbergen, Norway

S: up to 1.7 cm. D: Med.; Norway to Senegal, including Azores, Madeira, Canary Islands. G: this is another common species, frequently associated with cnidarians. Shown are animals on the severely nettling Stinging Bush Hydroid *Macrorhynchia philippina* (see p. 20). It is unknown how the skeleton shrimps manage to avoid being stung by the cnidocells of their host.

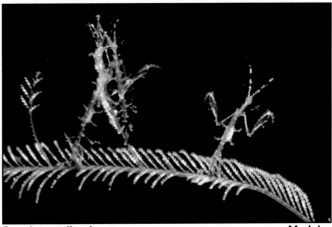

Pseudoprotella phasma   Madeira

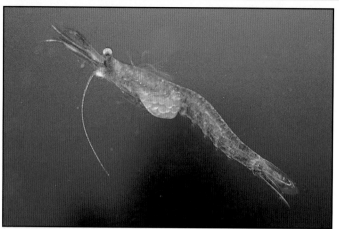

Leptomysis gracilis   **Netherlands, North Sea**

Bottom Opossum Shrimp
MYSIDAE (both pages)
S: 18 mm. D: Norway to Med.
G: most opossum shrimps are
only about 1 cm long. Many
species form swarms over the
bottom. They are then often
confused for juvenile fish.
Females posses a large ventral
pouch for holding the eggs and
the developing young (popular
name). The male places the
sperm into this pouch and the
eggs are fertilized there. The end
of the body forms a distinct tail
fan. At the base of this fan lie
two "statocysts" (balancing
organs), one of the most characteristic features of mysids. Photo:
female with (relatively few, large)
eggs in its brood pouch.

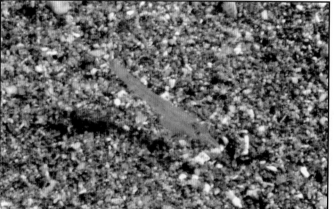

Leptomysis truncata   **Gran Canaria, Canary Islands**

Yellow Opossum Shrimp
S: up to 11 mm. D: Med., Black
Sea, Canary Islands. G: the yellow
colour shown in the photo is
typical for the species, although
other colour forms exist. The
species forms small swarms close
to the bottom. Often a single or
a few animals of this species join
a swarm of a different opossum
shrimp. The photo shown here
provides the first record for the
species for the Canary Islands
and thus the first record of the
species outside of the Mediterranean Sea. Many small species
believed to be endemic (i.e.
restricted to) for the well-
explored Mediterranean Sea
probably have simply been overlooked in the area outside.

Leptomysis lingvura   **Adriatic Sea**

Anemone
Opossum Shrimp
S: up to 17 mm. D: Med.; E-Atl.:
Norway to Morocco, Canaries.
G: this is a common species in
sea grass beds. It also frequently
forms swarms close to *Anemonia viridis* (p. 47). When danger
threatens they dive even deeper
between the tentacles of the
anemone. In contrast to several
other crustaceans associated
with this anemone (see for
instance *Inachus phalangium* on
p. 146), they are not immune to
the stinging action of the
anemone's cnidocells and have
to be careful not to touch any
of the tentacles! *Leptomysis
lingvura* most commonly lives
between 0.5 and 6 m depth.

S: 12 mm. D: Madeira, Canaries. G: very common at Madeira (swarms of hundreds of animals in shallow water). 5-30 m. Similar to the Med. *L. heterophila*, also frequently associates with other invertebrates, e.g. the sea urchin *Diadema antillarum*. <u>Below</u>: undescribed *Schistomysis* sp, also in large swarms of many hundreds over sand or sea grass at the Canary Islands.

***Leptomysis* undescribed species**   **Madeira**

S: 2.8 cm. D: Med.; North Sea to Morocco, Madeira, Canaries. G: long rostrum typical; common. 2-20 m. In swarms of up to 20,000 animals. In sea grass meadows, solitary individuals may be found swimming or even clinging to the leaves during the day. Opossum shrimps in temperate or tropical waters usually live less than one year, producing several broods per lifetime.

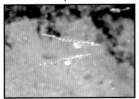

Siriella armata   **Isle of Man**

Chameleon Shrimp
S: up to 3.2 cm. D: Iceland to France; common in the Baltic Sea (see also the story "Long Distance"). G: large, common, shallow between plants near sand. Often in tide pools, also enters brackish water. Hormonally-controlled colour change (name), can adapt within a few minutes; transparent, yellow, yellow-green, brown, almost black.

Praunus flexuosus   **Isle of Man**

Mediterranean Boxer Shrimp
BOXER SHRIMPS, STENOPODIDAE

S: up to 7 cm. D: Med.; from Portugal to the Equator, including Azores, Madeira, Canaries. G: unmistakable because of its golden colour. The antennae usually are white but may be red. During the day in caves, coming out only at night. On rocky bottoms from shallow water down to about 700 m. Related Indo-Pacific species are cleaner shrimps and this has also been suggested for S. spinosus (the conspicuous white antennae seem to indicate it) but up to now there is no evidence for it.

Stenopus spinosus   Madeira

Mediterranean Rock Shrimp
ROCK SHRIMPS, SICYONIDAE

Size: up to 8 cm but usually less than 6 cm.
Distribution: Mediterranean Sea; in the eastern Atlantic from southern Portugal to the Equator.
General: this species lives on sandy, muddy and shelly bottoms and in seagrass beds from shallow water down to 120 m. In some areas of the Mediterranean, the Mediterranean rock shrimp is fished for and marketed but, because of its very hard armour, it is not highly esteemed.

Sicyonia carinata   Ionian Sea, Greece

Pink Shrimp
PANDALID SHRIMPS, PANDALIDAE

Size: up to 16 cm but usually less than 8 cm.
Distribution: from Iceland and the Faroes to the English Channel; cold W-Atlantic.
General: this species can be encountered on rocky and soft bottoms. There are 10-12 small spines on the long rostrum. There is a small spine on the carapace, just below the eye. The Pink shrimp lives from the intertidal down to about 1000 m . In some areas of the NE-Atlantic it is fished for. On sandy bottoms it is much paler than shown here.

Pandalus montagui   Norway

Plesionika narval   Ibiza, Spain

Unicorn Shrimp, Narval Shrimp
PANDALID SHRIMPS, PANDALIDAE

S: 9.5 cm without the rostrum which can be almost as long. D: Med.; SW-Spain to St. Helena, Azores, Madeira, Canaries, Cape Verdes; Red Sea, Indo-Pacific. G: to about 900 m. In shallow water, it hides in caves during the day and thousands of animals may cover the walls. At night they emerge but often stay together in large groups. Individuals are first males and later change into females. As in probably all family members, the eggs carried on the belly of the females are blue in colour.

Hippolyte prideauxiana   Costa Brava, Spain

Feather Star Shrimp
HIPPOLYTID SHRIMPS, HIPPOLYTIDAE

S: up to 2.5 cm. D: Mediterranean Sea; from western Scotland and western Ireland to the Canary Islands, including Madeira but not yet recorded from the Azores. G: as the name indicates, this species lives on feather stars (Antedon bifida and A. mediterranea, p. 265), where it is perfectly camouflaged. It used to be called Hippolyte huntii and lives from shallow water down to about 60 m. It probably feeds on the particles collected by the feather star.

HIPPOLYTIDAE

S: 3 cm. D: Med.; Norway to Canaries, Azores, Madeira. G: on a wide range of substrates, variable in colour: on seagrass green (animal below, put on rock for photo), otherwise grey, red, brown. Often associated with cnidarians, e.g. Macrorhynchia philippina (large photo; p. 20).

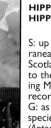

Hippolyte varians   Madeira

Seagrass Shrimp

HIPPOLYTIDAE (this page)
S: males up to 3 cm, females up to 5 cm. D: Med.; Ireland to Morocco. G: mainly lives between seagrass or algae, down to 30 m, and frequently is green in colour. Below: the Hidden Shrimp *Eualus occultus* (1 cm) hides below stones, also on stem of *Telmatactis cricoides* (p. 54).

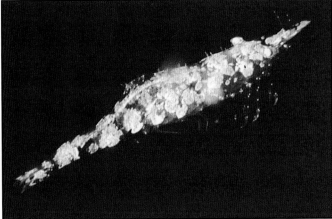

Hippolyte inermis   Costa Brava, Spain

White-striped Cleaner Shrimp

Size: up to 6 cm.
Distribution: in eastern Atlantic: Madeira to Ascension Island, Canary Islands, Cape Verde Islands; tropical W-Atl.
General: this beautiful cleaner shrimp is a simultaneous hermaphrodite: every large animal is a male and female at the same time. Usually, *L. grabhami* lives in pairs. Author PW has checked 188 groups and singletons at Madeira and the Canaries. In 41% of these cases, a single animal was encountered, in 54% 2, in 2% 3, and in 3% 4 animals. That is, most *L. grabhami* (65% of the 313 animals recorded) live in pairs, only 25% alone (mostly juveniles).

Fish apparently know where a pair of cleaner shrimps lives. They go there frequently to get rid of parasites (especially larvae of gnathiid isopods, see p. 111). The shrimps eat these parasites and thus get their food delivered to their home. At Madeira and the Canary Islands, the Atlantic Damselfish *Chromis limbata* is the most common client (top photo) but the White-striped Cleaner Shrimp cleans many different species of fish, including sting rays, morays and groupers. When cleaning groupers, they even enter the mouth of the large predator without being swallowed.

Lysmata grabhami   Madeira

Lysmata grabhami   Fuerteventura, Canary Islands

Lysmata seticaudata   **Costa Brava, Spain**

Monaco Cleaner Shrimp
HIPPOLYTIDAE (this page)

S: up to 5 cm. D: Med.; from the French Atlantic coast to the Canary Islands, including the Azores and Madeira. G: a locally common species that sometimes acts as a cleaner shrimp. However, where *L. grabhami* (above) is common (Madeira, Canaries), *L. seticaudata* appears to be outcompeted as a cleaner and has not yet be seen cleaning fish, as it commonly does in the Med. Recorded on a variety of bottoms, from shallow water down to 60 m depth. This species is fished for in some areas and sold in fish markets.

Thor amboinensis   **Madeira**

Squat Shrimp

S: up to 2 cm. D: in the eastern Atlantic from Madeira to the Cape Verde Islands. G: this is an unmistakable species, often associated with cnidarians. It has been recorded in association with many different species of sea anemones, such as the Club-tipped Anemone *Telmatactis cricoides* (<u>photo</u>) and recently also *Anemonia viridis* and also on many different species of coral. When excited it holds its tail up and waves it. The Squat Shrimp is usually encountered in groups of several animals (up to 18 at the Canary Islands).

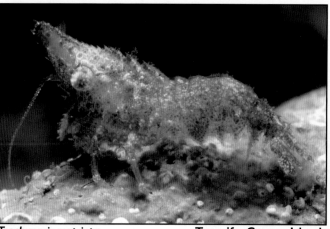

Trachycaris restricta   **Tenerife, Canary Islands**

S: 2 cm. D: Canary Islands to St. Helena. G: extremely difficult to detect, perfectly blends with the rocks it is sitting on. May not be as rare as it is supposed to be. Recorded from rocky substrates down to 50 m depth. A closely related western Atlantic form is now considered a separate species. <u>Below</u>: red morph.

HANDY TOOLS

The claws of crabs and lobsters display remarkable diversity in form and function. They are the crustacean's ultimate survival tools, finely adapted to the needs of each species: cutlery for feeding, weapons for defence, shovels for digging, signalling devices and reproductive aids. Robert Elner and Roger Hughes report.

All claws work on the same basic mechanical system. The moveable "finger" at the top of the claw is a simple lever with a hinge. The lower part of the finger, below the hinge, is connected to a large contracting "closer" muscle and, above the hinge, there is a smaller distending "opener" muscle. As the closer muscle contracts it pulls the finger down and squeezes any object against the lower, fixed finger. The

The European Lobster has two differently shaped claws. The large claw is used for crushing shells while the lighter one is a cutting tool.

action of each claw is a trade-off between power and speed of closure. Bulky claws with short fingers will have a lever system with a high mechanical advantage and deliver slow, powerful forces while slim claws with long fingers can nip rapidly. Similarly, the shape of the fingers, size and type of the muscles, as well as the form of the claw teeth, all influence claw action – varying from vice-like crushing,

The strong crushing teeth of the right claw of *Chaceon affinis* are at the base of the claw.

PHOTOS: PETER WIRTZ

to rapid cutting or scissoring, and scraping. So, while eyes are said to be windows to the human soul, claws can be viewed as windows to the life style of crabs and lobsters.

Dimorphism: some crabs and lobsters have overcome the limitations of the trade-off between claw speed and power by having a larger claw that is strong but slow and a smaller claw that is fast but weak. This "dimorphism" not only increases the repertoire of claw applications but also the combination of both claw types can be more effective in feeding. With tough molluscs, for instance, the fast claw holds and manipulates the prey while the slow claw squeezes the shell.

Tools with teeth: the mechanics of the claw lever system are such that the forces produced are more powerful nearer the hinge than the tip – hence, crabs and lobsters prefer to crush armoured prey near the base of their claws, where broad molar-like teeth can support the proportionately greater forces.

Hallmarks for strength and size: in the evolutionary "arms-race" between predators and prey, crabs and lobsters have developed progressively stronger claws in response to better armouring of their molluscan prey. The American Lobster (*Homarus americanus*) has the largest claws of any crustacean. *Carcinus maenas* feeding on a large mussel.

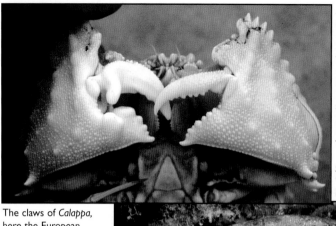

A 17-kg-male had a crusher almost 40 cm in length and 50 cm in girth. Forces of over 25 kg have been recorded from mid-way along the crusher claw of a large American Lobster. However, it is likely that these claws evolved as signals of reproductive prowess, since they appear larger than necessary for feeding and defense.

Green Crab (Carcinus maenas) claws: the Green or Shore Crab is a small but pugnacious predator along the coasts of

The claws of Calappa, here the European C. granulata, are unique devices.

Europe and North America – it is remarkable for feeding on far larger molluscs than similar sized crabs of other species. When confronted with molluscs stronger than the maximum forces exerted by its claws, this crab is adept at

Long, thin, fast: the claws of a portunid crab, Cronius ruber.

breaking into the prey at weak spots, such as the hinge or edge of the shell. However, if the prey's armour fails to succumb to such tactics, the crab resorts to repeatedly squeezing the shell in the same area with lesser pressure. This "pulsing" can go on for several minutes and results in minute fractures within the prey shell extending and joining together until it eventually cracks open.

Calappa: external appearances can be deceptive, particularly in the case of box crabs (Calappa). The first impression is that these tropical crabs have large and power-

Male of the majid crab Stenorhynchus lanceolatus holding a female. Note the difference in claw size between the sexes!

ful claws – however, the reality is that their claws are not particularly robust. The size of the closer muscle is limited and much of the claw is actually ornamentation. Indeed these broad but slim claws seem primarily adapted to digging and acting as a screen for channelling water currents while the crab is buried in sand. Yet, box crabs are still most effective mollusc predators, and compensate for the weakness of their claws by having an unusual hooked peg and cusp near the base of the right claw. The device has a massive mechanical advantage and acts as a "tin-opener" to either progressively peel away the shell off snails or crush bivalves.

Portunid crabs, such as the Swimming Crab Cronius ruber, have a pair of slim claws with needle-like teeth. These rapid-action claws, in combination with paddle-like hind legs for swimming, make portunids effective predators on fish and other soft-bodied, fast-moving prey.

Majid crabs show a marked sexual dimorphism in both body and claw size. The male's claws alter dramatically in size and shape at the final moult to full maturity. These changes, along with physiological shifts in the closer muscles, enable the male to better defend a mate as well as hold her firmly. Unfortunately for the females, the power of the males' grasp can scar and crush their limbs and attempts by other males to pull them away may result in the loss of legs. While males that have not reached their final moult can mate and inseminate females, they are at a competitive

Above: the claws of a male of the grapsid crab *Grapsus adscensionis* serve not only to scrape algae from the rock. They are also display organs in courtship and in aggressive encounters.

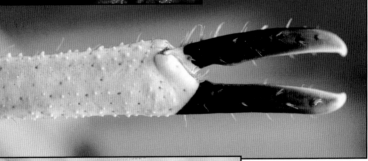

Left: obviously a multi-purpose tool – the right claw of a male of the majid crab *Herbstia condyliata*.

disadvantage against fully mature males that are equipped with large claws.

Tips to success: modified claw tips of herbivorous crabs can be important clues to their feeding behaviour. For example, spoon-shaped tips enable Sally

Above: the rather weak claws of *Paramola couvieri* have an unserrated cutting edge.

Lightfoot Crabs (*Grapsus* species) to scrape a living on the algal film covering wave-splashed rocks on tropical shores.

Left: the claws of the dromiid sponge crab *Dromia personata* look like the mouth of a predator! They probably afford a good grip on any prey item.

SNAPPING SHRIMPS, ALPHEIDAE

S: 3.5 cm. D: Med.; SW-Britain to Ascension, incl. island groups. G: colour variable, on rocky and soft bottoms, in seagrass, shallow to 180 m. Below: *Athanas nitescens*. 2 cm, Med., Norway to the Equator, on a variety of bottoms, may be associated with *T. cricoides* (p. 54). The light dorsal stripe is almost always present.

Alpheus macrocheles   Madeira

Holthuis' Snapping Shrimp
ALPHEIDAE

S: 2 cm. D: Cape Verdes to Ascension. Canaries? G: lives on rocky to sandy bottoms and between algae from the intertidal down to about 30 m depth. Below: *A. dentipes*, Mediterranean Sea, Bay of Biscay to Gulf of Guinea, on a variety of bottoms, shallow down to about 70 m.

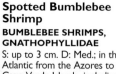

Alpheus holthuisi   Tenerife, Canary Islands

Spotted Bumblebee Shrimp
BUMBLEBEE SHRIMPS, GNATHOPHYLLIDAE

S: up to 3 cm. D: Med.; in the E-Atlantic from the Azores to the Cape Verde Islands, including Madeira and the Canary Islands. G: the cut-off appearance of the face is typical for members of this family. The unmistakable Spotted bumblebee shrimp lives on a variety of bottoms, from shallow water down to at least 30 m. It has been recorded with the sea urchin *Arbacia lixula* and the sea anemone *Telmatactis cricoides* but these associations apparently are rather casual and of short duration.

Gnathophyllum elegans   Adriatic Sea

Striped Bumblebee Shrimp
GNATHOPHYLLIDAE
(this page)

Size: up to 3 cm.
Distribution: Canary Islands; tropical western Atlantic.
General: the exact pattern of the stripes of this unmistakable species appears to be different in each individual. The Striped Bumblebee Shrimp lives from shallow water (tide pools even) down to about 50 m depth. It has been recorded in association with several echinoderm species, such as *Arbacia lixula, Coscinasterias tenuispinis* and sea cucumbers. The exact nature of such associations (and their duration) is unknown. *G. americanum* perhaps feeds on these echinoderms.

The second large photo is also from the Canary Islands (Gran Canaria). It shows a tiny animal (about 6 mm in length), obviously belonging to the genus *Gnathophyllum*. Nobody had recorded this species before it was photographed in a few metres depth. Probably it is an undescribed *Gnathophyllum* species. However, it just might be the (strikingly differently coloured) juvenile of *Gnathophyllum americanum* or *Gnathophyllum elegans*.

Gnathophyllum americanum   **Tenerife, Canary Islands**

Gnathophyllum sp   **Gran Canaria, Canary Islands**

Telle's Bumblebee Shrimp
S: up to 4 cm, only 3 animals known. D: Canary Islands.
G: the underwater photographer Arthur Telle lives on Gran Canaria. He has a fantastic eye for "small things". He not only detected the still undetermined *Gnathophyllum* shown directly above but also this shrimp (named in his honour) that was placed into a new genus. *G. tellei* appears to be associated with sea stars *(Ophidiaster ophidianus* or *Coscinasterias tenuispina)* in shallow water. Adult animals perhaps live in pairs, as is known for the related Pacific sea star-eating species *Hymenocera picta*.

Gnathophylleptum tellei   **Tenerife, Canary Islands**

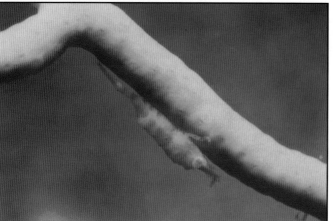

Balssia gasti   **Gran Canaria, Canary Islands**

ROCK SHRIMPS, PALAEMONIDAE

(both pages)
Size: up to 2 cm.
Distribution: western Mediterranean Sea; in the eastern Atlantic from the Azores to the Cape Verde Islands, including Madeira and the Canary Islands.
General: this small shrimp has been found in association with many different cnidarians, such as for instance *Antipathes*, *Gerardia* or *Leptogorgia*. The upper photo shows it, perfectly adapted in colour, on the yellow gorgonarian *Lophogorgia vimnalis*, the small photo, also from Gran Canaria on the red gorgonarian *Lophogorgia ruberrima*. The lower large photo shows it on a colony of *Gerardia* sp from Madeira. It has also be recorded from sponges in the Mediterranean Sea and lives from about 10-120 m depth.

Balssia gasti   **Madeira**

Brown-striped Shrimp

Size: up to 6 cm.
Distribution: Mediterranean Sea; in the E-Atlantic from Madeira to the Equator; tropical western Atlantic and Indo-Pacific.
General: this species can be locally common, especially in caves. It has been recorded with the sea anemone *Telmatactis cricoides* but this association is a casual one and of short duration. It is said to clean fish but this report needs confirmation. *Brachycarpus biunguiculatus* lives from shallow water down to about 50 m depth.

Brachycarpus biunguiculatus   **Madeira**

Rockpool Shrimp

S: up to 6 cm. D: Med.; from
S-Norway to Namibia, including
Azores, Madeira, Canaries and
Cape Verdes; Suez Canal; introduced into the Caspian Sea.
G: this is one of the few shrimp
species active during the day. It
lives in tide pools and shallow
water, down to about 10 m
depth. If you stand in shallow
water with bare feet and feel
some creature tickling you and
about to pull out some hairs,
this is most likely to be the cul-
prit. The pattern of golden
spots and dark stripes on the
transparent body of this shrimp
is quite variable.

Palaemon elegans   **Portugal**

Common Shrimp

Size: up to 11 cm but rarely
more than 8 cm.
Distribution: Mediterranean
Sea; from western Scotland to
the Canary Islands, including
the Azores and Madeira.
General: this species lives from
shallow water down to about
40 m depth. It prefers rocky
substrates and also can be
found in caves and in seagrass
meadows. It is active only at
night and usually much more
conspicuously striped than the
Rock shrimp. In some areas it
is fished for and sold in the
fish market.

Palaemon serratus   **Aegean Sea, Greece**

Plain Shrimp

Size: up to 7 cm.
Distribution: Med.; in the E-
Atlantic from Norway to
Morocco, including the Azores
but not Madeira and the Canary
Islands; Caspian Sea.
General: lives in seagrass meadows and on sandy bottoms in
sheltered lagoons and bays, from
shallow water down to 12 m
depth. It is quite tolerant to
brackish water and can reach
high densities in lagoons. In
autumn, it migrates into deeper
water where it spends the winter. There are no dark stripes
on the brownish body. In some
areas, *P. adspersus* is fished for.

Palaemon adspersus   **Baltic Sea**

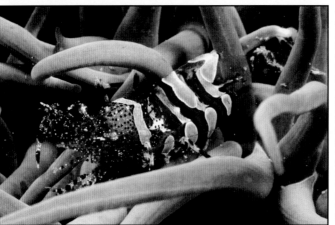

Atlantic Partner Shrimp
COMMENSAL SHRIMPS,
PALAEMONIDAE (both pages)
S: up to 3 cm. D: in the eastern Atlantic, from the Channel Islands to the Canary Islands; not in the Mediterranean Sea. G: this species has until recently be confused with the Med. *P. aegylios* (see below). As it was originally described from Jersey Island, the name *sagittifer* is the correct one for the Atlantic species. All 3 species on this page can be recognized by their colour pattern. *P. sagittifer* lives in association with *Anemonia viridis*, down to 10 m, on hydrozoans and *Antipathella* down to 40 m.

Periclimenes sagittifer   **Bay of Setúbal, Portugal**

Mediterranean Partner Shrimp S: 3 cm. D: W-Med., Adriatic. G: often called *P. sagittifer*. However, the true *sagittifer* lives only in the E-Atl. and is distinctly different (compare photos). All 3 spp on this page can be recognized by their colour pattern. *P. aegylios* lives in association with the anemones *Anemonia viridis*, *Condylactis aurantiaca* and *Cribrinopsis crassa* down to about 20 m.

Periclimenes aegylios   **Slovenia, Adriatic Sea**

Amethyst Partner Shrimp
S: up to 3 cm. D: Mediterranean. G: this shrimp lives with the sea anemones *Anemonia viridis*, *Aiptasia mutabilis* (large photo), *Alicia mirabilis*, *Cribrinopsis crassa* (new host record by C. d'Udekem d'Acoz) down to about 20 m depth. Below (Adriatic Sea): with *Cereus pedunculatus*. The spotting of the pink bands is distinctive.

Periclimenes amethysteus   **Malta**

Transparent Partner Shrimp

Size: up to 2 cm.
Distribution: Mediterranean.
General: even though this
species can be found in
association with the sea
anemone *Condylactis aurantiaca*
(p. 48), with Gorgonaria and
with Alcyonaria, it is by no
means restricted to such
association. It can also occur –
at high densities sometimes –
in seagrass meadows and
between algae, from shallow
water down to about 90 m
depth. Because it is almost
completely transparent,
Periclimenes scriptus is easily
overlooked.

Periclimenes scriptus   Slovenia, Adriatic Sea

Black Coral Shrimp

Size: up to 2 cm. Distribution:
Azores, Madeira, Canary
Islands, Cape Verde Islands.
General: this species lives on
black coral of the genus
Antipathella (p. 78), below
25 m depth. Author PW found
it at Madeira in 1995. When
later looking for this species
on black coral in other places,
he found it in the islands listed
above. It apparently is a widely
distributed common species
that was overlooked because
its transparent body with a single red line blends in perfectly
with the coral branches. Usually, many individuals inhabit an
Antipathella bush.

Periclimenes wirtzi   Madeira

Fan Mussel Shrimp

Size: up to 2 cm.
Distribution: Mediterranean
Sea; Azores to St. Helena Island
and Angola, including Madeira,
the Canaries, the Cape Verdes.
General: this species lives inside
the large fan mussels *Pinna nobilis*
and *P. rudis* (p. 233). In some
areas, every fan mussel contains
them. Looking down into the
open slit of the mussel, one can
often see the upward-turned
abdomen of the female. Usually
a pair lives in a *Pinna*, sometimes
only a solitary animal. Not only
males but also females have, on
rare occasions, be seen outside
the shells.

Pontonia pinnophylax   Faial Island, Azores

Pontonia manningi   **Cape Verde Islands**

Manning's Partner Shrimp

PALAEMONIDAE (both pages)
Size: up to 3 cm.
Distribution: Canary Islands, Cape Verde Islands; in the western Atlantic from North Carolina to Gulf of Mexico. General: this transparent shrimp lives in bivalves such as large *Spondylus* species (p. 235) or *Pecten, Aequipecten* and *Chlamys*. It has been found from 15 to about 70 m depth. As a rule, there is only a single shrimp in every bivalve. Thus, to reproduce, at least one of the sexes (probably the male) has to leave its host in search of a mate.

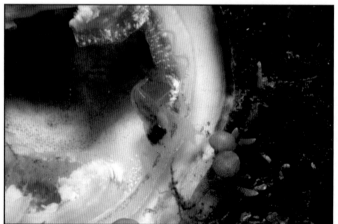

Pontonia pilosa   **Cape Verde Islands**

Hairy Partner Shrimp

S: photographed animal about 1 cm long. D: only one individual known, see photo. G: when diving on the NW-coast of São Tiago, author PW opened a few large bivalves in search of symbiotic decapods. In a *Pseudochama radians* in about 10 m depth, he encountered this small transparent shrimp. It obviously belonged to the genus *Pontonia*. In March 2002, the specialist for that genus, Charles Fransen at the Natural History Museum in Leiden, the Netherlands, described it as a new species, *Pontonia pilosa,* characterized by many small hairs all over the body (not visible in photo).

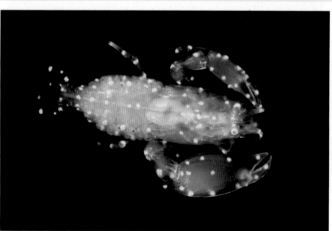

Ascidonia flavomaculata   **Tenerife, Canary Islands**

Sea Squirt Partner Shrimp

Size: up to 2 cm.
Distribution: Med.; in the E-Atl. from Morocco to Guinea, including the Canary Islands. General: as the name indicates, this species (which used to be called *Pontonia flavomaculata*) is covered by yellow spots (Latin *flavus* = yellow, *maculatus* = spotted). It lives in large tunicates, for instance *Ascidia mentula* or *Phallusia mammillata* (p. 284), from 15-50 m. As a rule, there is only a single shrimp in every tunicate. Thus, to reproduce, at least one of the sexes (probably the male) has to leave its host in search of a mate.

Sea Urchin Partner Shrimp

S: 2 cm. D: Madeira, Canaries; Caribbean. G: difficult to detect. First of all, not every sea urchin has one. Secondly, it is perfectly camouflaged and looks just like a sea urchin spine. And when you come close, the sea urchin rapidly moves its spines and the shrimp swims to the other side of the sea urchin. Usually only one shrimp per sea urchin, clinging head down to a spine. It is still not known what the shrimp feeds on. It could be a parasite feeding on the soft living tissue covering the sea urchin's spines.

Tuleariocaris neglecta   Madeira

Gorgonian Partner Shrimp

Size: up to 15 mm.
Distribution: Cape Verde Islands.
General: diving on the northwestern coast of São Tiago Island, Cape Verde islands, author PW searched for symbiotic shrimps. On the gorgonarian *Leptogorgia gainii* (p. 42), in 20-30 m depth, he found large numbers of a shrimp that turned out to be an undescribed species.

Later, the same species was encountered on the whip coral *Stichopathes lutkeni*. While the shrimp was living in groups of many individuals on the large gorgonarian, only a single animal was found on each whip coral. The upper large photo shows a female, the lower large photo shows a male.

The last three pairs of legs are curved and allow the shrimp to strongly grasp the branch of the gorgonarian or the whip coral it is sitting on.

Before the discovery of this species at the Cape Verde Islands, the genus *Pseudocoutierea* had only been known from the western Atlantic and from the eastern Pacific.

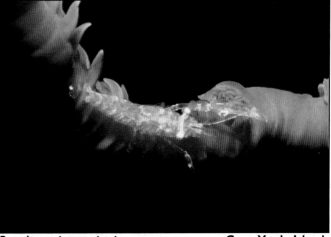

Pseudocoutierea wirtzi   Cape Verde Islands

Cinetorhynchus rigens   La Gomera, Canary Islands

Eastern Atlantic Dancing Shrimp
HINGE-BEAK SHRIMPS, RHYNCHOCINETIDAE

Size: up to 6 cm.
Distribution: in the E-Atlantic from the Azores to the Cape Verde Islands.
General: at night, one can sometimes see hundreds of shrimps of this species on rocky bottoms and one wonders, where they are during the day. They hide in caves (upper photo) and in cracks in the rock.

Unlike other shrimps, hinge-beak shrimps can move the long, sabre-shaped rostrum up and down. It is connected to the head by a joint. The adaptive value of this unique construction is, however, completely unknown.

When excited (for instance by the light of a diver), *Cinetorhynchus rigens* moves with small quick steps turning the body frequently. Thus its popular name "Dancing Shrimp". When approached closely, the shrimps performs a mighty leap, suddenly sitting on the rock one to two metres from its previous place. *Cinetorhynchus rigens* can be found from shallow water down to at least 25 m depth.

The sister species *Cinetorhynchus manningi* lives in the western Atlantic.

Cinetorhynchus rigens   Madeira

Crangon crangon   Baltic Sea

Brown Shrimp
CRANGONID SHRIMPS, CRANGONIDAE

Size: up to 9 cm but rarely more than 6 cm.
Distribution: from the White Sea and northern Norway to Morocco; Mediterranean Sea.
General: this species can be locally common on sandy and muddy bottoms, down to about 130 m depth, and is fished for in many areas. It also enters estuaries. During the day the Brown Shrimp is buried in the sand.

Common Spiny Lobster

PALINURIDAE (this page)

S: 40, max 50 cm. D: British Isles to S-Morocco, Azores, Madeira, Canaries; Med. (except SE). G: rocky bottoms, 5-160 m, in cold waters mainly 10-30 m, in warm waters deeper. Active at night, hides during the day. Like all family members, without claws or pincers, except females which have pincers on 5th leg pair and use them to handle and clean the eggs. Frequently in groups in rock fissures, with just the long antennae sticking out. Can produce a loud, squeaking noise by rubbing the base of the antennae against the head. Regularly in Med. Fish markets. *P. vulgaris* is a synonym.

Palinurus elephas   **Corsica, France**

Cape Verde Spiny Lobster

Size: up to 50 cm.
Distribution: this species is only known from the Cape Verde Islands.
General: in the Cape Verde Islands, this species is fished for with lobster pots and exported. It lives from 50 to at least 300 m depth, on rocky bottoms. It closely resembles *P. mauritanicus*, from which it differs in the shape of the frontal horns. Almost nothing is known about the biology of this species.

Palinurus charlestoni   **Cape Verde Islands**

Brown Spiny Lobster

Size: up to 38 cm.
Distribution: from the Canary Islands to St. Helena Island; in the western Atlantic along the coasts of Brazil.
General: note the different name of the genus. This species has its northern distributional limit at the Canary Islands, i.e. just where the Common spiny lobster has its southern limit. It lives from shallow water to about 35 m depth. Where it is common (in the Cape Verde Islands, for instance) it is fished for intensively. In some areas, females carry eggs already with a body size of about 10 cm.

Panulirus echinatus   **El Hierro, Canary Islands**

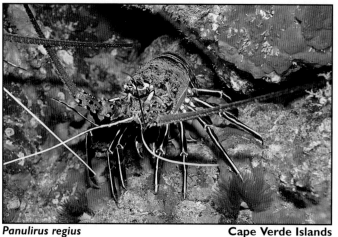

Panulirus regius   **Cape Verde Islands**

Royal Spiny Lobster
PALINURIDAE

S: 30, max 46 cm. D: S-Morocco to Angola; probably accidentally introduced into W-
Med. and the Spanish Atlantic
coast. G: this species lives from
shallow water down to about
40 m depth, on rocky bottoms.
In the Cape Verdes, it has been
fished for so intensively that it
is now much rarer than it used
to be. From shallow water
(where it could be picked up
by snorkelling) it has virtually
disappeared. In deeper water it
can sometimes be seen in
groups of many animals in fissures in the rock, with just the
antennae sticking out.

Scyllarides latus   **Zakynthos, Greece**

Mediterranean Slipper Lobster
**SLIPPER LOBSTERS,
SCYLLARIDAE**

S: up to 45 cm but rarely more
than 30 cm. D: Med.; S-Portugal
to Cape Verdes. G: the antennae
of slipper lobsters are modified
into shovels. This one lives on
rocky and rocky/sandy bottoms
down to 100 m depth. It is
active at night. During the day it
hides, frequently inside caves.
Large animals can sometimes be
encountered in open daylight.
The species has, however,
become rare in almost all of its
range, due to severe over-fishing.
It feeds on molluscs, mainly
limpets (*Patella*, see p. 164).

Scyllarus arctus   **Faial Island, Azores**

Small European Locust Lobster
SCYLLARIDAE

S: up to 10, rarely 15 cm. D:
Med., British Isles to Canaries,
Azores, Madeira. G: on rock,
sand/mud to 50 m. Hides by day
in dark places, often in groups
of several animals. See also p.
116. Below: *S. pygmaeus*, 5 cm.
Medit., Azores to Cape Verdes.

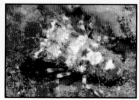

European Lobster
LOBSTERS, NEPHROPIDAE
(this page)
S: up to 62 cm long (and 8 kg in weight), but rarely more than 40 cm long.
D: from the Lofoten Islands and Norway to Morocco; Med. except the south-eastern part, but present in the Black Sea.
G: the European lobster lives in inshore waters, usually down to about 60 m, exceptionally down to 150 m depth. It prefers rocky bottoms but can also be encountered on gravel and even sand. It is a night-active species, much sought after by commercial fishermen. The natural colour of this species is blue; it turns red only when it is boiled!

Females carry eggs from early autumn and developing young until April or May.

Do not attempt to play with this species. The powerful claws can easily cut a finger. Left and right claw are different, one for crushing (bivalve shells and gastropod shells) and for manipulating and for cutting (see also "Handy Tools"). The crushing claw may be the right one or the left one.

Homarus gammarus   Adriatic Sea

Homarus gammarus   Helgoland, North Sea

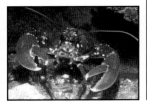

Norway Lobster
Size: up to 24 cm, but rarely more than 15 cm.
Distribution: from the Faroe Islands to the Canary Islands; western and central Mediterranean Sea.
General: the Norway lobster lives on muddy bottoms, from 15 m to 870 m. It inhabits complex burrows in the mud and leaves them only at night, to hunt for small crustaceans and worms. Females carrying eggs can be found throughout the year. The eggs are carried for c. 9 months! The species is of considerable commercial importance and mostly caught by trawling.

Nephrops norvegicus   Sogndalsfjord, Norway

Enoplometopus antillensis **Cape Verde Islands**

Enoplometopus antillensis **La Gomera, Canary Islands**

Red Atlantic Reef Lobster
**REEF LOBSTERS,
ENOPLOMETOPIDAE**
(this page)

Size: up to 11 cm.
Distribution: Madeira, Canary Islands, Cape Verde Islands, Gabon, São Tomé, St. Helena; western tropical Atlantic from the Bermudas to northern Brazil.
General: this beautiful little lobster is night-active. Inside caves, it can also be encountered during the day. The circular pattern on the "cheeks" and the red antennae are typical for this species. For a long time, only *E. callistus* (see below) had been recorded from the Canary Islands-even though *E. antillensis* is much more common there-because the two species were confused. When a diving light falls on it, it raises its claws in defence and tries to disappear into a dark crevice. The Red reef lobster lives on rocky shores, from 5 m to about 200 m depth. It is a tropical species that reaches its northern limit in the E-Atlantic at Madeira (as do many other tropical species). The lack of records from the mainland coast of Africa is probably due to the fact that not much research (and even less diving) has been done there.

Enoplometopus callistus **Gran Canaria, Canary Islands**

East Atlantic
Reef Lobster
Size: up to 11 cm.
Distribution: Canary Islands, Ghana, Nigeria.
General: this species has long been confused with the previous one. However, it does not have the circular markings on the "cheeks" and has brilliantly white antennae. It is also much less common then the Red Atlantic reef lobster. It lives on rocky shores from 40 m to about 200 m depth but can only very rarely be encountered more shallow than 100 m depth. The fishermen in the Canary Islands sometimes catch it in their traps.

SHRIMP LOBSTERS, AXIIDAE

Size: the photographed animal is about 5 cm long (without claws). Distribution: São Tomé.
General: the suborder Thalassinidea, generally called "Mud Lobsters", contains strange species that look like a cross between a shrimp and a lobster. They live in complex burrows in sand or mud. Some, especially those of the family Axiidae, leave their burrows at night. Author PW encountered this animal during a night dive at São Tomé in 15 m. Experts for the group, asked to identify the species from the photo, said that this is an undescribed species.

Axiidae new species   São Tomé

Mediterranean Ghost Shrimp
GHOST SHRIMPS, CALLIANASSIDAE

S: body 8 cm. D: Med.; Ireland to Canaries. G: large photo: female, small photo: male. Claws of different size in both sexes. In burrows, entrance: 1-5 cm wide depression with central hole; exit: similarly sized sandy cone.

Callianassa tyrrhena   Adriatic Sea

UPOGEBIIDAE

S: body 4 cm. D: Med.; French Channel coast to Mauritania, Canaries. G: shallow, in burrows in sand or mud. May occur in high densities; dug up, used for bait. Filters organic material. Below: male *Callianassa truncata*. In muddy sand, 2-57 m, Med., Gulf of Gascogne to Morocco.

Upogebia pusilla   Gran Canaria, Canary Islands

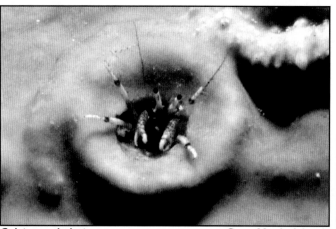

Calcinus tubularis   Cape Verde Islands

Sedentary Hermit Crab
HERMIT CRABS, DIOGENIDAE
(this page)
S: 1 cm. D: Med.; Azores to Gulf of Guinea. G: females often in empty tubes of worm snails and sedentary polychaetes, unable to move around. Usually hold legs spread, ready to grasp at passing objects. Males in snail shells, moving around freely (below).

Dardanus calidus   Crete Island, Greece

Common Mediterranean Hermit Crab
S: body 11 cm. D: Med.; Azores to Cape Verdes. G: common, on rocky and soft bottoms, shallow down to c. 100 m. Frequently, the sea anemone *Calliactis parasitica* (p. 53) is growing on its shell. Below: *Calcinus talismani*, to about 1 cm, in shallow water. Colour pattern of legs is typical.

Dardanus pectinatus   Cape Verde Islands

West African Hermit Crab
S: body 10 cm. D: W-Africa, Cape Verdes. G: colour pattern and fine horizontal lines on claws typical. 10+ m, on rocky and sandy bottoms. Below: *Diogenes pugilator*, locally common on sand, down to 40 m, can run with an amazing speed. Med., E-Atl., perhaps also in Indo-Pacific.

Prideaux' Hermit Crab

PAGURIDAE (this page)
S: body 6 cm. D: Med.; Norway to Cape Verdes. G: shallow to c. 250 m. Almost always associated with *A. carciniopados* (p. 53), which completely envelops the shell inhabited by the hermit. Below: *P. anachoretus,* very common in Mediterranean Sea, temperate eastern Atlantic.

Pagurus prideaux Norway

Common Northern Hermit Crab

S: 10 cm. D: Murmansk, Faroes to S-Portugal. Not Med. G: common, on sand, mud, shell, rock bottoms, from the intertidal down to c. 450 m. *B. undatum* (p. 184) is the preferred shell for larger animals but inhabits a great variety of shells. Sometimes with *C. parasitica* (p. 53) or *H. echinata* (p. 22).

Pagurus bernhardus Norway

S: 8 cm. D: Iceland, Norway to English Channel; cold W-Atl. G: on hard and soft bottoms, 5-1000 m. The animal in the photo has hydrozoans of the genus *Hydractina* or *Podocoryne* growing on its shell. Below: Hairy Hermit Crab *P. cuanensis,* locally common on soft, hard bottoms, shallow water down to 250 m, Med., southern Norway to South Africa.

Pagurus pubescens Norway

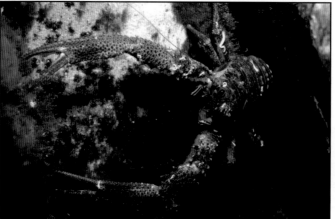

**SQUAT LOBSTERS,
GALATHEIDAE (this page)**

S: up to 6 cm long. D: Med.;
from S-Norway to the Cape
Verdes. G: below stones and in
cracks in the rock during the
day. From shallow water down
to about 145 m. Below: *G. faiali,*
10 cm, 5-350 m, S-Portugal to
Mauritania, Madeira, Canaries.

Galathea squamifera   Faial Island, Azores

Spiny Squat Lobster

S: 9 cm. D: Med.; S-Norway to
S-Morocco. G: bright red and
blue colour makes it an unmistakable species. Rocky bottoms
(also in caves), down to at least
180 m. Below: *G. nexa,* N-Norway to Canary Islands, Med.,
on hard bottoms and in seagrass meadows, to 800 m.

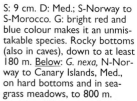

Galathea strigosa   Croatia, Adriatic Sea

**Long-clawed
Squat Lobster**
S: 6 cm. D: Norway to Portugal; Med. (except SE). G: 30-
300 m. In burrows on sand,
mud. In Med. usually too deep
to be seen by divers.
Below: *Munidopsis polymorpha,*
1 cm, only known from a lava
cave on Lanzarote, Canaries.
There it lives in great density.

Munida rugosa   Jossenfjord, Norway

Northern Stone Crab
STONE CRABS, LITHODIDAE

S: up to 14.5 cm. D: E-Atl.: the
Faroes and Norway to the
British Isles; W-Atlantic: Canada
to Maine. G: this species is
found on soft bottoms, from 5
to about 800 m. Females carry
eggs from December to April
the following year. The animal
seen here has a large sea anemone *Bolocera tuedidae* attached
to its back. Thus, it is not only
camouflaged but also protected
by the stinging cells of the
anemone. Records of this
species from south of the British
Isles are probably confusions
with *Maja squinado* (p. 147).

Lithodes maja   **Norway**

King Crab
LITHODIDAE

S: leg span up to 1 m. D: N-Pacific; introduced into to Barents
Sea, now spreading south along
the coasts of N-Norway. G: in
summer in 200-300 m but in
shallow water from November
to May. Commercially valuable,
was introduced into the Barents
Sea as early as the 1930s and
then again in the 1960s. Has also
appeared in the last 10 years on
the coasts of N-Norway. Each
year it is now encountered in a
fjord a bit further south than in
the previous year. Biologists predict that it will eventually reach
as far south as N of British Isles.

Paralithodes camtschatica   **Barents Sea**

Mole Crab
MOLE CRABS,
ALBUNEIDAE

Size: up to about 4 cm.
Distribution: Med.; in the
eastern Atlantic from the
Azores to Ghana, including
Madeira and the Canary
Islands.
General: this species lives in
current exposed sandy bottoms, from the water's edge
down to about 35 m depth.
Divers are unlikely to see a
living animal because the egg-
shaped body is burrowed in
the sand. The moulted skin of
A. carabus can sometimes be
seen on sandy bottoms.

Albunea carabus   **Tenerife, Canary Islands**

Bearded Crab
BEARDED CRABS, HOMOLIDAE

Size: up to 5 cm long. Distribution: Mediterranean Sea; from the Bay of Biscay to the Gulf of Guinea, including the island groups. General: the last pair of legs of this crab is no longer used for walking. It is permanently turned upwards and is used to hold an object over the crab, often a pieces of sponge, or a piece of algae, or some other things. For the photo, the photographer removed the algae carried by the crab but gave them back after taking the photo. See also the story "Never Without Umbrella".

Homola barbata   **Faial Island, Azores**

Atlantic Sponge Crab
SPONGE CRABS, DROMIIDAE

S: up to 9 cm wide. D: Azores, Madeira, Canaries, Cape Verdes, Ascension Island. G: the last two pairs of legs of the sponge crabs are modified. Young animals use them to carry a piece of sponge over the body (see "Never Without Umbrella"). Older ones no longer carry sponges. Perhaps because the last two pairs of legs no longer serve for walking, the Atlantic Sponge Crab uses the claws for walking in a way reminiscent of the knuckle-walk of a gorilla. It lives on rocky bottoms, shallow down to about 100 m depth.

Dromia marmorea   **Madeira**

Linnaeus's Sponge Crab

Size: up to 9 cm wide. Distribution: Mediterranean Sea; from south-western Great Britain to the Western Sahara. General: this species and the Atlantic Sponge Crab are very closely related. A covering of soft, velvety hair gives a furry appearance to both species and has resulted in the nickname "Teddy Bear Crabs". Young animals and even some adults carry a piece of sponge with the modified last pair of legs. The sponge is carefully cut to size. *D. personata* lives on rocky bottoms from shallow water down to c. 100 m.

Dromia personata   **Corsica, France**

DORIPPID CRABS, DORIPPIDAE

S: body without legs 4 cm. D: Med.; E-Atl.: S-Portugal to South Africa, including the Canary Islands. G: the last two pairs of legs of this crab are turned upwards and end in a small claw. They are used to hold an object (a piece of sponge, a shell, a large tunicate, or even a sea anemone) as protection over the body. The flattened body is rather hairy. Usually light brown to pink. On muddy and muddy-sandy bottoms from 10-900 m depth. Note the numerous *Ditrupa arietina* (p. 97) on the bottom below the crab.

Medorippe lanata   French Mediterranean

Larger-spotted Shame-faced Crab
SHAME-FACED CRABS, CALAPPIDAE

S: up to 11 cm wide. D: Med.; Bay of Biscay to Cape Verdes, including the other island groups. G: on soft bottoms, 10-400 m. Shame-faced crabs owe their name to the habit of holding the broad claws in front of the face as if ashamed. Claws specialized for opening snails: the left pointed claw holds the snail, while the right powerful claw cuts a piece out of the snail's opening. This procedure is repeated until the shell is cut open along its winding. Shame-faced crabs are the crabs with a tin-opener!

Calappa granulata   Aegean Sea, Turkey

Lesser-spotted Shame-faced Crab
CALAPPIDAE

S: up to 7 cm width. D: from the Azores to St. Helena Island, including Madeira, the Canaries, and the Cape Verde Islands; westernmost Med. G: this crab is similar to the Larger-spotted Shame-faced Crab but the spots are much smaller. At Madeira and the Canaries, where it is common on sandy bottoms, it can be seen walking around during daylight, often followed by a Wide-eyed Flounder (as in the photo) which snaps up small animals fleeing from the crab. From shallow water down to about 80 m.

Cryptosoma cristata   Madeira

Ebalia edwardsii   **Tenerife, Canary Islands**

LEUCOSID CRABS, LEUCOSIIDAE

S: about 1 cm wide. D: Med.; E-Atl.: S-Portugal to Canary Islands. G: an uncommon species, found on soft bottoms (from mud to sand to gravel), from shallow water to about 200 m depth. During the day, it is buried in the substrate and therefore (and because of its small size) rarely seen. It may, however, be not as rare as previously thought. With its thick shell and polygonal body, it looks rather like a small stone, when seen under water. There are several similar *Ebalia* species, difficult to distinguish.

Ilia nucleus   **Croatia, Adriatic Sea**

Pebble Crab
LEUCOSIIDAE
Size: body up to 3 cm in diameter.
Distribution: Med.; E-Atl.: S-Spain to the Cape Verde Islands (but not recorded from Madeira or the Canaries). General: the round body and the extremely long claws make this species unmistakable. It varies from cream to dark orange in colour. It lives on soft and hard bottoms and in seagrass meadows, from shallow water down to about 160 m depth. The small eggs are literally encapsulated between the abdomen and the sternum of the female.

SPIDER CRABS, MAJIDAE
S: body up to 6 cm long. D: Arctic to Bay of Biscay; cold NW-Atlantic. G: *H. coarctatus* and *Hyas araneus* (<u>below</u>) live in the same area of distribution, on hard and sandy bottoms, from 5-500 m depth. The easiest way to tell them apart is their colour: *Hyas araneus* is greyish brown while *Hyas coarctatus* is reddish.

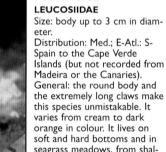

Hyas coarctatus   **Norway**

MAJIDAE (this page)

S: body of large males up to 5 cm long. D: Med.; Bay of Biscay to the Canaries. G: the photo shows a pair, the males not only being larger but also having proportionally larger claws than the female. It was taken in a cave, a common type of habitat for this species. From shallow water down to about 80 m. The lower small photo (Cape Verdes) shows the closely related H. rubra. It is known from hard bottoms, down to 75 m, from the Canaries to the Gulf of Guinea. Acanthonyx lunulatus (upper small photo) lives between plants (therefore its green colour) in shallow water, often in areas exposed to strong wave action, in the Med. and from the Azores to the Gulf of Guinea. Body up to 2 cm long.

Herbstia condyliata   **Faial Island, Azores**

Long-legged Spider-crab

Size: body up to 1.5 cm long. Distribution: Mediterranean; in the eastern Atlantic from Norway to the Strait of Gibraltar. General: there are many similar looking species in the genus *Macropodia*. They really resemble long legged spiders. They usually live between algae, on hard and soft bottoms and in seagrass meadows, where they are extremely difficult to detect. *Macropodia rostrata* has been recorded from the intertidal down to about 200 m depth.

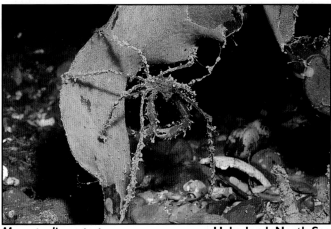

Macropodia rostrata   **Helgoland, North Sea**

Anemone Spider Crab
SPIDER CRABS, MAJIDAE
(both pages)
S: 2 cm. D: Med.; Shetland Is. to the Canaries, Madeira. G: in the northern part of its range, this crab lives on hard and soft substrates, while in the Med. and from the Portuguese Atlantic coast southwards this species is (almost) always found in association with sea anemones. *Anemonia viridis* is the most common host (upper photo); lower: two animals on the Club-tipped Anemone *Telmatactis cricoides*. In most cases, there is only one crab per anemone, sometimes two and very rarely three.
A study on the biology of this crab (using individually marked animals) has shown that females are stationary, only rarely moving to a different anemone, while males rove at night, in search of females. When copulating with a female, the males seal off the sperm of all previous males that still remain in the sperm pouch of the female with a cement-like layer. *I. phalangium* sometimes cut and eat the tips of *Anemonia viridis*. Below: *I. thoracicus,* not with sea anemones, 3+ cm, 10-100+ m.

Inachus phalangium   French Mediterranean

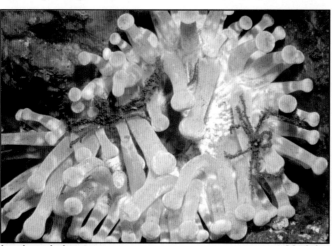

Inachus phalangium   Madeira

S: 5 cm. D: Mediterranean Sea; Atlantic coast of Portugal. G: lives on soft and hard bottoms (especially in association with calcareous red algae) and in seagrass meadows, 15-90 m. Despite its red colour it is difficult to detect because – like many spider crabs – it masks itself with pieces of plants. There are two humps on the back of the stout body and numerous such humps along the sides. The two flattened rostral spines are close together and form a "T" at the tip. The knobbly joints of the legs are also characteristic of the species. In the western Med., it reproduces from May to August.

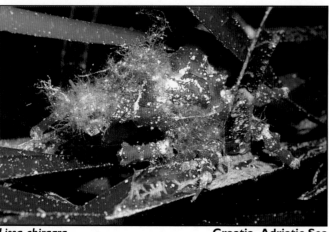

Lissa chiragra   Croatia, Adriatic Sea

Atlantic Spiny Spider Crab

S: to 35 cm. D: E-Atl.: southern North Sea to Guinea. G: eastern Atlantic "sister species" to the purely Mediterranean *M. squinado* (see below). One of the many differences between the two species is the more egg-shaped body of *M. brachydactyla,* which also reaches a larger size. Found on hard/soft bottoms, 3-100 m. Often masked with pieces of algae. After moulting, these algae are carefully transferred to the new shell. The claws of males are much longer and bigger than those of females. Fished for and consumed as a delicacy.

Maja brachydactyla   Madeira

Lesser Spider Crab

S: up to 6.5 cm long, 4.5 cm wide. D: Med.; E-Atl.: Portugal to Senegal. G: this species is frequently confused with young of *M. squinado* or *M. brachydactyla.* Like its larger cousins, it is frequently masked with pieces of plants. The main distinctive feature (fewer but relatively larger spines along the sides of the body) is therefore difficult to see in living animals. *Maja crispata* lives on hard and soft bottoms and in seagrass meadows from shallow water down to about 100 m depth. In the old literature, it is called *Maja verrucosa.*

Maja crispata   Ibiza, Spain

Mediterranean Spiny Spider Crab

S: to 25 cm. D: Med. G: a recent study has shown that this species is restricted to the Med. and the Atlantic *Maja* must be recognized as a separate species *(brachydactyla,* see above). *M. squinado* is more flattened and does not grow as large as its Atlantic sister species. On hard and soft bottoms, down to about 170 m. Body often masked with algae attached to special hooks. The crab usually uses the most common algae of the area where it happens to be – thus perfectly blending with its environment. In some areas of Med. of considerable commercial importance.

Maja squinado   Costa Calida, Spain

Stenorhynchus lanceolatus   **Madeira**

Eastern Atlantic Arrow Crab
SPIDER CRABS, MAJIDAE
(this page)
S: leg span 20 cm. D: Madeira to Angola, Canaries, Cape Verdes, Gulf of Guinea islands. G: unmistakable, hard and soft bottoms, 5-100 m. Sometimes associates with the sea anemone *T. cricoides* (p. 54) or the tube anemone *P. dohrni* (p. 61) but this association is a casual one: the crab stays only a few hours or perhaps a day. Frequently, one can see pairs of this species, the male (slender abdomen) holding onto the female (pouch-shaped abdomen) with a claw. The male has just copulated with the female and is now guarding her from copulations by other males. This is called "post-copulatory mate guarding" (see "Handy Tools"). In contrast to most majid crabs, this species does not mask itself with pieces of algae. The English name "arrow crab" is due to the very long, arrow-like rostrum. There is a report that the species has been observed cleaning moray eels at the Canary Islands. This report needs confirmation.

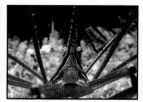

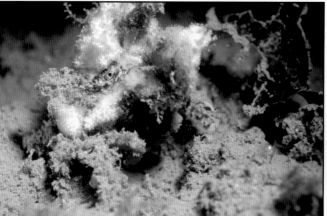

Stenorhynchus lanceolatus   **La Gomera, Canary Islands**

S: 4 cm. D: Mediterranean Sea; Isle of Man to Cape Verdes, including the island groups. G: *Pisa* spp are heavily masked, for identification sponges etc have to be removed (the shape of the rostral horns is an important feature). On soft and hard bottoms, 15-160 m. <u>Below</u>: *P. nodipes*, Med., English Channel to Cape Verdes.

Pisa armata   **Portugal**

PARTHENOPID CRABS, PARTHENOPIDAE

S: body 2 cm long; from "elbow" to "elbow" 8 cm wide. D: Cape Verdes to Gulf of Guinea, São Tomé. G: triangular body and long, massive arms characteristic of parthenopid crabs. The body posture figured, with "elbows" straight to the sides, is typical of these crabs. Usually encountered on gravel and on soft bottoms, hiding below stones during the day. Author PW photographed *D. bouvieri* in about 10 m. It has been recorded down to about 90 m. There are several, similar looking species belonging to the genus *Parthenope* in the Med.

Daldorfia bouvieri   **Cape Verde Islands**

Helmet Crab
HELMET CRABS, CORYSTIDAE

S: up to 4 cm. D: Med.; E-Atl.: S-Norway to Gibraltar. G: lives just below the surface of sandy or sandy-muddy substrate, 5-115 m. The long pair of the 2nd antennae forms a tube the tip of which reaches the surface and through which water is drawn downwards to bathe the gills. The crabs occasionally come to the surface at night. The photo shows a pair: male recognizable not only by its larger body size but also by its much larger claws. During strong storms, large numbers of this crab are sometimes washed ashore.

Corystes cassivelaunus   **French Mediterranean**

Circular Crab
CIRCULAR CRABS, ATELECYCLIDAE

S: body up to 4 cm long. D: Med.; in the E-Atlantic from the Faroe Islands to South Africa, including the Canaries and the Cape Verde Islands (but not recorded from the Azores and Madeira). G: this species lives on sand and gravel bottoms, from 10-300 m depth. It can be locally quite common. The reddish-brown body is almost circular (thus *rotundatus*). The closely related *A. undecimdentatus* is covered with coarse hair. It is larger and does not reach as far north as *A. rotundatus*, being quite common in the Bay of Biscay.

Atelecyclus rotundatus   **North Sea**

Cancer pagurus   **German Baltic coast**

European Edible Crab
CANCRID CRABS, CANCRIDAE

S: 28 cm wide. D: N-Norway to S-Portugal; W-Med., N-Adriatic. G: rocky, sandy bottoms, intertidal to 100 (rarely deeper, to 500) m. Reaches an age of 20+ years, large females produce up to 3 million (!) eggs per clutch. The small Med. populations may have been introduced by man but a Pleistocene fossil from the S-Med. coast indicates that they could be remnants from colder periods, now trapped in cold parts of Med. (but see "Trapped"). Global warming may now wipe them out there, too. Photo: starting to open a clam.

Pirimela denticulata   **Norway**

PIRIMELID CRABS, PIRIMELIDAE

S: up to 2 cm wide. D: Med.; in E-Atlantic from Norway to the Cape Verdes, including Madeira and Canaries, recently also recorded in the Azores. G: attractively coloured, lives between algae, on soft bottoms and gravel (in which it buries itself), and in seagrass meadows and has been found from the intertidal down to about 180 m depth. It does, however appear to be quite rare below 6 m depth. It is locally common in the NE-Atlantic Ocean and slightly rarer in the Mediterranean.

Bathynectes maravigna   **Faial Island, Azores**

SWIMMING CRABS, PORTUNIDAE

S: up to 8 cm wide. D: Med.; E-Atl.: the Shetland Islands to the Canary Islands, including the Azores and Madeira. G: what a stunningly beautiful crab! Unfortunately, you are not very likely to see it while SCUBA diving. It usually lives below 200 m depth (down to 1500 m), on sandy and muddy bottoms, sometimes close to hydrothermal vents. To encounter it in 60 m depth is a noteworthy occasion! The long spines on the body and on the arms increase the effective size of the animal and make it difficult to handle for a predatory fish.

Shore Crab
PORTUNIDAE (this page)

S: up to 8 cm wide. D: from Iceland, N-Norway and Faroes to Mauritania; westernmost Med.; often introduced (see the story "Long Distance").
G: commonest crab in shallow NE-Atlantic. On soft and hard bottoms, in seagrass meadows, down to about 70 m, highest density in a few metres. Enters estuaries, moves offshore in winter. Quickly buries into the sand when threatened. Colour dark green to grey, often orange below. Often collected as bait, sold in a few fish markets but commercially not important.

Carcinus maenas   Baltic Sea

Mediterranean Shore Crab

S: up to 7.5 cm wide.
D: Med.; Canary Islands.
G: very similar to *Carcinus maenas*. The few subtle differences cannot be seen under water. Intermediate forms have been found on the southern coast of Portugal and in the aquarium the two "species" readily hybridise. The bottleneck of the Strait of Gibraltar probably causes reduced gene flow between the Atlantic and the Med. animals, allowing some morphological differentiation. The Venetians eat this crab when it is soft (newly moulted) and call it "moleche".

Carcinus aestuarii   Adriatic Sea

Insular Shore Crab

S: 6 cm. D: Madeira, Canaries, Cape Verdes, Gulf of Guinea islands, Ascension. G: entirely insular, not yet found on African coast. As in all swimming crabs, tips of 5th leg pair form paddles, crabs can swim rapidly. Below: Wrinkled Swimming Crab *Liocarcinus corrugatus*, Med., Orkneys to Angola, on hard bottoms.

Laleonectes vocans   Cape Verde Islands

Navigator Swimming Crab

PORTUNIDAE (this page)
S: 4 cm wide. D: Med.; Norway to Mauritania. G: frequently called *Macropipus arcuatus*. On soft and shelly bottoms, intertidal to 40, max 100 m. *L. holsatus* (below) is a very active swimmer. On soft bottoms, Iceland to Morocco, shallow to 400 m.

Liocarcinus navigator   **Grevelingen Sea, Netherlands**

Red-eyed Swimming Crab

S: 10 cm wide. D: Norway to W. Sahara; W-Med. G: when feeling threatened, this common species rears up with claws spread wide. Red eyes are characteristic. The purple body is covered with very short dense hairs. On rocky bottoms, down to about 30 m. Occasionally hides in *Anemonia viridis* (below).

Necora puber   **Isle of Man**

Lanzer Swimming Crab

Size: up to 6 cm wide. Distribution: entire Mediterranean Sea; in the eastern Atlantic from the Azores to the Cape Verde Islands. General: this species lives on soft and shelly bottoms, down to about 50 m. It has conspicuous eye-spots on its swimming legs. When feeling threatened, it rears up and raises its claws; then it rapidly burrows backwards into the sand. Many swimming crabs show similar behaviour.

Portunus hastatus   **Cyprus**

ROUND CRABS, XANTHIDAE

(this page)
S: up to 3 cm wide. D: Canaries to Gulf of Guinea. G: lives in association with Zoantharia such as *Palythoa* and *Parazoanthus* spp (p. 63). Intertidal down to 30 m. Below: Wrinkled Crab *Paractaea monodi*, Med., Azores to Cape Verdes, on rocky bottoms, down to about 70 m depth.

Platypodiella picta   Cape Verde Islands

Velvet Crab

S: up to 6 cm wide. D: Mediterranean Sea; E-Atl.: W-Scotland to the Gulf of Guinea. G: this species, formerly called *X. incisus*, lives on rocky bottoms, from shallow water down to about 40 m. It is quite variable in colour, not only a beautiful blue as in the photo but also red or brown. There are several similar-looking species in the genus *Xantho*, in particular *X. pilipes* that differs in having legs with a marginal fringe of hair. This is a locally common species but in some areas it is extensively collected for bait and for human consumption and has actually become rare.

Xantho hydrophilus   Faial Island, Azores

Jaguar Round Crab

S: up to 6 cm wide. D: Mediterranean Sea; Canary Islands. G: locally common, on soft and hard bottoms from shallow water to about 15 m depth. Reproduces in W-Med. from May to September. Below: *X. pilipes*, on rock, gravel. Mediterranean, Norway to Angola.

Xantho poressa   Adriatic Sea

153

Yellow Shore Crab
ERIPHIID CRABS, ERIPHIIDAE

S: up to 8, rarely 13 cm wide. D: Med.; Bay of Biscay to Canaries, including Azores and Madeira; has invaded the Suez Canal. G: this locally common species lives from the intertidal down to 6 m depth, at most. During low tide, it frequently remains out of the water, fleeing into a small crevice when feeling threatened. In the Azores (where few shore birds live) *Eriphia verrucosa* is active during the day, while in the Med. it is active at night and during dawn and dusk. In some areas, this sturdy species is collected for human consumption.

Eriphia verrucosa   Faial Island, Azores

Very Hairy Crab
HAIRY CRABS, PILUMNIDAE

S: 3 cm wide. D: Med.; Azores to Canaries. G: one of many crustaceans that occasionally hide near *Anemonia viridis*. Rocky bottoms, down to 20 m. Below: *Globopilumnus africanus*. More globular in body shape than, but almost as hairy as *P. villosissimus*.

Pilumnus villosissimus   Madeira

Mud Runner
ANGULAR CRABS,
GONEPLACIDAE
S: up to 4 cm wide.
D: Mediterranean Sea; in the E-Atlantic from Great Britain to South Africa, Madeira, Canaries (but not recorded from the Azores). G: the clawed arms of males are four to five times as long as the body (but not as long in females). In both sexes, the eyes are on long stalks that can be folded back into protective grooves. The Mud Runner constructs complex, branching burrows in mud and muddy sand, from shallow water down to about 600 m depth. It can be locally common.

Goneplax rhomboides   North Sea

Chinese Mitten Crab
SHORE CRABS, VARUNIDAE

Size: body up to 8 cm long.
Distribution: originally from
China and Korea; Baltic and
North Sea, Netherlands to
Portugal; North America.
General: claws partly covered
by a dense mat of hair, more
strongly in males than in females.
Adults in fresh waters. Egg-lay-
ing and hatching in estuaries or
coastal regions. Larvae develop
in the sea, young migrate into
fresh water. Crabs can migrate
up to 1300 km upriver! Their
burrows can cause damage to
river banks. Considered a
delicacy in China!

Eriocheir sinensis   Netherlands, North Sea

Sally Lightfoot
SHORE CRABS, GRAPSIDAE

S: 5 cm wide. D: Azores, SW-
Portugal to Namibia, Ascension.
G: day-active, spends most of its
time just above the water line,
where it is splashed by waves.
Pulls algal cover off rocks and
eats it. Also scavenger, cannibal-
istic predator. <u>Below</u>: adult male.

Grapsus adscensionis   Faial Island, Azores

**TALON CRABS,
PLAGUSIIDAE**
Size: up to 3 cm wide.
Distribution: from south-western Portugal to Ascension
Island; recently it has also been
found in the Mediterranean
Balearic Islands and at the
coast of Sicily, where it is
spreading rapidly; tropical
western Atlantic.
General: this very flat crab
lives on rocky bottoms, down
to about 30 m depth. It is a
day-active, rather "nervous"
creature that, at the least
disturbance, zigzags speedily
into a hiding place. It often
seeks shelter under the spines
of sea urchins.

Percnon gibbesi   Madeira

TALON CRABS, PLAGUSIIDAE
Size: up to 4 cm wide.
Distribution: from the Azores to Ascension Island, Madeira, Canaries, Cape Verdes, and the islands in the Gulf of Guinea; tropical western Atlantic. General: at first glance, this species looks similar to grey *Grapsus adscensionis* (compare with previous page) but note the difference in colour and in the frontal area of the carapace. Lives on rocky cliffs, directly at the water line and down to at most 20 m depth. At night, it often leaves the water to run about on the rocks. Collected for human consumption in some areas.

Plagusia depressa   Faial Island, Azores

Ghost Crab
FIDDLER CRABS, OCYPODIDAE
S: up to 5 cm wide. D: E-Med.; Mauritania south to Angola, Cape Verdes, Gulf of Guinea islands. G: Ghost crabs live on sandy beaches, where they dig burrows in the intertidal. They are active day and night and run away very fast when approached. The long eyestalks are typical; they can be folded back into protective grooves on the front of the carapace. See the story "Trapped" to explain the curious fact that this species lives along the coasts of West Africa and in the eastern Mediterranean Sea but not in the area in between.

Ocypode cursor   Cape Verde Islands

West African Fiddler Crab
OCYPODIDAE
S: up to 5 cm wide. D: southeastern Portugal (Algarve) to Angola, Cape Verdes, Gulf of Guinea islands. G: the only eastern Atlantic fiddler crab, biggest species of the genus. On muddy or muddy-sandy beaches, where males and females construct burrows. Males have one claw (left or right) greatly enlarged (up to 40% of the male's weight!) and try to attract females by waving it. Females prefer males with larger claws but do not discriminate between right-handed and left-handed males.

Uca tangeri   Sierra Leone

NEVER WITHOUT UMBRELLA

To protect themselves from detection by predators, spider crabs of the family Majidae place fragments of seaweeds on small hooks on the body. Dromiid and homolid crabs have invented a different method for the same purpose.

The Bearded Crab *Homola barbata* carries objects like a clump of algae.

All species of the family Homolidae have the last, fifth, pair of legs modified: they are shorter and thinner than the other legs and instead of touching the ground they are permanently turned upwards. This special pair of legs is used to hold an object over the body of the crab. The most common species of the family in the Mediterranean Sea and the eastern Atlantic is the Bearded Crab, *Homola barbata*. During a night dive at Madeira, I encountered a bearded crab holding a clump of algae in its hindmost pair of legs. To photograph the special legs, I removed the algae from the crab.

Young Atlantic Sponge Crabs *Dromia marmorea* carry sponges for protection.

The poor crab looked rather unhappy without its umbrella, so I replaced the algae after taking the photos. Most bearded crabs carry a piece of sponge instead of algae but I have also seen one individual that clasped a branch of the encrusting anemone *Gerardia savaglia*.

The sponge crabs, family Dromiidae, even derive their name from the habit of carrying sponges. In sponge crabs the last two pairs of legs, the fourth and the fifth, are modified in such a way that they can no longer be used for walking. *Dromia personata* and *Dromia marmorea* cut a piece of sponge to give it the right size and then hold it with the special legs. Very large animals of these two species often no longer hold sponges: the habit appears to be confined to smaller individuals. Because the last two pairs of legs are useless for walking, sponge crabs use their claws instead! The tips of the claws tred the ground in a manner reminiscent of the knuckle-walk of gorillas.

Squilla mantis   **Adriatic Sea**

Spottail Mantis Shrimp
SQUILLIDAE
S: 25 cm. D: Med.; Portugal to
Angola, Mad., Can. G: double eye-
spot on tail. In U-shaped burrows
on sandy-muddy bottoms from 10
to 250+ m. Like praying mantis, all
mantis shrimps have a pair of
enlarged raptorial arms used to
capture prey; these arms may
either have sharp elongated spines
and spear the prey or they have a
club-shaped, heavily calcified joint
and smash the prey. **All 4 spp
shown are spearers.** Strike of
arms is one of the fastest movements (3-8 ms) in animal kingdom.
Day-active, visually hunting. Very
complex eyes on highly mobile
stalks (see "Invertebrate Vision").

Pseudosquilla oculata   **Tenerife, Canary Islands**

PSEUDOSQUILLIDAE
S: to 8 cm. D: in (sub)tropical
waters world-wide incl. Azores,
Madeira, Canaries, Cape Verdes,
Gulf of Guinea, St. Helena. G:
eye-spots on carapace. Shallow
to 100 m. Below (São Tomé):
Lysiosquilla hoevenii, Lysiosquilli-
dae, 26 cm, Cape Verdes, Senegal to Angola. Common off
West Africa, on soft bottoms
from shallow water to 30+ m.

S: 7 cm. D: Med.; Wales to Madeira. G: claws slender. On mix
of mud, sand, gravel, to 100+ m.
Until Rohan Holt discovered a
large bed (c. 62 acres) with burrows (up to 11/100 m², horizontally elongated U-shape, 45 cm
long, 16 deep, entrance 2 cm in
diameter) at Cardigan Bay, the
species was known only from
planktonic larvae and cod stom-
achs along the British coast.

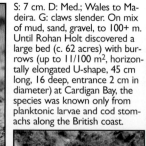

Rissoides desmaresti   **Cardigan Bay, Wales**

NYMPHONIDAE

S: trunk length up to 9 mm, leg span up to 9 cm. D: all around the Arctic, E-Atl.: coasts of Norway. G: sea spiders do look like spiders but do not belong to the true spiders (which do not live in the sea). Pantopoda (Greek) = "all legs". Indeed, the body of the sea spiders is so small that in many spp some of the organs such as the gonads and part of the gut are in the legs! Number of legs variable, with some spp having 4 pairs of them, others 5, and some even 6. Most spp suck on sea anemones, hydrozoans or moss animals and are therefore likely to be found near them. More than 1000 different spp. Many are <2 cm long but some Antarctic spp reach a leg span of 75 cm. *Nymphon* spp are characterized by a slender body. In addition to the 4 walking legs, they bear a pair of pincer-like feeding appendages and a pair of much shorter "legs" to carry the eggs (males). *Nymphon* spp belong to the more active among the normally rather sluggish sea spiders; *N. gracile* can even swim. <u>Below</u> (Barents Sea): *N. grossipes,* same D as *N. elegans,* leg span to 5 cm.

Nymphon elegans   **Norway**

S: leg span 3.5 cm. D: Norway to W-Africa, Azor.; Med., Black Sea. G: in the Pantopoda, males carry the eggs: balls of up to 1000 are glued to a special pair of legs and a male may carry eggs from different females. Littoral to 10+ m. <u>Below</u> (Baltic Sea): *Pycnogonum littorale,* 2 cm, arctic Norway to S-Spain. Sucks on sea anemones, stauromedusae, polychaetes, sea cucumbers. Shallow to 800 m.

Endeis spinosa   **Gulf of Genoa, Italy**

FOREST DWELLERS

Dense forests of big brown seaweeds are a dominant feature in shallow water on the rocky Atlantic coasts of northwest Europe, providing a sheltered home for innumerable invertebrates. Sue Scott describes how the kelp copes with sometimes unwelcome colonisers.

Like forests on land, dense stands of the kelp *Laminaria hyperborea* provide a variety of microhabitats for animals. Different creatures live on the forest floor, in the crevices in the branched holdfast, and attached to the rough stipes. Inside a kelp holdfast (the root-like processes the kelp uses to cling to the rock), small animals are safe from grazing urchins and other predators.

The moving frond is a more difficult place to colonise, as the kelp plant constantly produces slippery mucus to deter settlers, but a few animals manage to thrive even here. By the end of the summer, the kelp becomes covered in fuzzy growths of the hydroid *Obelia geniculata,* and large white patches of the bryozoans *Membranipora membranacea* and *Electra pilosa,* while the little blue-rayed limpet *Helcion pellucidum* grazes the fronds.

Animal growth across its frond is a serious problem for the kelp plant, because it blocks out the light the kelp needs to grow. *Laminaria hyperborea* has an

Like forests on land, kelp provides a variety of microhabitats for animals.

interesting way of dealing with this – sometime between late winter and spring, it sheds the whole frond, complete with animals, and grows a brand new, clean one! In the photo, the old frond covered in bryozoans is ready to

Inside a kelp holdfast, small animals are safe from predators.

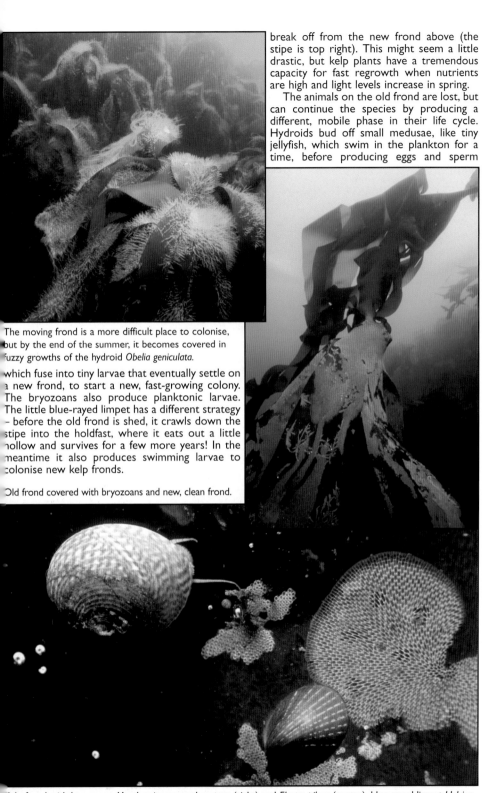

break off from the new frond above (the stipe is top right). This might seem a little drastic, but kelp plants have a tremendous capacity for fast regrowth when nutrients are high and light levels increase in spring.

The animals on the old frond are lost, but can continue the species by producing a different, mobile phase in their life cycle. Hydroids bud off small medusae, like tiny jellyfish, which swim in the plankton for a time, before producing eggs and sperm

The moving frond is a more difficult place to colonise, but by the end of the summer, it becomes covered in fuzzy growths of the hydroid *Obelia geniculata*.

which fuse into tiny larvae that eventually settle on a new frond, to start a new, fast-growing colony. The bryozoans also produce planktonic larvae. The little blue-rayed limpet has a different strategy – before the old frond is shed, it crawls down the stipe into the holdfast, where it eats out a little hollow and survives for a few more years! In the meantime it also produces swimming larvae to colonise new kelp fronds.

Old frond covered with bryozoans and new, clean frond.

Kelp frond with bryozoans *Membranipora membranacea* (right) and *Electra pilosa* (centre), blue-rayed limpet *Helcion pellucidum* (bottom, right of centre), spirorbid worm tubes (left) and Grey Topshell *Gibbula cineraria* (top left).

Chiton olivaceus   **Crete Island, Greece**

Green Chiton
CHITONIDAE

S: 4 cm. D: Med., Algarve, Tanger. G: as in all chitons, the shell consists of 8 interlocked plates, also called "coat-of-mail shells". In this species, the plates form a distinct longitudinal keel on the back of the animal. The broad girdle around the shell plates is distinctly granulated, due to the presence of small, triangular overlapping scales. Olive-green marbled white, red, yellow. Common, can be found below stones from the water line down to 40 m. The small objects on the girdle are foraminiferans; despite consisting of only a single cell, they are visible to the naked eye (see "Giant Single Cells"). Below (Crete): *C. corallinus,* Mediterranean Sea, 2.5 cm, 15-100 m.

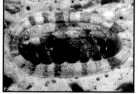

Concentric Chiton
LEPIDOCHITONIDAE

S: 3 cm. D: N-Spain south to Canaries; W- and E-Med. G: 7-10 conspicuous ribs on the sides of the plates and on the head and rear tail plates. Cream to light brown. From the water line down to 40+ m. *Chiton canariensis* (small photos; Chitonidae) resembles *C. olivaceus* but does not live in the same area, namely W-Africa and the Canary Islands. Colour grey to red and striped.

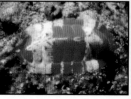

Lepidopleurus cajetanus   **Crete Island, Greece**

Grey Chiton
ISCHNOCHITONIDAE
S: 2.5 cm. D: S-Norway, Shetland Is. to Strait of Gibraltar; W-Med. G: very common, usually on the underside of stones, intertidal downwards. Plates rough to the touch. Colour variable, patches of yellow, red, green. <u>Below</u>: *Tonicella marmorea,* Iceland, Norway to Great Britain, to 200 m.

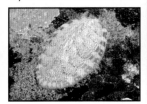

Lepidochitona cinerea   Helgoland, North Sea

Ribbed Chiton
ACANTHOCHITONIDAE
S: 4 cm. D: Brittany/France to Canaries, Azores, Madeira; Med. G: 8 plates with a longitudinal keel in the middle. 18 conspicuous tufts of bristles on the girdle. 0-50 m. Colour variable, yellow to brown, pink to brightly red. <u>Below</u>: *Ischnochiton rissoi,* Ischnochitonid., common, Med., 3.5 cm.

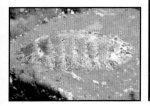

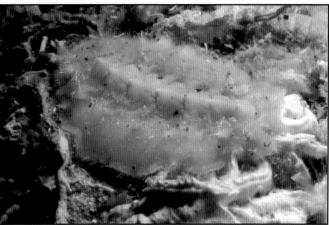

Acanthochitona fascicularis   Faial Island, Azores

Celtic Shoresnail
ONCHIDIIDAE
S: 15 mm. D: S-Great Britain to Madeira; W-Med. G: Looks like a nudibranch (p. 199) but is an air-breathing lung-snail. Grazes on diatoms and small plant material during low tide, hides in air-filled rock crevices during high tide.

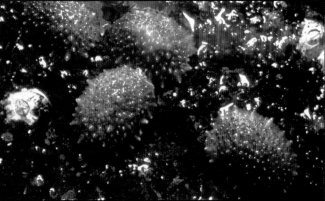

Onchidella celtica   Faial Island, Azores

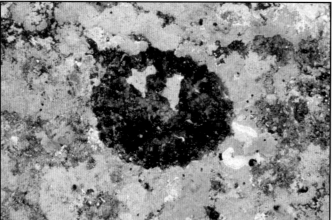

Patella lowei **La Palma, Canary Islands**

Lowe's Limpet
LIMPETS, PATELLIDAE

S: up to 7 cm. D: Madeira. G: there are many different limpet species all along the coasts of Europe and Western Africa, most of them living in the intertidal. Prehistoric rubbish dumps analysed by historians have shown that even the northern, bitter-tasting species were eaten by our ancestors (see "Appetising"). Overfishing has caused the near disappearance of many populations. As limpets are important grazers of algae, the coasts are much more densely covered by algae where man collects limpets.

Ansates pellucida **Isle of Man**

Blue-rayed Limpet
PATELLIDAE

S: up to 2.3 cm. D: from Iceland and Norway to continental Portugal but not on Belgian coast or to the east of them. G: this beautiful little limpet used to be called *Patina pellucida.* It lives, usually in groups of several animals, on large brown algae, down to about 30 m. The blue markings tend to disappear in older individuals. Small animals graze on microalgae growing on the kelp fronds. Large animals can excavate holes in the holdfasts of kelp, which may lead to the plant becoming torn off during storms.

Acmaea virginea **São Jorge Island, Azores**

Pink-rayed Limpet
ACMAEIDAE

S: 12 mm long, 4 mm high. D: Iceland, Norway to Cape Verdes; Med. G: pale cream to dark green and red. On stones from shallow water to 100 m, feeding on algae, especially encrusting red algae. Below: *Emarginula paivana,* Fissurellidae, 15 mm, has a tiny slit at the front of the shell.

Ormer
ABALONES, HALIOTIDAE

S: <10 cm. D: Med.; Channel Is. to Morocco. G: the series of holes along the outer edge of the flat shell makes abalones unmistakable. Clings to the lower side of stones, intertidal to 30 m. Feeds on algae, especially soft red ones. Edible, over-collected.

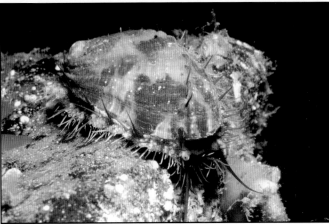

Haliotis tuberculata   Porto Santo Island, Madeira

Painted Topshell
TOPSHELLS, TROCHIDAE

S: 2, max 3.5 cm high. D: Med.; Lofoten, Norway to Canaries. G: 1-300 m. Differs from *C. conulum* (below) by its broader shape, less polished surface. Below (Azores): considered by some experts as a separate species called *C. lusitanicum*.

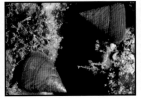

Calliostoma zizyphinum   Norway

Shining Topshell

Size: up to 2.7 cm high.
Distribution: Med., Madeira, Canary Islands.
General: at first glance, this species is quite similar to *C. zizyphinum* (above). It differs from it by its more slender shape, less granulated first whorls and more polished surface. It is most common below 20 m and can reach 200 m depth. The photo shows the most common form but, like *C. zizyphinum*, it is variable in colour. A small violet form appears to be associated with sponges.

Calliostoma conulum   Crete Island, Greece

Umbilicated Monodont
TROCHIDAE (this page)
S: 2.5 cm. D: Med. G: many similar Med. *Gibbula* spp. Photo: *G. u.*
forma *"nebulosa"*, differs from
"latior" by being taller spired,
glossier, with more pronounced
colour pattern. Below: *Clanculus
bertheloti*, Az., Mad., Can. Female
keeps eggs in deep groove on
base of shell until larvae hatch!

Gibbula umbilicaris   **Cyprus**

Freckled Monodont

S: 1-2, max 3.8 cm. D: Med.,
adjacent Atl. coasts. G: used to
be called *Monodonta turbinata*.
Colour pattern species-typical.
On rocky shores, from the
intertidal down to a few metres
depth. Below: *Jujubinus pseudo-
gravinae*, at night in a large tide
pool in the Azores, about 1 cm.

Osilinus turbinatus   **Crete Island, Greece**

Arctic Monodont

Size: up to 10 mm in diameter.
Distribution: a circumboreal
species (this means: all around
the Arctic). In Europe as far
south as the British Isles.
General: this species lives from
the intertidal zone down to
400 m depth and is most commonly encountered on brown
seaweeds or stones. It differs
from other *Margarites* species
by its smooth, fragile shell. The
nacreous shine of the shell is
characteristic for the species.

Margarites helicinus   **Spitsbergen, Norway**

Rough Star Shell
TURBAN SHELLS, TURBINIDAE
S: 7 cm. D: Med.; Azores, Portugal to Canaries. G: unmistakable, shell often covered by algae. Can close opening with thick operculum (below). Opercula used in jewellery since ancient times; amphorae filled with them found in Roman shipwrecks. Nowadays still used to make cuff-links.

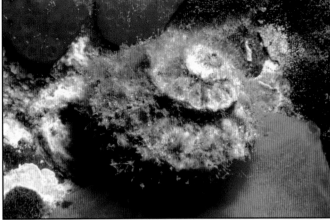

Bolma rugosa   Madeira

Mediterranean Cerith
CERITHS, CERITHIDAE

Size: usually about 2.5 cm long.
Distribution: Mediterranean Sea; Canary Islands.
General: there are many similar looking *Cerithium* species and the species are quite variable. The rather stout *Cerithium rupestre,* for instance, can have a smooth shell (as in the photo) or a spiny one. It lives in shallow water on rocky and rocky-sandy bottoms. The animals in the unusual photo apparently are scavenging on a dead sea urchin.

Cerithium rupestre   Costa Brava, Spain

Common Cerith
S: up to 7 cm long. D: Med. G: a locally common sp that lives in shallow water, on sandy and muddy bottoms. The species *C. alucaster* is similar in size but more slender and lives in deeper water. Below (Azores): the tiny (1 cm long) *Bittium latreillii.* There are many similar looking *Bittium* species.

Cerithium vulgatum   Crete Island, Greece

Tower Snail, Muddy Auger
TURRITELLAS,
TURRITELLIDAE
S: up to 5 cm.
D: Mediterranean Sea; E-Atl.:
continental Portugal to Madeira.
G: the high, pointed shell is
typical of the genus, which
comprises three further European species. Most shells are a
uniform brown but a second
colour pattern, also shown in
the photo, is not uncommon.
The species lives on rocky and
sandy bottoms. It is rare in
shallow water. Below 15 m
depth, at Madeira, *Turritella
turbona* can locally reach densities of more than 50 animals
per m².

Turritella turbona   Madeira

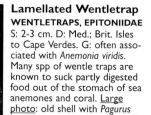

Lamellated Wentletrap
WENTLETRAPS, EPITONIIDAE
S: 2-3 cm. D: Med.; Brit. Isles
to Cape Verdes. G: often associated with *Anemonia viridis*.
Many spp of wentle traps are
known to suck partly digested
food out of the stomach of sea
anemones and coral. <u>Large
photo</u>: old shell with *Pagurus
anachoretus*. <u>Below</u>: living snail.

Gyroscala lamellosa   Madeira

Milky White Eulimid
EULIMIDS, EULIMIDAE
S: females to 13 mm in diameter.
D: E-Atl.: Madeira to São Tomé.
G: most eulimid snails are parasites on echinoderms. Some are
only loosely attached, can crawl
away in search of pair partners,
others are firmly attached and
probably do not change hosts. *E.
leucophaes* belongs to the latter
group. Usually, 2 animals live on
a *Diadema* sea urchin, the larger
one being the female. If the large
animal dies, the male changes
sex and turns female, waiting for
a new pair partner to arrive.
The combination large female
plus small male maximises the
output of offspring for both!

Echineulima leucophaes   Madeira

Philippi's Eulimid
EULIMIDAE

S: up to 5 mm. D: Med.; Azores (new record), Canary Islands. G: Locally common parasite on the sea urchins A. lixula, P. lividus, S. granularis. Below: Melanella alba, 2 cm, a parasite on sea cucumbers, Norway to Med. Both loosely attached, also found without their hosts.

Vitreolina philippi   **Pico Island, Azores**

Rough Periwinkle
PERIWINKLES,
LITTORINIDAE

S: up to 2 cm high. D: Atlantic coast of Europe. G: periwinkles are the dominant snails in the intertidal. Most species are rather inconspicuous, small brown jobs, but Littorina saxatilis is an attractive exception. As the photo shows, the species is quite variable, yellow or red or purple or brown. This is an air-breathing marine snail, found in crevices on the upper shore and among brown algae. Because of its tolerance to reduced salinities, it can also live on estuarine mudflats. The Rough periwinkle bears live young.

Littorina saxatilis   **North Sea**

Greater Worm-Shell
WORM-SHELLS,
VERMETIDAE

S: tube up to 10 cm long, diameter of aperture up to 15 mm. D: Med. G: vermetids cannot move around. They live in tubes fastened to the substrate and these tubes are easily confused with those of some polychaetes. Worm-Shells feed by secreting a mucous thread that captures plankton. Every now and then, they pull in the mucus and eat it plus all that adheres to it. S. arenarius is the largest Med. Worm-Shell. Locally common on rocks from about 5 m downwards. In contrast to most vermetids, it does not have an operculum.

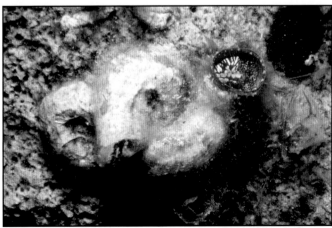

Serpulorbis arenarius   **Crete Island, Greece**

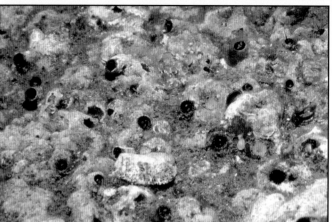

Unidentified Worm-Shell
VERMETIDAE
S: coil up to 15 mm in diameter.
G: difficult to identify. An expert for whom author PW collected numerous species (Madeira, Azores) was unable to identify a single one of them. This one reaches densities of several 100 per m² on shallow rock. <u>Below</u> (Canaries): *Vermetus triquetus*.

Unidentified Worm-Shell   **Madeira**

Persian Conch
CONCHS, STROMBIDAE

S: up to 6 cm long, usually 4 cm.
D: E-Med.; Persian Gulf. G: only European family member. Probably accidentally introduced into Mediterranean with ballast water (see "Long Distance"), now common in eastern Med. Large eyes unmistakable. In shallow bays on mixed bottoms, feeds on algae. Pushes itself forward in a curious stepwise fashion by stemming its elongated operculum against the bottom. See the story "Trapped" for *Strombus latus*, which lived there during warmer, preglacial times.

Strombus persicus   **Crete Island, Greece**

Spiny Lamellariid
LAMELLARIIDS,
LAMELLARIIDAE

S: up to 4 cm but usually <2 cm.
D: Med.; in E-Atlantic from the Lofoten Islands to the Canary Islands, including Azores and Madeira; in the W-Atlantic from Florida to Brazil. G: lamellarids are usually confused with nudibranchs. Shell is reduced to a small, thin remnant below the mantle tissue, not visible in the living animal. *L. perspicua* hides below stones by day, shallow down to 1200 m . In the Med., it spawns from April to May. Deposits its eggs in the mantle tissue of tunicates.

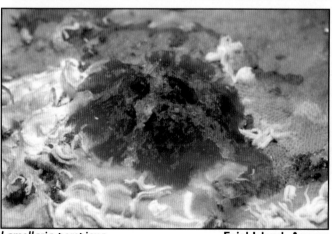

Lamellaria perspicua   **Faial Island, Azores**

Porcellaneous Slipper
SLIPPER LIMPETS,
CALYPTRAEIDAE

S: up to 2 cm. D: from Canaries southwards along the coast of W-Africa, including Cape Verdes. G: large calyptraeids are sedentary and filter feeding. Individuals are male first and turn female later. In stacks of animals of the slipper limpet *C. fornicata* (see "Long Distance"), the lower big animals are female, the upper small animals are male. Large animals are filter-feeding, while the small males move around and feed by grazing. Photo: light-shelled male on larger dark female, attached to *Conus ermineus*.

Crepidula porcellana   Cape Verde Islands

Flea Trivia
TRIVIAS, TRIVIIDAE

S: up to 9 mm. D:Mediterranean Sea; Azores, Canary Islands. G: when undisturbed, this species (like all Trivias) covers the shell with two folds of the mantle. On rock bottom, down to at least 30 m depth, differs from *T. arctica* by a smooth area on the dorsal side of the shell.

Trivia pulex   São Miguel Island, Azores

Ribbed Trivia

S: up to 10 mm but usually smaller. D: Med.; in E-Atlantic from Norway to Gibraltar. G: frequently called *T. europaea*. As a comparison with the photos above shows, *T. arctica* differs from *T. pulex* not only in shell structure but also in the colour of the mantle tissue of living animals. It lives on rocky bottoms, down to about 200 m depth, and feeds on tunicates. Animals from the Med. tend to be smaller than those from the north-eastern Atlantic (a general rule, applicable to many species of animals with a similar distribution).

Trivia arctica   North Sea

Purpuradusta gracilis **Cyprus**

Graceful Cowrie
COWRIES, CYPRAEIDAE
(this page)
S: 2 cm. D: Indo-Pacific; E-Med.
G: Red Sea immigrant (see p. 254). When undisturbed, cowries hold two folds of the mantle over the shell. When porcelain came from China to Europe it was named after the "porcelain snails" (and not vice versa!).

Erosaria spurca **Madeira**

Dirty Cowry

S: up to 2, rarely 3 cm.
D: Mediterranean; in E-Atlantic from Madeira to St. Helena, including Canaries and Cape Verdes. G: the mantle tissue bears many small, branched protuberances. A common species, the most likely cowry to be encountered by a diver.

Fallow Cowry

S: up to 6.5 cm. D: Med.; in E-Atlantic from Azores to Ascension Island, including Madeira, Canaries, Cape Verdes. G: largest cowry in our area. Unmistakable due to 2 dark spots at each shell end. Like the other cowries shown, active at night, most likely found inside caves.

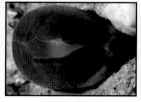

Luria lurida **Faial Island, Azores**

Cave Ovula
EGGSHELLS, OVULIDAE
S: up to 15 mm.
D: western Med.; eastern
Atlantic: continental Portugal
to Angola, including the
Canary Islands.
G: *N. spelta* lives on gorgonians,
from shallow water down to
80 m. In the Med. it is usually
found on *Eunicella* and *Paramuricea,* in the Canaries on the
red *Lophogorgia ruberrima* or
the yellow *L. vimnalis* (p. 42).
The mantle of the snail always
has the same colour as the
gorgonian it lives on (through
uptake of pigments from the
host, on which it feeds?). It can
move with surprising speed.

Neosimnia spelta　　　　Costa del Sol, Spain

Dwarf Red Ovula
OVULIDAE

Size: up to 15 mm.
Distribution: Mediterranean
Sea; in the eastern Atlantic at
the Canary and Cape Verde
Islands.
General: this species is more
globular, less elongated than
Neosimnia spelta. It mainly lives
on red coral *Corallium rubrum,*
from 20-120 m depth, but has
also been found on other
Gorgonaria species (p. 40) and
on *Alcyonium* (p. 35). The
colour of the mantle tissue is
quite variable. On *Corallium* it
usually is bright red.

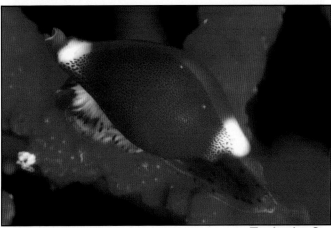

Pseudosimnia carnea　　　　Tyrrhenian Sea

Pale Moon Shell
MOON SHELLS, NATICIDAE
S: to 22 mm high. D: circumpolar sp, in Europe south to
Iceland and North Sea. G: used
to be called *Lunatia pallida.* Mud
and clay bottoms, 10-1200 m.
Below: *Euspira pulchella,* used to
be called *Polinices nitida.* Locally
common, up to 16 mm high, on
sand, from N-Norway to Med.

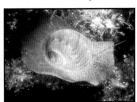

Euspira pallida　　　　Spitsbergen, Norway

CLEAN ME

More than 120 fish species from 29 different families are known to clean other fish. They pick small parasites off the skin of their clients and eat them. Nineteen shrimps and two crabs have also been recorded as cleaners.

RAIMUND HÜBNER

In the Mediterranean Sea, *Lysmata seticaudata* can occasionally be seen cleaning fish, such as moray eels.

More than half of the crustacean cleaners belong to the genus *Lysmata*, a total of ten species from the Mediterranean Sea, the eastern Atlantic, the western Atlantic, the Indian Ocean and the Pacific Ocean. As in the fishes, some species clean only occasionally; others are professionals that derive all their food in this way. In the Mediterranean Sea, *Lysmata seticaudata* is an occasional cleaner; fish like *Symphodus melanocercus* and *Thalassoma pavo* are the professionals there.

In the eastern Atlantic, the White-striped Cleaner Shrimp *Lysmata grabhami* is a truly professional cleaner. It lives in pairs at fixed places, frequently close to a giant sea anemone *Telmatactis cricoides*. Fish know where the cleaner shrimps are living and come there to be cleaned. Frequently many fish queue in front of these cleaning stations and patiently wait their turn.

The White-striped Cleaner Shrimp cleans not only harmless plankton-eating fish species like the Atlantic damselfish *Chromis limbata* and micro-carnivores (eaters of quite small

PETER WIRTZ

Open wide please! *Lysmata grabhami* acts as a dentist for the Atlantic damselfish *Chromis limbata*.

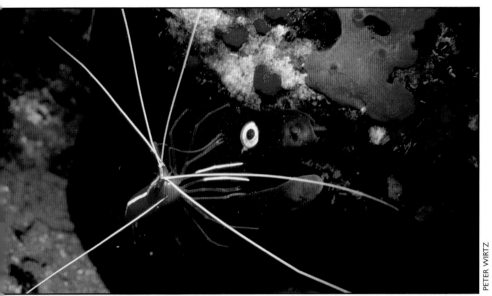

PETER WIRTZ

This cleaner shrimp apparently is not afraid to be eaten by its client, a *Muraena augusti*.

animals) like the pufferfish *Sphoeroides marmoratus* but also predators like the Tiger Moray *Enchelycore anatina*. Is it somehow protected against being preyed on? If yes, then this protection is not 100 per-cent effective: the Blacktail Comber *Serranus atricauda* and the Madeira Scorpionfish *Scorpaena madeirensis* both were seen to eat a *Lysmata grabhami*.

When potential clients approach the home of the White-striped Cleaner Shrimp the shrimp per-forms a curious dance, waving its conspicuous white antennae. This is probably a signal to the fish to come closer. Many cleaner shrimps have brilliantly white antennae. However, not all shrimps with white antennae are cleaner shrimps. The Mediterranean Boxer Shrimp *Stenopus spinosus* is sometimes called a cleaner shrimp but apparently it has never really been observed cleaning.

Until now, only two crab species have been reported as cleaners. The Columbus Crab eats animals and plants growing on the turtles on which it lives. At the Canary Islands, Alberto Brito observed the Eastern Atlantic Arrow Crab *Stenorhynchus lanceolatus* cleaning the Mediterranean Moray and the Tiger Moray – but cleaning is apparently a rare behaviour for this species.

HELMUT DEBELIUS

Despite its appearance, the Golden shrimp *Stenopus spinosus* is probably not a cleaner. Photo from Ibiza, Spain.

175

Hebrew Moon Shell
MOON SHELLS, NATICIDAE
S: 4 cm. D: Med. G: muddy and sandy bottoms, in 10+ m. Like all moon shells, a mollusc predator: it bores a small hole into the shell of a bivalve or another snail (a process that can take several hours) and then inserts the proboscis through this hole and scrapes out the soft bits. <u>Upper small ph.</u>: Josephine's Moonshell *Neverita josephinia*, shallow, on sand, Med. <u>Lower</u>: typical spawn.

Natica hebraea   Ionian Sea, Greece

Spotted Moon Shell
S: up to 4 cm high. D: Med. G: the spotted colour pattern makes this beautiful species quite unmistakable. Size and number of the spots varies. The Spotted moon shell lives on sandy and muddy bottoms, from about 10 to 80 m. <u>Upper small photo</u> (from large tide pool, Azores, at night): *N. adansoni*, Med., Azores to Cape Verdes. <u>Lower</u> (Canary Islands): *N. dillwynii*, which lives in the same area as *N. adansoni*.

Natica stercusmuscarum   Crete Island, Greece

MESOGASTROPODA

Giant Tun
TUN SHELLS, TONNIDAE

S: 20, max 30 cm. D: world-wide in temperate & tropical waters. E-Atl.: Azores-Ascension. Med. G: by day buried in sand, only partly visible, emerges at night to prey on bivalves, echinoderms, especially sea cucumbers. <u>Below</u>: Spotted Tun *T. maculosa*, W-Atl., occas. W-Africa, Canar., Madeira.

Tonna galea   Crete Island, Greece

Senegal Helmet
HELMETS, CASSIDAE

Size: up to 10 cm long but rarely more than 7 cm. Distribution: in the eastern Atlantic from the Canary Islands to St. Helena; also in tropical western Atlantic. General: the shell of this unmistakable species is solid and quite heavy. Some experts consider the West African form a subspecies, *Cypraecassis testiculus senegalica*. It lives on sandy bottoms, from about 10 m down to several hundred metres depth, and is a predator of sea urchins.

Cypraecassis testiculus senegalica   Cape Verde Islands

Mediterranean Bonnet
CASSIDAE

S: 12 cm. D: W-Med.; Azores to Cape Verdes, Madeira, Canaries; W-Atl. G: on sandy bottoms, shallow down to 20+ m. *Phalium saburon* (W-Med., N-Spain to W-Africa) is quite similar but even more globular in shape and has closer spiral ridges. <u>Below</u>: the spawn of *Phalium granulatum*.

Phalium granulatum undulatum   Madeira

MESOGASTROPODA

Charonia lampas Madeira

Knobbed Triton
TRITONS, RANELLIDAE
(this page)
S: up to 32 cm.
D: Med.; in the E-Atlantic from the English Channel along the coast of West Africa.
G: this triton differs from the Atlantic Trumpet Triton (below) by having an orange-red body and a broader shell bearing distinct nodules. It lives on rocky and sandy bottoms, from shallow water down to 700 m, feeding on echinoderms and bivalves. The sea star *Echinaster sepositus* (p. 279) appears to be one of its preferred prey. Triton females guard the egg capsules for several weeks.

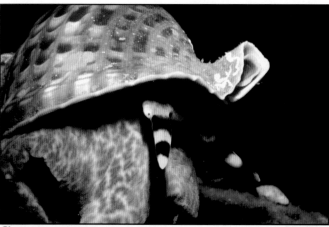

Charonia variegata Madeira

Atlantic Trumpet Triton
S: up to 23 cm. D: tropical and subtropical waters of both sides of the Atlantic; eastern Med. G: the Atlantic triton differs from the Knobbed triton (above) by having a yellow-cream coloured body and a more slender shell without distinct nodules. It lives on rocky or gravel bottoms, generally in shallower waters than the Knobbed triton. The Guanchas, the indigenous population of the Canary Islands, used this species as trumpets. See the story "Trapped" for an explanation of its curious distribution pattern.

Neapolitan Triton
S: to 17 cm. D: W- to C-Med.; temperate and tropical E-Atl.; W-Atl., IP. G: the many "hairs", placed in perfect rows, make the species unmistakable. It feeds on other snails and on bivalves, which are first paralysed with a secretion from the mouth. Small photo from Gran Canaria, Canary Islands.

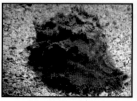

Cymatium parthenopeum Faial Island, Azores

Pitted Frog Shell
FROG SHELLS, BURSIDAE

Size: up to 7 cm.
Distribution: Med.; in the eastern Atlantic from the Azores to the Cape Verde Islands.
General: the deep grooves along the outer edge of the aperture characterize this species. It lives on rocky bottoms in 10-100 m. While rare in the Med., it is quite common at the Azores, where it often enters the traps of fishermen. The female guards the eggs for some time. This is a predatory species, feeding on large polychaetes. When capturing a polychaete, the snail injects a paralysing poison.

Bursa scrobilator   **Faial Island, Azores**

Crowned Heteropod
HETEROPODS, FIROLIDAE
S: 30 cm. D: Med.; Atlantic. G: this fantastic animal belongs to a group of snails adapted to life in the plankton. They do not have a shell and the gelatinous body is transparent. A large flap on the belly makes undulating or beating movements and propels the animal. Males have a sucking disk on this flap to hold onto the female. Two well-developed eyes are clearly visible. These snail are predators that grasp other animals in the plankton, such as small crustaceans or fish larvae, with their long proboscis and swallow them. The photo is an excerpt from a video tape.

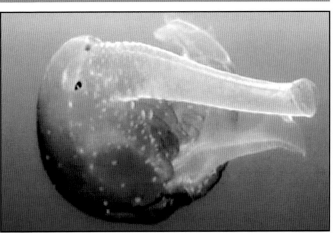

Pterotrachaea coronata   **Costa Brava, Spain**

Banded Murex
MUREX SHELLS, MURICIDAE
S: 5, max 10 cm. D: Med.; Azor. to Canaries. G: on mud, sand, 5-100 m. Appears to like polluted harbours. The elephant trunk-like front of shell is typical. Many animals congregate for spawning (photo). Fished for commercially in Med. In ancient times, it was used to produce a purple dye.

Hexaplex trunculus   **Cyprus**

HOUSE EXCHANGE

Hermit crabs hide the soft rear end of their body in a snail shell. The crab grows; the shell, however, does not. Thus, hermit crabs periodically need a new shell. To find an empty shell of the right size is a very rare event. But there is another possibility. Peter Wirtz tells us how hermit crabs deal with housing problems...

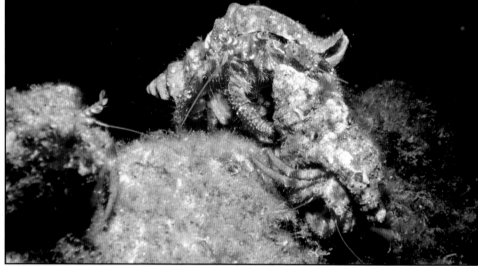

PHOTOS: PETER WIRTZ

Hermit crabs *(Dardanus calidus)* need an empty snail shell to protect their soft abdomen. But most shells are occupied!

Two hermit crabs facing each other are waving their claws and their antennae as if talking in sign language. Suddenly one of them leaves its house and, rapidly afterwards, the second animal also crawls out of its house. For a moment, they are both completely naked – for hermit crabs probably more a dangerous than an erotic situation. Quickly the first crab enters the house vacated by the other crab while the second one slips into the house of the first. The two hermit crabs have exchanged houses.

Because available houses are so rare, many hermit crabs find themselves in houses that are too small to be comfortable. If they encounter a house that is a little bit too large they may have to use it. Thus, there are both crabs with houses too large and crabs with houses too small running around in the same area. What better way than to exchange them if they are meeting and if both partners are willing? After the exchange, both hermit crabs are occupying houses better suited to their size.

Thus the theory. But is it true? Do both partners profit from an exchange in houses? By offering a large choice of empty houses to hermit crabs, investigators determined "the perfect house" for each size of hermit crab. They were then able to say if, after an exchange of houses, both partners really had come closer to the perfect state.

The answer is: mostly yes, but frequently not. Both partners in a house exchange had gained in about two thirds of the cases.

What about the other cases? A closer look at the behaviour of these crabs showed that pure force was involved. Sometimes one of the two hermit crabs would grab the claws of the other one and pull. It would also bang its own shell against that of the other crab in a series of rapping bouts. Eventually, some of the crabs thus attacked would give up their house and would, of course, have no choice than to use that of the aggressor in exchange.

Finding an empty shell is a rare event. But will it fit the hermit's size?

Phyllonotus duplex   **Cape Verde Islands**

Duplex Murex
MUREX SHELLS, MURICIDAE

Size: up to 11 cm.
Distribution: coasts of West
Africa, south to Angola.
General: this species lives on
rocky and sandy bottoms. Like
probably all muricid snails, it is
a predator and scavenger on
dead animals. Author PW
observed an individual that
was entering its head and anterior body into the aperture of
the shell of a *Cypraecassis testiculus* (p. 177) larger than
itself.

Stramonita haemastoma   **Madeira**

Red-mouthed Rock-shell
DOGWINKLES, THAIDIDAE

S: up to 4, max 11 cm. D: Med.;
both sides of the subtropical and
tropical Atlantic (in E-Atl. as far
north as the Channel Islands). G:
the sp can be recognized by the
red lining of the mouth, which,
however, is visible only when the
snail is lifted up. Has reached sad
fame as an indicator organism
for stanniferous boat paints.
Even at minute concentrations in
the water, these "anti-fouling"
paints cause a partial sex change
in the females of many snails:
females develop a penis and
become sterile. In the vicinity of
some ports, 100% of the female
snails are deformed in this way!

Nucella lapillus   **Jersey, Channel Islands**

Atlantic Dogwinkle
THAIDIDAE

S: up to 4 cm. D: Greenland to
Gibraltar; W-Atl. G: this is a
very variable species, from
pale grey or cream to shades
of brown, with or without
stripes. It lives in the intertidal,
where it mainly preys on barnacles. It also scavenges on
dead animals, which it can
smell from a distance through
its long siphon. On open-sea
coast, animals are small and
broad, whereas in more sheltered areas they are taller. In
the old times, dog whelks
were used to produce a purple
dye, like some members of the
family Muricidae.

Lamellose Coral-shell
CORAL SHELLS,
CORALLIOPHILIDAE

S: up to 4 cm but rarely more than 2.5 cm. D: Med.; Azores to Canaries. G: feeds on a variety of cnidarian prey. Sucks out the stomach contents of coral such as *Balanophyllia europaea* (p. 70) or *Cladocora caespitosa* (p. 67) or bores into the stalk of sea anemones. Photo: with *Anemonia viridis*, which appears to be the preferred host of larger *C. meyendorffi*. The sp is a sex changer: animals change from male to female sex at about 10 mm. Most common one of several, rather similar European *Coralliophila* spp.

Coralliophila meyendorffi   Madeira

Woody Horse Conch
HORSE CONCHS,
FASCIOLARIIDAE

Size: up to 6 cm.
Distribution: Mediterranean Sea. General: this is a locally common species in the eastern Mediterranean, less common in the western Mediterranean. It lives in shallow water, on rocky shores. It is a predator, preying on other molluscs. The species of the family Fasciolariidae have a very long proboscis. The animal in the photo is in the process of inserting its proboscis into the tube of a Giant Worm Shell *Serpularia vermicularis*.

Fasciolaria lignaria   Crete Island, Greece

Sicilian Spindle
FASCIOLARIIDAE
S: up to 55 mm. D: Med. G: on stony, sandy and muddy bottoms from shallow water down to about 50 m. The colour pattern of the shell shown in the photo makes it unmistakable but uniformly coloured animals also exist. Below: the spawn of a related species, *Latirus armatus*.

Fusinus syracusanus   Cyprus

Buccinum undatum   **Baltic Sea**

Common Whelk
WHELKS, BUCCINIDAE
(this page)
Size: usually around 6 cm, exceptionally to 14 cm.
Distribution: in the eastern Atlantic from N-Norway to Gibraltar; in the western Atlantic from the Arctic to New Jersey.
General: the Common whelk lives on sandy, muddy and shingle bottoms, from shallow water down to about 100 m depth. It is a scavenger, feeding on dead animal matter. This is a very variable species, in shell shape, sculpture and colour. There is a considerable fishery for this species in northern Europe, where it is regarded a delicacy, and large amounts are exported to the Far East.
Lower large photo: an animal with spawn. The typically shaped egg mass – a cluster of egg capsules – is about the size of an apple. Tiny, perfectly shaped whelks hatch from it.
Small photo below: The Striated Whelk *B. corneum* is a locally common species in shallow water in the Mediterranean Sea. It grows to 7 cm but is usually about 3 cm long.

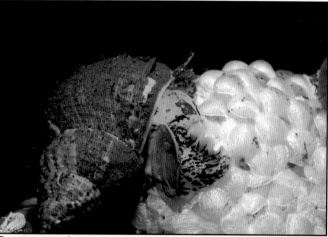

Buccinum undatum   **North Sea**

Canarian Dwarf Triton

S: 6 cm. D: Madeira, Canaries, West Africa. G: when author PW took this photo, he was not aware that this is considered to be a very rare species. It lives on sandy and sandy-rocky bottoms in shallow water. The Med. *C. reticulatum* looks similar. Below (Azores): *Pollia dorbignyi*, 2 cm.

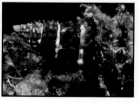

Colubraria canariensis   **Madeira**

Netted Nassa
MUD SNAILS, NASSARIIDAE
S: 3 cm. D: Mediterranean; Norway to Canaries. G: on sand, mud, 1-40 m. Mud Snails are expert scavengers. Swinging their long proboscis, they follow the scent of a dead animal and move with astonishing speed. <u>Below</u>: *N. denticulatus*, 2.5 cm, W-Africa, Madeira, Canaries.

Nassarius reticulatus   **Gran Canaria**

Adanson's Dove-shell
DOVE-SHELLS,
COLUMBELLIDAE
S: 2 cm. D: Azores, Madeira, Canaries. G: very similar to *C. rustica* (Med.). On rocky shores, in shallow water. <u>Below</u>: *Mitrella ocellata*, 1 cm, quite abundant in the rocky intertidal of the Cape Verdes. Tropics, on both sides of Atlantic and in Indo-Pacific.

Columbella adansoni   **Madeira**

Shiny Marginella
MARGINELLAS,
MARGINELLIDAE
S: 4 cm. D: W-Africa: Morocco to Guinea; also Canaries, Cape Verdes. G: predatory, in shallow water on rocky bottoms, in seagrass meadows. <u>Below</u> (Cape Verdes): two *Volvarina taeniata*, less than 1 cm, next to the peach snail *Berthellina edwardsi* (p. 197).

Marginella glabella   **Gran Canaria**

Spindle Miter
MITERS, MITRIDAE

S: 2, max 4.5 cm. D: W-Med.; Azores to Equator. G: easy to recognize when alive: body with bright yellow margin. On rocky shores, 5-50 m. <u>Below</u>: *M. zonata* female depositing eggs. Banded pattern unmistakable. From 30 to 1200 m, W-Med., Azores to Canary Islands. 5, max to 10 cm.

Mitra cornea **Faial Island, Azores**

Flame Olive
OLIVES, OLIVIDAE

Size: up to 4 cm. Distribution: coasts of West Africa, south to Angola. General: this beautiful species has the cylindrical body shape and shiny surface typical of the family. It can be recognized by its colour pattern of numerous flame-shaped lines (thus the name *"flammulata"*). It lives on sandy bottoms, from 8 m depth downwards. The Flamed olive is a predator that hunts at night, for small shrimp and small mussels.

Oliva flammulata **Cape Verde Islands**

Olla Volute
VOLUTES, VOLUTIDAE

S: 12 cm. D: S-Portugal to Morocco and Spanish Sahara. G: the photo shows only a shell of this species. The body of *Cymbium* spp is larger than the shell, cannot be retracted (<u>below</u>). Viviparous, give birth to small young. <u>Below</u> (Senegal): *C. glans*, common, Senegal to Gulf of Guinea.

Cymbium olla **Bay of Setúbal, Portugal**

Mediterranean Cone
CONE SHELLS, CONIDAE
(this page)

S: 4, max 7 cm. D: Med.; Atlantic coast of Portugal. G: in shallow bays, hides in sand or crevices by day, emerges to hunt polychaetes at night. Colour variable. Family with 400+ spp world-wide, only this one in Med. Cone shells are predators that catch large poly-chaetes, other snails, and even small fish by spearing them with a small harpoon connected to poison glands in the mouth. Dif-ferent cone spp have different types of venom, adapted to their most common type of prey. The venom of fish-eating species is also highly poisonous to man.

Conus mediterraneus   **Crete Island, Greece**

Butterfly Cone

S: 10, max 25 cm. D: from the Canary Islands southwards, along the coasts of W-Africa. G: this is the largest species in the family Conidae. It lives on sandy bottoms, from shallow water down to at least 35 m. Below: *C. guanche,* up to 5 cm, is only known from the Canary Islands.

Conus pulcher   **Tenerife, Canary Islands**

Turtle Cone

S: 7.5 cm. D: Cape Verdes; W-Atl.: Caribbean, N-Brazil. G: has been found as 120,000 years old fossils at the Azores! In preglacial times, the climate in N-Europe was much warmer ("Trapped..."). *C. ermineus* is a fish predator. Be-low (Cape Verdes): *C. genuanus,* found from Senegal to Angola.

Conus ermineus   **Cape Verde Islands**

INVERTEBRATE VISION

The sense of vision appears to be all too natural to us humans. But it was a long way along the paths of evolution until highly developed eyes, able to produce 3-D colour images, were available to living organisms. The biologists Peter Nahke and Peter Wirtz report.

PHOTOS: PETER NAHKE

A large number of invertebrates can "see" without eyes. Some cells of the skin are sensitive to light. Such light-sensitive cells may be scattered all over the body. Often, the light-sensitive cells are concentrated in patches. A transparent layer of protective tissue lies in front of the patch and a layer of dark pigment behind it. The dark layer shields the light-sensitive cells from light coming from other directions. Thus, these simple organs can not only perceive the presence or absence of light but also the direction the light is coming from! Organs of this type can be found in, for instance, jellyfish, many annelid worms and sea stars.

Directionality of vision is improved by setting the patch of light sensitive tissue in a shallow cup and – after further and further indentation – in a deep cup-shaped

Light-sensitive cells are scattered all over the surface of the sea star. At the tip of the arms, they are concentrated in a little red patch.

structure surrounded by dark pigment. Now, the light coming through the opening of the cup strikes only a part of the light sensitive area, the retina, and this already gives much more accurate information on where the light is coming

Although the eyes of sea hares appear just like tiny dark dots at the base of the rhinophores, they are highly developed and even equipped with lenses.

from. The vast multitude of organisms living on earth shows, still today, all intermediate forms in this sequence of eye development. Patches of up to 1000

Aeolid nudibranchs like this *Facelina auriculata* (Baltic Sea) have less than ten receptors cells in the "retina", but they do have a small lens. The tiny black dot at the feeler base is an eye.

light-sensitive cells in a shallow cup are common in flatworms. Limpets have a somewhat deeper cup. Deep cup-shaped light organs are common in annelids and gastropods.

Only a small change is now necessary to transform this structure into one that can perceive images. The size of the opening has to be reduced further and further until, finally, the light enters the hollow sphere through but a small hole and projects an inverted image onto the light sensitive cells at the rear. Such an eye, functioning like a pinhole camera, can be found in many gastropods.

A member of the genus *Strombus* holds the record of the highest number of receptor cells in the retina among the gastropods: 97,000! Plus a true lens, of course.

Each of the many eyes of this scallop (from Malta) has an area of vision of about 100 degrees.

In some snails the cup forming the eye is filled with a gelatinous transparent substance. This substance already acts like a lens: it collects light from a larger area and concentrates it onto a smaller area of the retina. From such a crude proto-lens, we move on gradually to the formation of a true lens at the entrance of the eye. Cuttlefish, squids and octopuses have a true lens and an eye remarkably similar to ours, although their ancestors developed the principle of an eye completely independently.

Eyes with a lens can be found in some jellyfish, some annelids, in arthropods with their compound eyes (a collection of many separate eyes pointing in different directions), some gastropods and bivalves, most cephalopods, and of course the vertebrates.

The scallops (*Pecten* species) have the most complex eyes among the bivalves. Up to 100 of them lie along the edge of the mantle tissue and look out for predators like sea stars. *Pecten* can see movements around it not only by comparing the images from different eyes but also with a single eye. Each eye has a lens and a cornea, and the unusual arrangement of a double-layered retina.

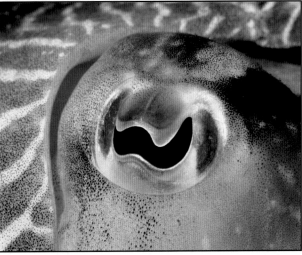

The pupil of the cuttlefish is special in that it is shaped in the form of a W.

Green-lined Paper-bubble
BUBBLE-SHELLS, HYDATINIDAE
S: 5 cm (shell), 10+ cm (extended animal). D: Az., Iberian peninsula to Madeira, Can., CV. W-Atl., IP. G: like most head-shield snails, spends the day buried in soft sediments to emerge at night. Author PW found the sp in a large tide pool of Faial, Azores, at night (northernmost record). Lower small ph.: *Micromelo undatus*, 3 cm, IP, trop. WA, Can., CV.

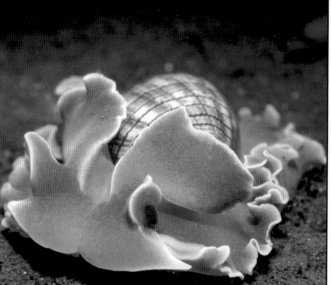

Hydatina physis — Faial Island, Azores

AGLAJIDAE

S: up to 4 cm. D: W-Med. to Cape Verdes. G: in members of the family Aglajidae, the shell is internal, in the rear part of the animal. *A. depicta* spends the day buried in muddy substrate. *Bulla amygdalla* (upper small photo), Bullidae, 5 cm, Atl. isl. (Madeira to São Tomé), Gabon. *Haminoea orteai* (lower), Atyidae, 2 cm, regionally/temporarily common, SE-Spain, Azores, Selvagens, Can.

Aglaja depicta — Costa del Sol, Spain

Black Sea Hare
APLYSIIDAE (this page)

S: largest European opisthobranch: up to 40 cm and 2 kg!
D: SE-Britain to Angola, Azores,
Madeira, Canaries, CV; Med.; RS.
G: black with red rim or brown.
Swims with flapping movements
of the 2 lobes on the back. "Sea
hare" due to 2 long rhinophores
on the head. All sea hares feed
on algae, thus live in shallow water. All are simultaneous hermaphrodites. Thus, two animals always make a pair. However, one
can encounter chains of mating
sea hares, each animal acting as a
male to the one in front and as a
female to the one behind.

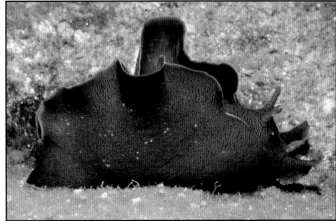

Aplysia fasciata   Faial Island, Azores

Annulated Sea Hare

S: 20 cm. D: circumtrop.; E-Atl.:
north to Madeira. G: ring-marks
on grey to light/dark brown body
typical. Has recently increased
in numbers: an effect of global
warming? 3-30 m. Can eject a
purple ink, containing "aplysiovi-
olin" from the red algae it feeds
on, when disturbed (photo).

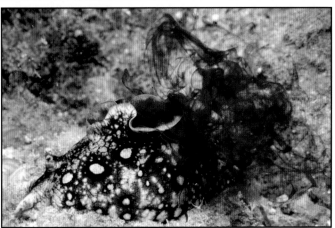

Aplysia dactylomela   São Tomé

Dotted Sea Hare

S: 10 cm. D: Norway to Can.;
most common sea hare in
Med. G: young animals (photo)
are lighter and more reddish
than adults. Can swim. Shallow
water down to 30 m. Below:
A. parvula, circum(sub)trop.,
Med., northern limit in E-Atl.:
Azores. Only up to 2 cm long.

Aplysia punctata   Norway

Aplysia depilans   Madeira

Depilated Sea Hare
APLYSIIDAE (this page)
S: 30 cm. D: SE-Britain to W-Africa, island groups; Med. G: most common sea hare in temp. E-Atl. 3-30+ m. Hides below stones by day, eats algae at night, digested by symbiotic gut bacteria (like in cows). Below: "vermicelli de mer", gelatinous egg strings put down in disorderly-looking lump.

Ragged Sea Hare
S: 12 cm. D: E-Med.; E-Atl.: W-Africa. W-Atl. G: tasselled appearance due to numerous hair-like skin papillae. Brilliant blue spots typical. See "Trapped" for a possible explanation of curious distribution. Could also have entered the E-Med. only recently, via the Suez Canal.

Bursatella leachi   Ionian Sea, Greece

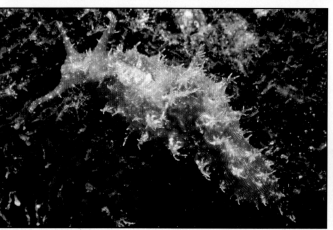

Blue-ring Sea Hare
S: 5 cm. D: circumtropical. E-Atl.: Cape Verdes, Selvagens, Azores. G: iridescent blue spots ringed orange, many long skin papillae typical. Often called *S. longicauda* (different sp). Below: Warty Sea Hare *Dolabrifera holboelli*, circumtropical. In eastern Atlantic northern limit at Madeira. 4 cm.

Stylocheilus striatus   Faial Island, Azores

192

HERMAEIDAE
(this page)
S: up to 1.5 cm. D: Med.; Azores to Canaries; Florida. G: almost all sacoglossa cut into plant cells and suck out the contents (only 3 spp eat the eggs of other opistho-branchs). Most are only 1-3 cm long and live in very shallow water. Their greenish colour is due to the chlorophyll of the plants they feed on. Most are specialists and feed on only a few plant spp. *A. formosa* has numerous elongated green "cerata" with many small white spots on its back. Night-active. Author PW encountered a mass occurrence in 5-50 cm depth (!) during a night dive in a large tide pool at Faial Island, Azores.

Aplysiopsis formosa   **Faial Island, Azores**

S: up to 1.5 cm. D: western Mediterranean Sea; Azores to Canaries. W-Atl. G: feeds on green plants in very shallow water. Hiding between bubble-shaped stands of *Valonia* (one of its food plants) it may even be found above the water level at low tide. <u>Below</u>: *Placida cre-moniana,* Mediterranean Sea, Azores to Canaries. To 1 cm.

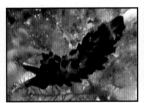

Ercolania coerulea   **Faial Island, Azores**

S: up to 6 cm. D: western Mediterranean Sea; Morocco to Senegal, Canary Islands; Caribbean. G: the many trans-parent, leaf-like "cerata" are typical, the branches of the digestive gland are visible inside. <u>Below</u>: Glass Slug *Cyerce antil-lensis,* Caliphyllidae, Caribbean, recently found in the Azores. Cerata sticky, easily detach.

Polybranchia viridis   **Gran Canaria, Canary Islands**

Ornate Elysia
ELYSIIDAE (this page)
S: 5 cm. D: circum(sub)trop.; in E-Atl. north to Azores. G: most *Elysia* are green, famous for being "solar powered": eat green algae, incorporate the plants' chloroplasts into their own body tissue where they continue to photosynthesise! Below: *E. viridis*, Norway to SA; Med. Common, 2 cm.

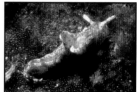

Elysia ornata　　　　　Faial Island, Azores

Timid Elysia

S: 3 cm. D: Med.; Cape Verdes; Cuba, Florida. G: unmistakable. Feeds on *Acetabularia* in spring to summer, changes to *Padina* in autumn. Has a curious "hopping" way of locomotion. Tastes bad due to polypropionates, fish soon avoid it. Below: *Elysia margaritae*, W-Med., Azores to Canary Is.

Elysia timida　　　　　Elba Island, Italy

Hope's Elysia

S: 1.5, max 3 cm. D: Med., in Atl. slightly N of Strait of Gibraltar. G: colour variable (below: Costa del Sol, Spain), but unmistakable in Med., due to elongated body, short parapodia. *T. picta* (E-Atl., e.g. Madeira, Canar.) similar. Distinction between *Elysia* & *Thuridilla* by shape of teeth! 2-25 m.

Thuridilla hopei　　　　　Cyprus

Golden Sponge Snail
TYLODINIDAE

S: 4 cm. D: Med.; E-Atl.: S-Britain to St. Helena I. G: the umbrella snails are a small group that used to be combined with the Pleuro-branchomorpha (p. 196) in a group called "Notaspidea".

    This snail looks rather like a yellow limpet (p. 164). 4-25+ m. The species is not as rare as one might think; it is just difficult to detect on its host. When you see a Golden Sponge *Aplysina aerophoba* (p. 16) that shows signs of being fed on look at it for some time. You are likely to "suddenly" see one, if not several, Golden Sponge Snails. Did you see that there are two animals in the photo? Background: a string of eggs attached to the sponge. <u>Below</u>: a single animal.

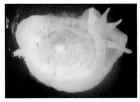

Tylodina perversa   **Madeira**

Warty Umbrella Snail
UMBRACULIDAE

S: 18 cm. D: Med.; Azores to São Tomé. W-Atl. G: during the day, hidden in a rock crevice, partially buried in sand, or sitting on the sponge it is feeding on. Locally common. 4-80+ m. Colour variable, grey, bluish, pink, green, brown; often with dark spots. <u>Upper small photo</u>: two snails on sponge. <u>Lower</u>: spawn.

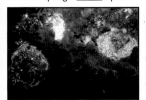

Umbraculum umbraculum   **Madeira**

Pleurobranchus testudinarius　　Faial Island, Azores

Turtle Snail
PLEUROBRANCHIDAE (both pages) S: 25 cm. D: Med.; Azor., Canaries; also Brazil. G: one of the largest European opisthobranchs. Hides by day in caves or below stones, 20+ m. Young brilliant orange with violet polygonal lines around humps. Eats tunicates, molluscs. <u>Below</u>: spawn, can be white, pink, lilac.

Gomez-Snail
S: up to 5 cm. D: Cape Verdes. G: quite common, during the daytime in 4-20+ m. <u>Below</u>: a *Pleurobranchus* sp (Azores, Madeira, Canaries) closely related to *P. garciagomezi*, but it differs in colour, skin texture, body shape, and behaviour: while *P. garciagomezi* is day-active, this undescribed sp is active at night.

Pleurobranchus garciagomezi　　Cape Verde Islands

Pleurobranchaea meckeli　　Costa del Sol, Spain

Meckel-Snail
S: 15 cm. D: Med.; Azores, Canaries. G: locally common on sand, mud, 20-90 m. Feeds on cnidarians, polychaetes, amphipods (e.g. *Pseudoprotella phasma*; see p. 113), nudibranchs, ascidians, nemertines, small fish etc. <u>Below</u>: *Pleurobranchus membranaceus*, 12 cm, North Sea-W-Med.

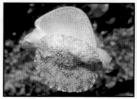

Peach Snail

S: 5 cm. D: Azores, Madeira, Canaries, Cape Verdes; W-Med. G: common, down to 40 m. The animal shown is slightly darker than normal. Hiding in crevices in the rock or below stones by day. *B. aurantiaca* (Med.) is similar in appearance. <u>Below</u>: the characteristic spawn of this species.

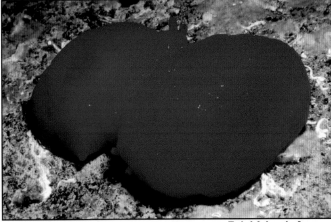

Berthellina edwardsi   Faial Island, Azores

S: up to 3.5 cm. D: western Mediterranean; Canary Islands. G: easy to recognize by its typical ocellated colour pattern. It feeds on sponges. <u>Below</u>: *Berthellina citrina*, world-wide in temperate waters, Med. It is similar to but much lighter in colour than *B. edwardsi* (compare above). *B. citrina* studied in Japan live for only 1 year.

Berthella ocellata   Sicily, Italy

S: to 2 cm. D: Med.; Canaries, Selvagens Is., Azores (first record); trop. W-America. G: very flat. 2-25 m. Colour variable but most animals have white blotch in centre of back. <u>Below</u>: *B. plumula*, Norway to Med., 2-20 m, 6 cm. Light area on back has been suggested to mimic sponge opening. The main diet is the sponge *Oscarella lobularis* (p. 11).

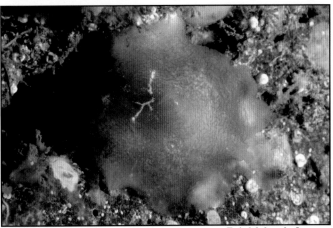

Berthella stellata   Faial Island, Azores

JANOLIDAE

S: 8 cm. D: S-Norway to Canaries; Med. G: the Arminacea are the smallest suborder of the nudibranch snails, consisting of two rather different types of animals, both shown on this page. Family members posses numerous "cerata" on the back and feed exclusively on bryozoans. The cerata contain branches of the hepatic gland, clearly visible in the large photo. Colour morphs of *J. cristatus:* blue (large photo, Crete); orange to light brown (small photo, North Sea). Tips of cerata always blue. On rocky bottoms, 3-30+ m. Feeds on bryozoans (genus *Bugula,* p. 251). The spawn consists of a pale string wound around the same moss animals; the eggs are in distinct packets, giving a beaded appearance to the spawn.

Janolus cristatus   Crete Island, Greece

ARMINIDAE

Size: up to 10 cm in length. Distribution: European Atlantic coasts and Mediterranean Sea. General: in the family Arminidae, the back of the snail shows a series of longitudinal grooves. The species of this family generally feed on cnidarians.

Armina tigrina lives on sandy-muddy bottoms and mostly stays buried below the surface. It emerges at night to feed on sea pansies (Pennatularia) but even then it is difficult to detect because it usually is covered with mud. In the Mediterranean Sea, it can be locally common in shallow water.

Armina tigrina   Costa del Sol, Spain

<<< A nudibranch's egg-mass in a Sicilian reef.   **199**

TRITONIIDAE
S: up to 5 cm. D: Med.; Azores and Portugal to Canaries. G: the members of the nudibranch sub-order Dendronotacea usually have more or less branched respiratory appendages along the sides of the body. A fringed or smooth veil overlies the mouth. Retractile rhinophores have large distinctive sheaths at the base. Dendronotaceans feed mainly on cnidarians. *M. blainvillea* (long considered a Med. endemic) can be recognized by its typical colour pattern. It lives from shallow water down to about 50 m depth and feeds on various Octocorallia. When it feels threatened it sometimes swims by strong contractions of the body.

Marionia blainvillea — Faial Island, Azores

TRITONIIDAE
S: 2 cm. D: only Med. G: can be common in shaded habitats but also found in brightly lit areas. Feeds on soft coral (Alcyonaria), e.g. *Paralcyonium spinulosum* (p. 36). The two photos, taken at the same place, show two different colour patterns. The dark longitudinal lines (hence Latin name *"striata"*) are the characteristic feature of the species.

Tritonia striata — Costa Brava, Spain

DENDRONOTIDAE
S: 10 cm. D: Arctic to France; NW-Atlantic. G: can be locally common. Feeds on hydrozoans (*Tubularia*, p. 19), colour variable. Gills, oral veil, rhinophore sheaths extended into branched processes. Below: *Tritonia hombergii*, Tritoniidae. 20 cm! Many rounded tubercles are characteristic. Also pink, brown. To 80 m. Feeds on *Alcyonium digitatum* (page 35).

Dendronotus frondosus — Norway

DENDRONOTACEA

DOTIDAE

S: 3 cm. D: Norway to Spain. G: *Doto* spp live on hydrozoans and also deposit their eggs there, most are are less than 1.5 cm long, thus, this is a giant. Its only prey is the hydrozoan *Nemertesia antennina* (p. 21). Below (Azores): the tiny *D. fluctifraga,* also known from the Canaries, can be common on the hydroid *Sertularella polyzonia* in 25+ m.

Doto pinnatifida   Galicia, Spain

TETHYIDAE

S: 30 cm. D: Med.; Portugal to Gulf of Guinea. G: unmistakable, on sand, mud, 5-150 m. The oral veil of this species is especially large. Below (Patras): *Melibe fimbriata,* closely related, 14 cm, into Med. via Suez Canal. Both feed on crustaceans and other small animals in the soft bottom. The numerous cerata on the back are easily detached.

Tethys fimbria   Ibiza, Spain

PHYLLIROIDAE

S: 4 cm. D: Atl. G: when seeing this strange species for the first time, few people would suspect it to be a nudibranch. The 2 spp of *Phylliroe, atlantica* and *bucephala,* cannot be identified from photos but the animal shown was 4 cm long, while *P. bucephala* reaches only 2.5 cm. Both live in the oceanic plankton. The body is laterally compressed and they can swim with a wriggling movement. No cerata on back; only two very long rhinophores. The body is transparent, some organs can be seen in it. Feed on hydromedusae (p. 23). *Phylliroe* is one of the few nudibranch genera to exhibit bioluminescence (see also *Plocamopherus,* p. 215).

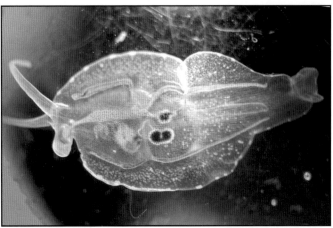

Phylliroe atlantica   Faial Island, Azores

Common Grey Seaslug
AEOLIDIIDAE (this page)

S: 6, max 12 cm. D: NE-Atl.: S to Spain; NW-Atl.; N-Pac. G: locally common (N-Europe). Large, flattened "cerata" cover body. Drab grey-brown, also orange. Aeolidians prey on Cnidaria, mostly hydrozoans. *A. pap.* eats anemones (photo: *Actinia fragacea*, p. 46).

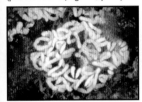

Aeolidia papillosa   **North Sea**

S: up to 4 cm. D: Great Britain to the Portuguese Atlantic coast. G: species feeds on sea anemones. Unlike other nudibranchs, it transfers sperm not during a copulation but with "spermatophores" attached to the partner's back, sperm then migrates to gonopore! <u>Below</u>: *A. sanguinea*, Ireland to Spanish Atlantic coast; Madeira.

Aeolidiella glauca   **Western Scotland**

S: up to 7 cm. D: Mediterranean Sea; France to Ghana; W-Atl., E-Pac. G: common, eats sea anemones (*Aiptasia mutabilis*, photo; *Anemonia viridis*). As in many aeolidians, the prey's stinging cells are stored in the cerata tips on the back (defence). <u>Below</u>: *Berghia coerulescens*, Med.; nearby Atl. south to Canary Islands. 7 cm.

Spurilla neapolitana   **Lanzarote, Canary Islands**

<<< *Flabellina babai*, Bay of Setúbal, Portugal   **203**

EUBRANCHIDAE

S: 2 cm. D: Norway to Canaries, Azores; W-Med. G: colour variable, photo: common pattern but tips of cerata also orange, white, body purple-black. 5-40+ m. Eats *Obelia*, *Aglaophenia pluma* (p. 20). Lower small ph.: *E. tricolor*, Arctic to France; cold W-Atl. 4 cm. To 80+ m. Eats *Obelia geniculata* (p. 23). Upper small ph.: *E. pallidus*, Iceland, Norway-W-Med.; NW-Atl. 2.5 cm. Eats *Obelia*, *Tubularia*.

Eubranchus farrani   **Croatia, Adriatic Sea**

FACELINIDAE

S: to 5 cm. D: Med.; Portuguese Atl. coast to Canaries. G: locally common, 3-30 m. Feeds on *Eudendrium* hydrozoans (p. 21). Found not only on rocky shores but also in seagrass beds. Photo (spawning pair) from 9 m. Lower small photo: *C. scintilla* is known from the Cape Verdes only, up to 1 cm, 3-17+ m. Upper small photo: *Facelinopsis marioni*, only known from W-Med., to 1.5 cm.

Cratena peregrina   **Costa Brava, Spain**

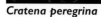

AEOLIDACEA

FACELINIDAE

S: 5 cm. D: Norway to Canaries; Med. G: colour variable, partly depending on the recently eaten food; bluish iridescence almost always apparent. Cerata on back in separate clusters. Eats hydrozoans. <u>Below</u>: Black-spotted aeolidian *Caloria elegans*, 1.5 cm, W-Med., Great Britain-Canar., Azor.

Facelina auriculata   **Croatia, Adriatic Sea**

FACELINIDAE

S: up to 5.5 cm. D: Norway to W-Med.; cold W-Atl. G: one of the most common aeolidians in N-Europe, but the description of an animal from Boston Harbour, Massachusetts, was the first one and thus is the valid one. Has a very broad foot and is broadest at the "shoulders". The two very long frontal tentacles, held foreward, are reminiscent of steer horns. It feeds on many different hydroids of the genera *Obelia*, *Eudendrium*, *Tubularia*, and others (see chapter on hydroids). In Denmark, there are two generations per year, the first one spawning in May/June, the second in September/October.

Facelina bostoniensis   **Sognefjord, Norway**

FAVORINIDAE

S: up to 9 cm. D: Med.; Atlantic coast of Portugal. G: this is the largest aeolidid in the Med. Cerata set in 5-6 horseshoe-shaped clusters. Light yellow to (more frequent) bright orange. Not only found on rocky, but also on soft, detritic bottoms to 35+ m depth. <u>Below</u> (12 m): its spawn.

Dondice banyulensis   **Costa Brava, Spain**

AEOLIDACEA

FAVORINIDAE

S: 2.5 cm. D: Murmansk to W-Africa; W-Med. G: feeds – like all genus members – on eggs of sea-hares, side-gilled snails, nudibranchs (photo), also on *Obelia* hydrozoans. Below (in a large tide pool on Faial, Azores): *Dicata odhneri*, 1.3 cm, to 17 m. Med.; Great Britain to Portugal.

Favorinus branchialis   **Baltic Sea**

FIONIDAE

S: up to 4 cm.
D: cosmopolitan in (sub)tropical waters; uncommon in the Mediterranean Sea, common in the Atlantic.
G: this is a species of the open seas. It lives on floating objects (a mode of life called "neustonic"), such as pieces of wood, on which the Goose Barnacle *Lepas anatifera* (p. 106) grows which *F. pinnata* eats. It can also be found clinging to, and feeding on *Velella velella* (p. 19). A keeled margin of the cerata is typical for the species but can only be seen by microscopic examination.

Fiona pinnata   **Madeira**

TERGEPEDIDAE

S: to 1, max 2 cm. D: Norway to Canaries; Med. G: a lovely little species. Colour pattern of cerata unmistakable. Feeds on the hydrozoan *Sertularella polyzonia*. First record from Azores (35 m) by author PW. Below: *C. thompsoni*, shallow, to 1 cm, only known from Spanish Atl. coast.

Cuthona caerulea   **Costa Brava, Spain**

FLABELLINIDAE
(this page)
S: up to 1.5 cm. D: Med. G: this species can be locally common, on rocky shores, from shallow water down to 10 m. The orange cerata have white tips; these are the "cnidosacs", where the stinging cells of the hydrozoan food are stored. Small photo: Elba Island, Italy.

Calmella cavolini Costa del Sol, Spain

S: up to 12 mm. D: Iceland and Norway to France; in cold W-Atl.: Nova Scotia to Cape Cod. G: feeds only on *Eudendrium* (p. 21). Shallow down to at least 33 m.
   Below (Azores): an undescribed *Coryphella*. Found repeatedly at Faial Island (in 5-10 m) and once in a cave (5 m) at Pico Island, Azores.

Coryphella gracilis Norway

S: up to 2 cm. D: only Cape Verdes. G: recently described, unmistakable, common in shallow water, to 25+ m.
   Below: oral tentacles of *F. lineata* with white longitudinal line that continues down onto head and body to form a median line. 10-400 m, Norway to Strait of Gibraltar; rare in the Mediterranean Sea.

Flabellina arveleoi Cape Verde Islands

Flabellina babai — Bay of Setúbal, Portugal

FLABELLINIDAE

(this page)
S: up to 5.3 cm long. D: Med. and Portuguese Atlantic coast. G: body hyaline, tips of cerata yellow or orange. 7-12 clusters of rather large cerata on each side of the back. Each cluster has 2-5 cerata, all originating from a common stalk. 2-20+ m. Below: at Costa Brava, Spain.

Flabellina affinis — Crete Island, Greece

S: up to 4 cm long. D: Mediterranean Sea, Atlantic coast of Portugal to Canary Islands. G: cerata in 6-9 clusters of 3-9 each. Feeds on *Eudendrium* (p. 21), down to 50 m, also deposits its egg-masses (purple like adults) in this bushy hydroid. Perhaps most common nudibranch in W-Med. Below: Crete, Greece.

Flabellina pedata — Ibiza, Spain

S: up to 2-3, max 5 cm. D: Norway to Gibraltar, Azores; western Mediter-ranean Sea, Adriatic. G: feeds on *Eudendrium* (p. 21). More reddish than *F. affinis*, cerata with white tips. One of the most common aeolid nudi-branchs in shallow waters. Below: the tiny *F. Ilerai*, Cape Verdes only, photo: 1 m depth.

FLABELLINIDAE

Size: photographed animal about 2 cm long. Distribution: only known from the Cape Verde Islands. General: this species has been described in 1998 on the basis of a single animal of only 4 mm length, found in 8 m depth at Sal Island. Author PW has seen several, much larger individuals, down to a depth of about 40 m, when diving on the north coast of São Tiago Island. Below: *F. ischitana,* Med. and Atlantic coast of Portugal, grows to a length of 2.5 cm. It is variable in colour and can closely resemble both *F. affinis* and *F. pedata.* Like these, it feeds on *Eudendrium* hydroids and all three species may even be found on the same bush of hydrozoans.

Flabellina bulbosa   Cape Verde Islands

GLAUCIDAE

S: 3 cm. D: all temperate and tropical oceans. G: this beautiful animal is floating, upside down, on the surface, buoyed by a gas bubble in the stomach. The belly, turned to the surface, is a deep blue colour and thus difficult to see against the dark blue of the water. In contrast, the back of the animal, turned down, is a brilliant white (below) and any fish looking up from below will have problems spotting it against the light sky. This type of colour, common in many animal species living near the surface of the water, is called countershading. Feeds on floating jellies, such as *Physalia* (p. 32), *Velella* (p. 19), and *Porpita* (p. 19). Like most aeolids, it stores the stinging cells of its prey in the tips of the cerata.

Glaucus atlanticus   Faial Island, Azores

GIANT WORM

The yarn made it as far as Germany: In the vicinity of the Croatian island of Rab, scuba instructor Andreas Krohn supposedly showed his customers the largest polychaete ever encountered in the Mediterranean – a huge worm nearly 2 m long! Reason enough for UW-journalist Thomas Gögl to investigate the seemingly incredible tale about an extraordinary marine giant. He had no way of knowing then just how much the local divers and fishermen appreciate this bristle worm.

PHOTOS: THOMAS GÖGL

Only at night will the longest worm in the Mediterranean present itself in all its beauty: *Eunice aphroditois*, also known along the Croatian coast as "drapulla", makes an excellent bait and is thus a welcome source of supplemental income.

Here one can see the enormous length of the giant worm *Eunice aphroditois* compared to a man.

Even at the more moderate depths within the reach of scuba divers the Mediterranean is still populated by numerous marine beings that we seldom catch sight of. But the existence of such a large creature in the 5-metre range was hitherto unknown to me. Of course, the drapulla, as the Croatians refer to the giant worm, lives in concealment. It is a benthic animal that likes to burrow deep into the muddy and gravely substrate. At night one can occasionally spot the exposed upper body of the animal as it looms over its sandy recluse in search of prey. It has five symmetrically positioned feelers that remind one of the appendages of a sea star. In addition, this worm has two pairs of pliers-like jaws, one of which is serrated along the edges. As soon as the feelers detect the slightest movement, the jaws will close around the potential food source. And that at an incredible speed! Eminences along the animal's underside enable it to move forward and grasp its quarry firmly. The giant worm is omnivorous, which means that it feeds on carrion as well as live prey.

Since the Croatians are quite fond of using the drapulla as bait, they have found an effective way to capture the animal in the daytime under the curious gaze of diving tourists. Even the Croatian youths have mastered the skill in order to supplement their allowances, as the fishermen are willing to pay up to 30 Euros for a grown specimen! The prime hunting season runs from spring to late summer. The method used is always the same: a foully smelling strip of fish is inserted into a homemade tubular trap and placed over the assumed hiding place of the worm. Finding the right spot is not an easy matter as the ground is usually covered with holes that have nothing to do with the worm. If the right hole is chosen, then the ever-hungry worm will soon smell the titbit and, abandoning all sense of caution, shoot out of its enclosure to slip headfirst into the tubular trap. There it will trip a release mechanism that causes a flap to trap it inside the tube.

But this merely completes the easier part of the task, as no more than a few centimetres of the worm actually project out of the hole. Now all depends on the submarine hunter's knack when it comes to controlling the buoyancy of the anatomically fitted trap. Styrofoam rings like those commonly used by the fishermen have proven to be especially effective in this particular case. If the worm hunters make the trap too light, the animal will probably be ripped apart; if it is not light enough, the giant worm will simply remain unharmed inside the trap and proceed to devour the bait.

By applying a constant and carefully calibrated tractive force for 10 to 20 minutes, the worm hunter is then able to pull the animal out of its hole without tearing off any of its appendages. Throughout this delicate procedure, the hunter keeps a sharp eye out for any fish looking for a free meal. The fish are welcome to the tempting delicacy once it is dangling in strips from a fishing hook. Furthermore, there is always the danger that once the prey has been pulled out of its hole by the Styrofoam ring it will shoot up to the surface and thus be lost.

Our giant worm even has a nice-sounding scientific name, *Eunice aphroditois,* which was given to it in 1788 by the Russian naturalist Pallas. It has similarly large relatives in tropical waters, but here in the Adriatic Sea it is definitely the longest representative of the lower life forms!

Top: this prospective bait already has its head stuck inside the trap and now needs to be "hoisted" very gently.
Right: this close-up shows head and anterior part of body of the giant worm in a man's hands.

DORIDACEA

ONCHIDORIDIDAE
(this page)
S: 3, max 7 cm. D: Iceland and
Greenland to Morocco; W-
Med.; NW-Atl., NE-Pacific. G:
"Fluffy" appearance caused by
soft papillae all over back. Cir-
cle of up to 9 gills on back.
Pure white to brown, purple
to black. Feeds on bryozoans.
<u>Below</u>: from Spanish Atl. coast.

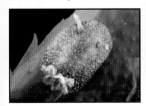

Acanthodoris pilosa   North Sea

Size: up to 2.5 cm.
Distribution: from Greenland
and Iceland to Denmark; also
in north-western Atlantic.
General: the back of this small
nudibranch is covered by
rounded tubercles with conical
tips. The body may be white
or yellow in colour. *Adalaria
proxima* feeds on encrusting
bryozoans such as *Membranipora membranacea* (p. 251) in
shallow water, down to about
60 m. In Britain, it spawns
from February to May.
    This species is often con-
fused with *Onchidoris muricata*
(<u>small photo</u>, Norway). One of
the differences is that the
tubercles of *A. proxima* have
pointed tops while those of *O.
muricata* are flattened or
rounded. The latter species
grows to 14 mm long and lives
in shallow water, from the
Arctic to the French Atlantic
coast. It feeds on encrusting
bryozoans and appears to be
especially fond of *Membranipora membranacea*. Instead of
white, it can also be yellow or
orange.

Adalaria proxima   Sweden

<<< The polycerid *Tambja ceutae*, Azores   **213**

S: 10 mm. D: Med.; Portuguese Atl. G: bright elongated papillae on white back and yellow rim around back. Eats encrusting bryozoans, preferentially in shaded locations, to 40+ m. <u>Below</u> (Norway): *D. luteocincta*, 11 mm, papillae not elongated. N-Norway to W-Med., <u>not</u> Canaries.

Diaphorodoris papillata   **Costa Brava, Spain**

TRIOPHIDAE

S: up to 3.5 cm. D: Scotland to Canary Islands; W-Med. G: all over the translucent white body, there are small, forked processes, yellow to orange in colour, which make the species quite unmistakable. It feeds on bryozoans in shallow water. <u>Below</u>: Spanish Mediterranean coast.

Crimora papillata   **Costa Brava, Spain**

TRIOPHIDAE

Size: up to at least 3 cm. Distribution: from the Azores to Angola; Mediterranean Sea. General: there are only a few scattered records of this species. It feeds on encrusting bryozoans. Author PW found it in the Azores from 1-25 m depth, below stones during the day and active at night. It can be recognized by the branched (Latin *"ramosus"*) processes along the sides of the body. The colour varies from pink to dark red.

Kaloplocamus ramosus   **Faial Island, Azores**

DORIDACEA

TRIOPHIDAE

Size: up to 3 cm.
Distribution: Madeira, Canary
Islands, Cape Verde Islands.
General: this is one of the
most common species of nudibranchs on the south coast of
Madeira. It is active at night,
hiding below stones during the
day. When touched at night, it
emits a surprisingly bright blue
light (and such bioluminescence is known for other
members of the genus *Plocamopherus*). When disturbed,
this species can swim with
alternating lateral contractions
of its body. It lives from shallow water down to at least
100 m depth.

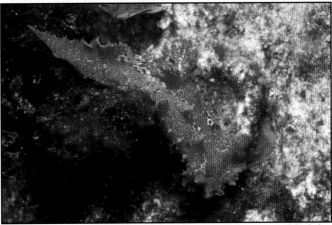

Plocamopherus maderae Madeira

TRIOPHIDAE

S: up to 6 cm. D: north coast of
Madeira. G: this is apparently an
undescribed species, so far only
known from the north coast of
Madeira. It differs from *P. maderae* (see above) in reaching twice
the size , being active during the
day, and in colour pattern. Below: another individual, same sp.

Plocamopherus sp Madeira

ALDISIDAE

S: up to at least 2.5 cm. D: Cape
Verdes only. G: author PW
encountered this endemic from
shallow water to about 15 m,
below stones and in a small cave.
Probably active at night. Below
(Madeira): *A. smaragdina*, 4 cm,
Spanish Atlantic coast, Azores to
Canaries. Often on red sponges.

Aldisa barlettai Sal Island, Cape Verde Islands

Sea Lemon
ARCHIDORIDIDAE

Size: up to 12 cm. Distribution: from Iceland to the W-Med. General: this is a locally common species in the northeastern Atlantic. The many short, blunt tubercles on its back are of two different sizes. The mottled colour probably serves as a camouflage and is quite variable. *A. pseudoargus* feeds on the Breadcrumb sponge *Halichondria panicea* (p. 13) and several other sponges. In the Atlantic, this species is mainly found in the intertidal, while in the Mediterranean it is more common in 50-200 m.

Archidoris pseudoargus   **Norway**

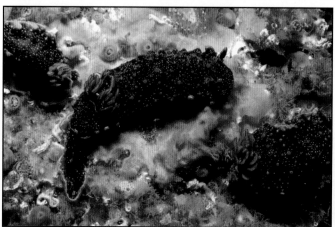

CHROMODORIDIDAE

S: up to 6 cm. D: Azores, Madeira, Canary Islands. G: in open daylight, 2-20 m, also in caves. Body from light green to dark blue, with many small red papillae. Below: *Cadlina laevis*, Cadlinidae. 3.2 cm, feeds on sponges, to 800 m depth. One of the few species with direct development.

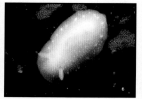

Glossodoris edmunsi   **Faial Island, Azores**

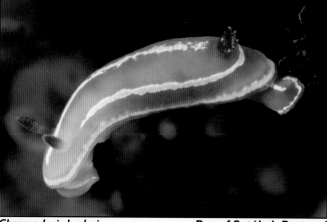

CHROMODORIDIDAE

S: up to 2.8 cm but usually 1-1.5 cm. D: from the French Atlantic coast to the W-Med.; Canary Islands. G: this is a locally common species that can be seen from 10 to about 50 m depth. It appears to prefer shaded places on hard bottoms and has also be found in *Posidonia* seagrass fields. The body colour varies from pale white to violet. The rhinophores and gills are dark violet. Three yellow-white bands run along the back, the outer ones uniting on the rear. Small yellow spots may also be present.

Chromodoris krohni   **Bay of Setúbal, Portugal**

Brito's Nudibranch

CHROMODORIDIDAE (this page) S: 2 cm. D: Azores, Gibraltar, Mad., Can.; Med. G: purple bands on light blue background typical. On rocky bottoms, 2-15 m. Below (Azores): Pink Nudibranch *C. purpurea*, 3, max 5 cm long. Azores to Cape Verde Islands, W-Med., on hard bottoms, down to about 15 m.

Chromodoris britoi   **Faial Island, Azores**

S: usually about 3, max 5.5 cm. D: Gulf of Biscay to Ghana; western Mediterranean Sea. G: the following three species are frequently confused. This one has several large yellow spots on the back that are surrounded by white or light yellow rings. Found in 5-60 m depth, feeds on sponges. Small photo below from Elba.

Chromodoris luteorosea   **Bay of Setúbal, Portugal**

S: up to 2.5 cm. D: in the eastern Atlantic on the southern coast of Spain; western Mediterranean. G: in contrast to the previous species, the (more numerous) yellow spots of this one are not surrounded by conspicuous light rings. From the intertidal to about 40 m. Below: *C. rodomaculata*, only known from the Canary Islands.

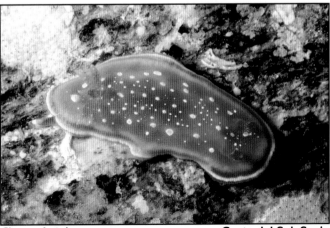

Chromodoris luteopunctata   **Costa del Sol, Spain**

Hypselodoris bilineata   **Madeira**

Double-lined Nudibranch
CHROMODORIDIDAE
(both pages)

Size: up to 3 cm. Distribution: Mediterranean Sea; in the eastern Atlantic from Portugal to Madeira and Morocco.
General: this is a common species at Madeira. It can be found on rocky bottoms down to at least 25 m depth. Only adult animals have the name-giving double yellow line *("bilineata")* along the back. In young animals the line is undivided and the young of this species can be confused with many other similar "blue *Hypselodoris*" species.

Hypselodoris midatlantica   **Faial Island, Azores**

S: up to 2 cm. D: Azores.
G: described 1990 from the Azores, where it is common in 3-25+ m. According to some authors, however, it might be a colour variant of *H. tricolor*.
Below: Three-coloured Nudibranch *H. tricolor*, western Mediterranean Sea, France to Canary Islands, locally common, in 3-25+ m, to 3.5 cm.

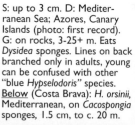

Hypselodoris fontandraui   **Lanzarote, Canary Islands**

S: up to 3 cm. D: Mediterranean Sea; Azores, Canary Islands (photo: first record).
G: on rocks, 3-25+ m. Eats *Dysidea* sponges. Lines on back branched only in adults, young can be confused with other "blue *Hypselodoris*" species.
Below (Costa Brava): *H. orsinii*, Mediterranean, on *Cacospongia* sponges, 1.5 cm, to c. 20 m.

Size: up to 5 cm but usually about 2 cm long.
Distribution: Mediterranean Sea; in the eastern Atlantic from the French coast to Morocco.
General: this is a locally common species on the Atlantic coasts of the Iberian peninsula, where it can be found throughout the year, with peak densities in April and May. From shallow water down to about 40 m depth. It is frequently seen on the sponge *Dysidea fragilis*, on which it feeds. This species is extremely variable in colour and many different colour morphs have been described. The <u>small photo</u> from Patras, Greece, shows one of the colour morphs of *H. villafranca*.

Hypselodoris villafranca   **Bay of Setúbal, Portugal**

S: up to 11 cm long.
D: Gulf of Gascogne to Spanish Mediterranean coast.
G: one of many similar blue *Hypselodoris* species. Adults can be recognized by the pattern of white spots on the body (see photos). Juveniles are very difficult to distinguish from several other species. Feeds on sponges of the genus *Dysidea*. From shallow water down to about 25 m. <u>Below</u>: a mating pair, Sesimbra, Portugal.

Hypselodoris cantabrica   **Bay of Setúbal, Portugal**

Hypselodoris picta   Costa Brava, Spain

Hypselodoris picta   Faial Island, Azores

Hypselodoris picta   São Tomé

Variable Seaslug
CHROMODORIDIDAE

Size: up to 13 cm.
Distribution: Mediterranean Sea; in the eastern Atlantic from the southern coast of Spain to Angola; in the western Atlantic from Florida to Brazil.
General: this very variable species has been described under many different names, the most common synonym is *H. elegans*. Jesus Ortea and co-workers recognized 5 subspecies. In the Mediterranean subspecies *H. p. picta* (upper large photo), the body is light blue and bears many yellow lines and spots, sometimes appearing almost entirely yellow.

The Azorean subspecies *H. p. azorica* (middle large photo) is easy to recognize because the many golden spots on the dark blue body do not form lines.

The subspecies *H. p. webbi* (upper small photo, from La Palma) has many yellow lines and spots on a dark blue body. It lives from southern Spain to the Canary Islands and in the western Atlantic.

The subspecies *H. p. verdensis* (lower large photo; lower small photo, from the Cape Verdes) has orange spots and lines on a blue-green body. It lives from the Cape Verde Islands to Angola.

The subspecies *H. p. tema* (not figured) is only known from Ghana. *Hypselodoris picta* can be found from shallow water down to about 50 m depth. It feeds on sponges of the genus *Dysidea*.

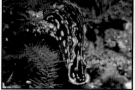

DORIDACEA

Leopard Seaslug

DISCODORIDIDAE (this page)
S: 10 cm. D: Med.; France-Canar.
G: often on its food, *P. ficiformis*
(p. 14). Even though this sponge
contains defensive compounds
(making it unpalatable to most),
the slug does not incorporate
them into its own tissue (as do
many opisthobranchs); calcareous spicules for defence. 4-20 m.

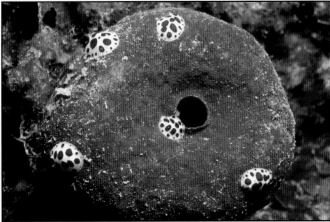

Discodoris atromaculata   **Malta**

S: 6 cm. D: Canaries, Madeira,
Porto Santo. G: *D. fragilis* was
considered a circum-tropical
species until it could be shown
that the Atlantic animals are
distinctly different. They were
then given the name *D. confusa*. The species lives on rocky
bottoms in 5-25 m. Below:
Paradoris indecora, Med., Portugal to Canary Islands; to 4 cm.

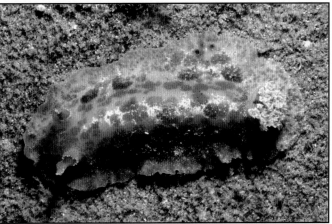

Discodoris confusa   **Porto Santo Island, Madeira**

S: 6.5 cm. D: Med.; Norway to
Canaries. G: eats sponges, e.g.
Hemimycale columella (p. 14) or
Mycale spp. 3-15+ m. Below:
Canary Sea Slug *G. perfossa*,
Canaries; Madeira. It is yellow
in colour, thus the name
Canary Sea Slug has a double
meaning. It grows to at least
3.5 cm and lives in shallow
water down to at least 20 m.

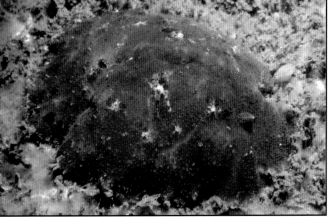

Geitodoris planata   **Faial Island, Azores**

PLATYDORIDIDAE

S: 10 cm. D: Med.; French Atl. coast to the Canaries. G: one of the most common nudibranchs in Med. and temperate eastern Atlantic. An analysis of its gut contents has shown that it feeds on many different species of sponges. During the day, it hides below stones, so that the conspicuous spawn of this species (upper small photo) is much more evident than the animals themselves. The lower large photo shows the typical "trailing" behaviour sometimes observed in this sp. Lower small photo: *Rostanga rubra* (Rostangidae), Med., E-Atl.: Norway to the Canary Islands. It also feeds on sponges. Up to 2 cm long.

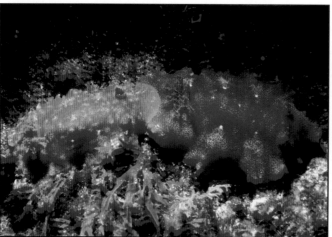

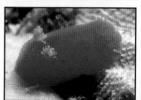

Platydoris argo   Faial Island, Azores

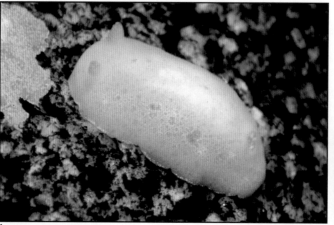

White Jorunna
KENTRODORIDIDAE

S: up to 5.5 cm. D: Norway to the Canary Islands; W-Med. G: feeds on sponges, e.g. *Halichondria panicea* (p. 13) and *Haliclona* spp, shallow to about 400 m depth. The body surface of this species resembles the surface of a sponge. Below: the same species from Helgoland, North Sea.

Jorunna tomentosa   Norway

DORIDACEA

Velvet Jorunna
KENTRODORIDIDAE

S: 3 cm. D: from the Spanish Atlantic coast south to the Canary Islands; Spanish Mediterranean coast. G: lives on rocky coasts, down to at least 10 m depth. Feeds on sponges. Has typical "velvety" appearance of all genus members. <u>Below</u> (Costa del Sol): a portrait of the same animal.

Jorunna onubensis Costa del Sol, Spain

POLYCERIDAE

Size: up to 20 mm.
Distribution: eastern Atlantic: from Norway to South Africa; western Mediterranean Sea. General: there are yellow-tipped processes all around the body of this species. Those at the front are held forward, those at the sides are curled upwards over the back of the animal. This is a locally common species, which feeds on encrusting bryozoans, such as *Membranipora membranacea* (p. 251), on which it is figured here.

The <u>small photo</u> from Madeira shows *Thecacera pennigera.* The white body is covered by many small orange, yellow and black spots. This species has a world-wide distribution in tropical and subtropical waters and feeds on bryozoans of the genus *Bugula* (p. 251).

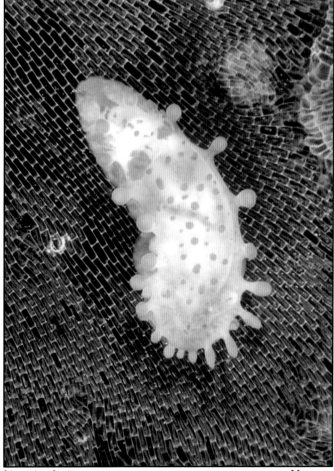

Limacia clavigera Norway

S: up to 4.8 cm. D: from Ireland to Gibraltar, including the Azores; W-Med. G: this unmistakable species, sometimes called *Greilada elegans,* feeds on bryozoans of the genus *Bugula* (p. 251), and lives in 5-25 m depth. Below: the same species from the Azores.

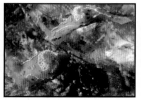

Polycera elegans   Ibiza, Spain

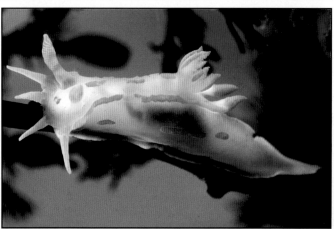

S: up to 4.5 cm. D: Norway to Madeira; western Mediterranean Sea. G: one of the most common nudibranchs of the NE-Atl. It feeds on bryozoans such as *M. membranacea* (p. 251) and on *Bugula* spp. Has 4-6 frontal processes. Also has a colour morph in which body is partly or completely black (below, Azores).

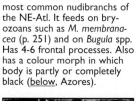

Polycera quadrilineata   Costa Brava, Spain

S: 4.5 cm. D: Faroes to W-Med. G: sometimes confused with *P. quadrilineata* but has 8-10 frontal processes and only sometimes yellow spots on back. Below: an animal photographed (but not collected) by Jorge Fontes at the Azores in about 8 m depth. It is an undescribed sp. Unfortunately, it was never seen again. 2 cm.

Polycera faeroensis   Bay of Setúbal, Portugal

POLYCERIDAE (this page)

S: up to 5 cm. D: Algarve to Strait of Gibraltar; Spanish Med. coast. G: several colour morphs exist. Body light or dark blue, the yellow (or bright orange) lines on it can be thinner or wider. On rocky bottoms, below 5 m depth, down to 30+ m. Small photo from same location.

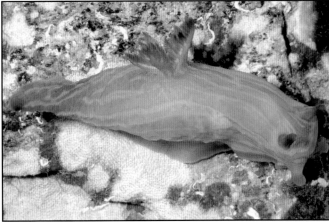

Roboastra europaea Costa del Sol, Spain

S: 6 cm. D & G: found in 20 m at São Tiago, Cape Verdes. Another individual from Sal Island was put into a little aquarium where it regurgitated a small *Tambja!* Below (Cape Verde Islands): this might be *Tambja marbellensis*, so far only recorded from Spanish Med. coast; it could also be a colour morph of *T. ceutae* (see next page).

Roboastra **undescribed species** Cape Verde Islands

S: up to 4.5 cm. D & G: both species shown here are known only from the Cape Verde Islands. On rocks down to about 30 m, feeding on blue bryozoans of the genus *Bugula*. Below: *T. fantasmalis* also lives on the rocky coasts of the Cape Verde Islands, down to at least 15 m. It grows to about 5 cm length.

Tambja simplex Cape Verde Islands

DORIDACEA

POLYCERIDAE

Size: up to 6 cm.
Distribution: Azores, Gibraltar, Madeira, Canary and Cape Verde Islands; Spanish Mediterranean coast.
General: this species was originally described from the Strait of Gibraltar (thus the name "ceutae"). It is one of the most common nudibranch species at the Azores, on rocky bottoms, in open daylight, from shallow water down to about 20 m depth.

The blue colour morph (upper large photo) is the one first described. The more yellow one is equally frequent at the Azores. Author PW has never seen matings between the two colour morphs and is still not entirely convinced that they are the same species.

The small photo is from Madeira.

See also the large photo of a mating pair on page 212.

Tambja ceutae   **Faial Island, Azores**

DENDRODORIDIDAE

S: 10 cm. D: Med.; Portugal to Can. G: with typical wavy mantle edge and soft appearance of the genus. Variable, mottled body can be cream, grey, pale green, light brown, light red. Edge not yellow (as in *D. limbata*). Below: *D. herytra*, N-Spain to Can., Az., Mad., 5-30 m. Pink, brown, 9 cm.

Dendrodoris grandiflora   **Elba Island, Italy**

DORIDACEA

DENDRODORIDIDAE

S: 7 cm. D: Med. G: variable; the mottled body can be grey, yellow, brown or black; can be recognized by a yellow mantle edge. Below (CV): *D. senegalensis*, only known from Senegal and the Cape Verde Islands. The photographed individual was about 4 cm in length.

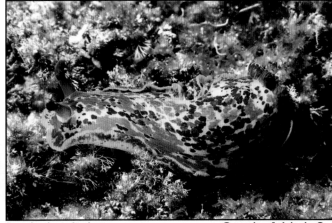

Dendrodoris limbata　　　　Croatia, Adriatic Sea

DENDRODORIDIDAE

S: 3 cm. D: N-Spain to Canaries (but not known from the Azores and Madeira); Spanish Med. coast. G: yellow body covered by thin white lines. Particularly common on the Atlantic coasts of Portugal and Spain, from 5 m downwards. Below (Cascais, Portugal): a copulating pair.

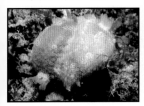

Doriopsilla areolata　　　　Bay of Setúbal, Portugal

PHYLLIDIIDAE

S: up to 4.5 cm. D: Med.; Canary Islands. G: this species can usually be found on the sponges on which it feeds, especially *Axinella cannabina* (photo) and *Acanthella acuta*. Its bright yellow to orange colour with large white tubercles make it unmistakable. *P. flava* (sometimes called *P. pulitzeri*) lives on rocky bottoms, usually below 20 m. It is the only Mediterranean member of this genus, which contains many tropical species in the Indo-Pacific. Albino animals, completely white, have been collected in dark caves.

Phyllidia flava　　　　Crete Island, Greece

Following pages: Common Mussel *Mytilus edulis*, Gulmarsfjorden, Sweden　**227**

Noah's Ark
ARK SHELLS, ARCIDAE

S: 7, max 11 cm. D: Med.; Algarve to Senegal. G: often covered with sponge *Crambe crambe,* then difficult to detect. Attached to rock, 4-100+ m. Below: Dog Cockle *Glycimeris glycimeris* (Bittersweet clams, Glycimeridae). Locally common, 2-80 m, Norway to Cape Verdes, Med. Sea.

Arca noae   **Crete Island, Greece**

Common Mussel
MYTILIDAE

S: 12 cm. D: circum-arctic, but not Arctic itself. NE- & NW-Atl.; California, Japan. G: probably the best known bivalve, commercially important. Purple-blue to light brown. High intertidal down to a few metres. Attach themselves to rock and to each other with threads ("byssus"). Because they attach to each other and to agglomerations of shells of dead animals, mussel beds can extend onto soft sediments. Filters up to 50 l water per hour. Main predators are sea stars (pull open the mussel and evert their stomach into it) and large crabs (crack the shell with their claws).

Mytilus edulis   **Baltic Sea**

Horse-Mussel
MYTILIDAE

S: 10, max 22 cm. D: Faroes, Iceland to Bay of Biscay. G: dark blue, 1-150 m. One end typically beak-shaped. Has byssus. Below: the holes made by *Lithophaga lithophaga.* Med., Spain to Angola. Bores into calcareous rock by secreting acid. Much sought after (delicious taste), now protected.

Modiolus modiolus   **North Sea**

Large Fan-Mussel
PEN SHELLS, PINNIDAE
(both pages)
S: to 100+ cm high. D: Mediterranean Sea. G: this is the
largest European bivalve. Due
to heavy collecting of this now
totally protected species, it is
rare to encounter animals larger than 60 cm high. The oldest
animal encountered in a study
at the Spanish Mediterranean
coast was 13 years old, at a
length of 45 cm. Large photo:
a dive instructor shows the
only remaining Fan-Mussel
(which he carefully protects) in
the vicinity of his dive centre
to the photographer.
   The strong, yellow-brown
byssus threads, used by the
animal to attach itself to the
bottom, were used to weave
cloth, such as probably the
famous golden fleece. The
shrimp *Pontonia pinnophylax*
(page 129) and the crab *Pinno-
theres pisum* can live inside the
shell of *Pinna* (see the story
"My Shell Is My Castle").
   Small photo below from
Crete Island, Greece. It shows
very well the cover of invertebrates and algae which usually
grow on large Fan-Mussels.

Pinna nobilis   Ibiza, Spain

Northern Fan-Mussel

Size: up to 25, max 35 cm.
Distribution: from S-Britain to
the western Mediterranean.
General: the third European
member of the family Pinnidae.
It is very rare to see this
species already in 50 m depth;
normally it lives below 100 m,
down to at least 600 m depth.

Altrina pectinata   North Sea

Spiny Fan-Mussel

Size: up to 40 cm high.
Distribution: all of the Mediterranean Sea; in the eastern Atlantic from the Azores along the coast of West Africa south to St. Helena Island; also found on the other side of the Atlantic Ocean in the Caribbean Sea.

General: its rough surface sculpture of wide open scale-like thorns set in rows along the shell's longitudinal axis distinguishes this species from the much smoother Large Fan-Mussel which has more, but less prominent, flatter scales. Young specimens of both cannot easily be determined to species. When not overgrown by sessile organisms, the colour of the clean shell is reddish brown.

Found on sandy and soft bottoms, especially in small sandy pits in the rocky littoral zone. The depth range of this large bivalve is from a few metres down to over 50 m.

This mussel almost always contains a pair or a single animal of the shrimp *Pontonia pinnophylax* (see the story "My Shell Is My Castle"). It is much rarer than the Large Fan-Mussel. Both species are used for human consumption but after overcollecting by man have become so rare that they nowadays are hardly seen in Mediterranean fish markets.

The upper photo was taken while snorkelling near a very shallow beach where the bottom was covered with beautiful *Caulerpa* algae. In the rather dirty water the photographer was surprised to find such a fine specimen of the Spiny Fan-Mussel.

Pinna rudis   Costa Blanca, Spain

Pinna rudis   Madeira

Pteria hirundo   **Faial Island, Azores**

Wing Oyster
WING OYSTERS, PTERIIDAE

S: 11 cm. D: Med.; Great Britain
to Angola, including Azores,
Madeira, Canaries. G: unmistakable, attaches itself with strong
byssus threads to the bottom or
(preferentially) to upright structures like gorgonians or black
coral. The rather thin shell of
this species is frequently overgrown by algae, bryozoans, polychaetes, which can make the
mussel difficult to detect.
   Pinctada radiata is similar
("wing" shorter) and has invaded
the Med. via the Suez Canal. See
"Red Sea Immigrants". Recently
also detected in the Canaries.

Aequipecten opercularis   **North Sea**

Queen Scallop
SCALLOPS, PECTINIDAE
S: 11 cm. D: N-Norway, Faroes
to Canaries and into W-Med. G:
while juveniles attach themselves
to the substrate with byssus
threads, adults are the most
actively swimming of all scallops.
They may suddenly clap the
valves together and move off,
swimming with the free margin
forward. By repeatedly "biting"
the water they can swim long
distances. The Queen Scallop
lives on sandy mud, gravel or
shelly ground down to a depth
of about 400 m. The large eyes
at the mantle edge can detect
movements (see also the story
"Invertebrate Vision").

Pecten jacobaeus   **Crete Island, Greece**

Pilgrim's Scallop
PECTINIDAE
S: 15 cm. D: Med.; Portugal to
Angola. G: upper (flat) valve with
14-17 angular ribs. Spanish pil-
grims used to attach the shell to
their coat or hat to honour Saint
Jacques. <u>Below</u>: Great Atlantic
Scallop *P. maximus*. Rib ridges
much rounder. Buried in ground.
1-250 m, Norway to Canaries.

Variegated Scallop
PECTINIDAE
S: 6 cm. D: Lofoten to Senegal; Med. G: extremely variable, pure white to almost black. Attaches to rock with byssus, often below stones. Shallow water down to 80 m. Below (Adriatic Sea): two differently coloured individuals of *C. glabra.* Atlantic coast of Portugal, Med. Sea, 7 cm, 5-900 m.

Chlamys varia   Madeira

African Thorny Oyster
SPINY OYSTERS, SPONDYLIDAE
S: 15 cm. D: Madeira to Gabon. G: lower shell cemented to rock, 10-40+ m, often overgrown, may have short spines. See also "My shell...". Below: European Thorny Oyster *S. gaederopus,* overgrown by *Crambe crambe* (p. 13). Spines very long (photo) to absent.

Spondylus senegalensis   Madeira

Saddle Oyster
SADDLE OYSTERS, ANOMIIDAE
S: 6 cm. D: Iceland, Faroes to Ghana; Med.; SW-Atl. G: lower shell very thin, firmly attached to hard substrate. Solid upper valve overgrows lower one. Common, often overgrown. 2-150 m. Below: *Pododesmus patelliformis,* 4 cm, Norway to Med. Recently found in the Azores.

Anomia ephippium   Crete Island, Greece

Gaping File Shell
FILE SHELLS, LIMIDAE
S: 3 cm. D: Lofotes to Canaries;
Med. G: divers rarely see this
brilliantly coloured shell. Below
stones in "nest" of byssus
threads, small stones; can spread
many long tentacles. <u>Below</u>:
Spiny File Shell *Lima lima,* warm
oceans of the world, Med. 7 cm.
Both spp can swim in small hops.

Limaria hians   Madeira

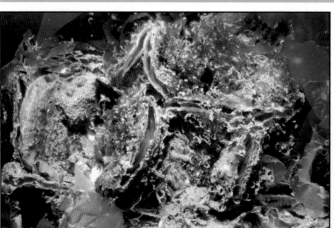

Common European Oyster
OYSTERS, OSTREIDAE
S: 11 cm. D: Norway-Morocco;
Med. G: only native European
oyster, shallow to 80 m, hard or
soft bottoms. Once considered
as food for the poor! <u>Below</u>:
Spoon Oyster *Neopycnodonte
cochlear* (Gryphaeidae). Iceland
to Angola, Med., 40-250 m.

Ostrea edulis   Italian Adriatic

MONTACUTIDAE

S: 4, max 8 mm. D: Norway to
Canaries. G: lives between the
spines of irregular sea urchins
such as *Brissus unicolor* (photo),
*Spatangus purpureus, Echinocardi-
um cordatum.* <u>Below</u>: Fleshy Tellin
Tellina incarnata (Tellinidae), Med.,
Great Britain to Canar., 4.5 cm,
in muddy sand, shallow to 85 m.

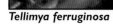

Tellimya ferruginosa   Tenerife, Canary Islands

Edible Cockle
COCKLES, CARDIIDAE

S: 5 cm. D: Barents Sea to Senegal. Not in Med. G: white to
brown. Shallow, in sand, gravel,
mud, up to 10,000 per m². Also
estuarine. Commercially fished.
<u>Below</u>: Tuberculate Cockle, *Acan-
thocardia tuberculata*. 5, max 9 cm.
Med., British Isles to Morocco.

Cerastoderma edule   Baltic Sea

Pea Mussel
SEMELIDAE
S: up to 15 mm. D: S-Ireland to
Canaries; Med.; Bermuda. G: this
tiny bivalve can reach enormous
densities, as the photo shows.
Divers are likely to overlook it
because all one can see are the
tiny, transparent siphons of the
mussels sticking out of the sand.
Recorded from 25-1800 m.

Ervilia castanea   Faial Island, Azores

Iceland-Cyprina, Quahog
ARCTICIDAE

S: 13 cm. D: Iceland, Faroes,
White Sea to Ria de Vigo, Spain.
NW-Atl. G: unmistakable, shell
heavy, yellowish to dark brown.
In mud, sand, gravel, 5-500 m.
Grows to 105 years of age! <u>Be-
low</u>: *Cardita calyculata* (Carditi-
dae), Med., temp. E-Atl. 1-200 m.

Arctica islandica   Norway

Rasp Short Razor
RAZOR CLAMS, SOLECURTIDAE

S: shell up to 10 cm. D: Med. G: the body of this strange, unmistakable species is much larger than the shell. It lives buried in mud or muddy sand in 2-15 m depth and can be locally common.

The two small photos from the Baltic Sea show the Sand Gaper *Mya arenaria* (Myidae, Soft-Shell Clams). It lives in mud or muddy sand or sand from shallow water to about 80 m depth. It reaches a size of 15 cm and is known from the White Sea and northern Norway to France, also in the north-western Atlantic and the northern Indo-Pacific. The species is heavily fished on the eastern coast of America.

Solecurtus strigilatus Sardinia, Italy

Warty Venus
VENUS CLAMS, VENERIDAE

S: 7 cm. D: Med.; Norway to SA. G: on all types of bottoms, 2-100+ m. Veneridae: largest marine bivalve family (500+ spp). Below: Brown Venus *Callista chione*, 10 cm, in sand, low water to 180 m, Med., S-Britain to Canar. Fished for in parts of the Med.

Venus verrucosa Crete Island, Greece

Chamber Venus

S: 5 cm. D: S-Norway to Cape
Verdes. G: ribs much finer, not
as knobbed as *V. verrucosa*. On
sand and gravel bottoms in 5-
200 m. Can be either white
(photos) or a dark chestnut
brown or a dark red. Main
predators are sea stars such as
Astropecten aranciacus (p. 274).

Venus casina   North Sea

WATERING POT CLAMS, CLAVAGELLIDAE

S: tube 4, shell 2 cm. D: Med.;
Canaries. G: starts life as normal bivalve but then bores into
sediment and mantle tissue
produces a tube-shaped "secondary shell". First record outside Med. 1994. Typical are 6-
16 tube edges. Below (Crete):
C. balanorum or *C. aperta*.

Clavagella melitensis   Tenerife, Canary Islands

TUSK SHELLS   SCAPHOPODA

Common Tusk Shell
TUSK SHELLS, DENTALIIDAE
S: 6 cm. D: Med. G: scaphopod
shells are slightly curved, open at
both ends. Head and foot are
protruded from the wider end.
Buries head down in soft ground,
feeds on detritus. Below: *A. enta-
lis*, 4 cm, common, North Sea.

Antalis tarentinum   Tuscany, Italy

PERFECTLY BUOYANT

Bones and tissue are heavier than water. To compensate, bony fish have a gas-filled swim bladder. Cephalopods have invented similar solutions.

Cuttlefish of the family Sepiidae carry a solid object in their bodies close to the back. This is called the "cuttlebone". The cuttlebone is very light: it consists of thousands of tiny chambers that are filled with gas. Because it is so light the cuttlebone provides the lift that compensates for the weight of the cuttlefish. As a result, the cuttlefish is neutrally buoyant that is, it hovers in the water without having to spend energy for swimming. When the cuttlefish grows and therefore becomes heavier, it simply adds a few hundred tiny gas-filled chambers to its cuttlebone.

The cuttlebone is like a solid swim bladder. These are from Common Cuttlefish *Sepia officinalis,* upper side on top, lower side below.

Perfectly buoyant: a European Common Cuttlefish hovers in the water.

Compared to the swim bladder of fish, the cuttlebone has the advantage of not changing its volume under changing pressure. When a fish swims downwards, increasing pressure compresses the swim bladder and the fish has to secrete more gas into it to maintain the correct volume of the swim

Shell of a *Nautilus pompilius* cut in half to show chambers.

bladder. Conversely, when a fish swims upwards, the swim bladder has a tendency to expand and the fish has to remove gas from it (by dissolving it into its blood) to maintain the correct volume of the swim bladder. In contrast, the cuttlebone always remains the same size.

The beautiful shell of the Nautilus also contains gas chambers, albeit much larger ones. As shown in the sawn shell depicted here, the chambers are connected by a small hole. In the live animal, a core of tissue extends from the body of the animal joining all these holes. The animal itself sits in the first chamber. Nautiluses can change their buoyancy by moving water in and out of the rear chambers. Even more surprising, when diving in depth with low oxygen concentrations, Nautilus not only lowers its metabolism and thus its oxygen demand but can also extract oxygen from the air in its buoyancy chambers. Nautilus is the only cephalopod with a SCUBA tank!

Sepia elegans   **Mediterranean Sea**

Elegant Cuttlefish
CUTTLEFISHES, SEPIIDAE
S: 9 cm. D: Med.; North Sea to Angola. G: 30-450 m. Recognized by the prominent extension of the body ("mantle") over the head (photo). This extension is caused by the cuttlebone of the animal (see "Perfectly Buoyant"). During winter, the Elegant Cuttlefish migrates into deeper waters (100-250 m), returning to shallow water in spring and summer to spawn. Females lay about 250 eggs. The fourth left arm of the male is modified with two zig-zag rows of tiny suckers. The lifespan of this species is only about 1.5 years. It feeds on small fish and crustaceans.

Sepia officinalis   **Porto Santo Island, Madeira**

Common Cuttlefish

S: 45 cm. D: Med.; S-Norway to Cape of Good Hope, into Indian Ocean. G: prefers sandy to muddy bottoms in 1-200 m. Females deposit up to 4000 grape-shaped eggs that hatch after 30-90 days. The 8 mm-hatchlings feed on caprellids (p. 113) during the first 3 months. Females born in spring spawn already in autumn, while females born in autumn spawn in spring the following year; thus two cycles alternate. Females die after spawning, while males may live up to 2 years. Main diet are small crustaceans, shellfish, small fish. See also preceding pages.

Sepiola atlantica   **Isle of Man**

Atlantic Bobtail Squid
BOBTAIL SQUIDS, SEPIOLIDAE
S: body 1.5 cm. D: Iceland to Morocco, not in Med. G: pair of rounded fins widely separated from each other. 2 to c. 300 m. Genus members with light organ within the gill cavity that houses luminescent bacteria (*Photobacterium fischeri*). Below: Analogous Bobtail Squid *S. affinis*, Med. only.

Stout Bobtail Squid
SEPIOLIDAE

S: body 9 cm. D: Greenland to Morocco; Med. G: for a bobtail squid rather large. 30-600 m, over sandy and muddy bottoms. Lives only one year. Most sepiolids cannot be identified from photos. <u>Below</u> (at night, 15 m, Crete): *Neorossia caroli*, normally deeper (100-1000 m). 5 cm.

Rossia macrosoma   **Sognefjord, Norway**

European Squid
COMMON SQUIDS, LOLIGINIDAE

S: body 40 cm. D: Scotland to Angola; Med. G: squids are torpedo-shaped animals with a pair of round/triangular fins. 1-500 m. Deposits jelly-like strings of eggs (<u>below</u>) on hard objects in shallow water. Fast predator feeding mainly on fish and crustaceans.

Loligo vulgaris   **Gran Canaria, Canary Islands**

Veined Squid
LOLIGINIDAE

S: body (without arms) 90 cm. D: Med.; S-Norway to West Africa; Red Sea. G: this large species is characterized by the distinctive markings on the sides of the body in larger animals. It usually lives below 100 m, down to 400 m depth.

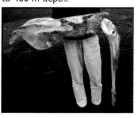

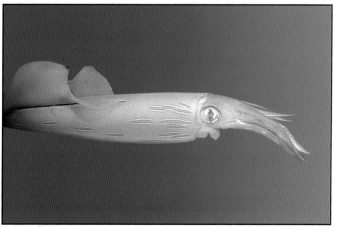

Loligo forbesi   **Faial Island, Azores**

Allotheutis subulata   **Portugal**

European Common Squid
LOLIGINIDAE

S: body 20 cm. D: Med. (rare); W-Baltic Sea to Mauritania. G: easily recognized by its very elongated tail, more so in males than in females (photo: young male). Over sandy and hard bottoms, shallow to c. 500 m. In S-North Sea, males and females arrive in shallow water in early summer, spawning season June-July. Hatching juveniles are 2 mm long and lead a planktonic life for the first 2-4 weeks; then they shift to the demersal habit of the adults. They grow at a rate of about 1 mm per day and live for 1-2 years. The food consists of small fish and crustaceans.

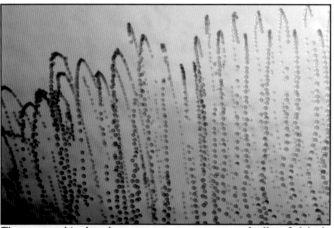

Thysanoteuthis rhombus   **Italian Adriatic**

Diamondback Squid
LOLIGINIDAE

S: body 1 m. D: world-wide in warm and temperate waters. G: the rare photo shows the planktonic egg mass of (probably) this species. Many squids of the open ocean release their tiny eggs in a large jelly-like sac. These egg masses of 60-150 cm length (10-20 cm in diameter) are rather fragile and transparent and easily overlooked. They drift in the currents, near the surface of the sea, until the larvae hatch. The eggs are pink to purple. Those in the photo appear to be young: no embryos are visible. See the cephalopod book in this series for a photo of an adult animal.

Eledone cirrhosa   **North Sea**

Horned Octopus
BENTHIC OCTUPUSES, OCTOPODIDAE

S: up to 40 cm. D: Norway and Iceland to W-Med. G: this stout, little, reddish-brown species lives in 20-500 (mostly 60-150) m. Most of the year, the sexes tend to segregate, females living in much shallower water than males. Has only a single row of suckers on the underside of each arm. A pale-coloured ridge encircles the rear body. Peak spawning time in the W-Med. is July; the female lays up to 1000 large eggs (around 8 mm in diameter). Lifespan in the W-Med. is 2-3 years but probably longer in colder waters.

Longarm Octopus
OCTOPODIDAE (this page)
S: body 9 cm, arms 30 cm.
D: Med.; Morocco to Angola.
G: long arms, small body typical.
On sand, mud to 350 m. Photo
(night, 15 m) may be first one of
this sp taken in the sea. Females
carry egg strings. When in danger, animals can sever arms near
the base as a decoy to predators.

Octopus defilippi   **Crete Island, Greece**

White-spotted Octopus
S: up to 60, max 150 cm total
length. D: in (sub)tropical
waters all around the world,
incl. Med. G: another rather
long-armed species, unmistakable because of its colour pattern of white spots on a red
body. The topmost pair of
arms is the longest. Active at
night, hiding during the day.
Despite its large range, little is
known about the biology of
this species. It lives in shallow
water and can even be found
in large tide pools. The <u>upper
small photo</u> of a strongly spotted animal is from Ibiza,
whereas the almost unspotted
animal in the <u>lower small pho-
to</u> is from Crete. Compare the
skin texture: like many other
octopods, *O. macropus* can
change their appearance by
raising or lowering small protuberances all over the body.

Octopus macropus   **Tenerife, Canary Islands**

Common Octopus

S: up to 1.3 m total length. D: Med., E-Atl.; real distribution unknown due to systematic confusion. G: common, 1-200 m. Author PW has observed octopuses crawling almost completely out of the water, feeling for crabs in rock crevices above the water line. Most populations have two spawning peaks per year, 1st in April/May, 2nd in Oct. Females produce 120,000-400,000 eggs (2 mm long), which they deposit in fuzzy looking strings in holes and then guard for 25-65 days (depending on water temp.). During this period, females stop feeding and frequently die after the hatching of the larvae. Main food are crabs, bivalves. As the Common Octopus has the habit to bring back its prey to its cave, the food habits were analysed by simply collecting remains (shells) from around the den. Colour change is extremely quick; when frightened, animals turn almost white, with dark rings around the eyes (<u>below</u>). Also hunts in open daylight. It is often accompanied by fish (wrasses, groupers) that hope to catch a crab or shrimp that flees from the octopus.

Octopus vulgaris   **Costa Brava, Spain**

Greater Argonaut
ARGONAUTIDAE

S: shell (<u>below</u>) 30 cm. D: trop. & temp. seas world-wide. G: open sea, at surface. Females have a membranous flap at end of 1st arm-pair that secretes, envelops, and holds a thin white calcareous shell in which the female resides and lays/guards eggs. Flaps change colour. Males only 2 cm, no shell.

Argonauta argo   **Faial Island, Azores**

WITH A DRILL AND WITH POISON

Archaeologists study the rubbish heaps of prehistoric cultures to detect what our ancestors were eating. Marine biologists of the University of the Azores do the same with the leftovers of the Common Octopus, scattered on the ground around its den.

Above: in front of the cave of the Octopus are the left-overs of his meals, in this case the bivalves *Rudicardium tuberculatum* (in the foreground), *Callista chione* (directly in front of the Octopus) and *Chamelea gallina*. Left: bore holes on the backs of crabs collected at Octopus dens.

The Common Octopus habitually carries into its den the snails, mussels, and crabs caught during its feeding excursions and eats them there. What is left over is simply chucked out of the cave.

By regularly collecting these leftovers, scientists can not only determine which prey species the Octopus is feeding on but even the quantities devoured.

When collecting the leftovers of Octopi, scientists of the University of the Azores even found the shells of two species of crabs that had never been recorded from the Azores. Ormers *(Haliotis tuberculata)* were the most frequent prey item. A closer look at the shells of the crabs showed that many of them bore drill holes. These holes were found not only on the back of the carapace but also on the claws.

The salivary glands of Octopi produce a paralysing poison and proteolytic (protein-dissolving) substances. The poison paralyses small crabs in less than thirty seconds. But of course it has to be injected first. To do this, the Octopus does not use its parrot-like beak but a set of small teeth that lay directly at the exit of the salivary gland. The poison not only paralyses the crabs but also dissolves their tissues within half an hour. The octopus can then slurp the brew. Whether the Octopus first drills the body of the crab and then the claws or the other way round is still not known and should be observed in an aquarium.

KAMPTOZOANS

KAMPTOZOA (ENTOPROCTA)

Barentsia discreta

Faial Island, Azores

S: 6 mm. D: all over S half of the globe; in the eastern Atlantic as far north as the Azores; Med. G: when the photographer saw these small animals on a stone in the harbour of Horta, Faial I., he thought that they were hydrozoans. But then the hydrozoans started to nod. Nodding when disturbed is the name-giving characteristic of the Kamptozoa (from the Greek *kamptein* = to nod). A muscle at the base of the stalk moves the whole stalk and the attached head rhythmically sideways. The German name "Kelchwürmer" (chalice worms) is a good description: they resemble a wine glass with a long and slender stem. The rim of the cup bears a single circlet of small tentacles. A sample of the Azorean colony was sent to the expert for this group of animals, Dr. Peter Emschermann at the university of Freiburg im Breisgau, Germany. He identified the species. With a length of 6 mm, *B. discreta* is a giant among the kamptozoans; most of the c. 150 spp measure only 0.1 to 1 mm. Many spp live on other invertebrates, for instance polychaetes or crustaceans.

MOSS ANIMALS

BRYOZOA

Neptune's Lace
S: 10+ cm in diameter. D: Med.; Norway to Azores. G: bryozoan colonies consist of many 1000 of tiny boxes. Each box houses a small polyp that can extend its head for filter feeding. Together, these boxes form a great variety of differently shaped colonies. In this book, the spp are arranged in a rather unscientific manner: first spp that resemble coral, then spp that look like plants and finally encrusting forms. The delicate colonies of *S. septentrionalis* are unmistakable. Very common in Med. Living colony pink; dead areas quickly overgrown by green algae. In dark places, such as cave entrances, and in 25+ m. <u>Below</u>: unidentified moss animal, Azores, the polyps are extended.

Sertella septentrionalis

Sardinia, Italy

Pentapora fascialis   Gallinara Island, Italy

HIPPOPORINIDAE

S: 15 (40) cm high, colonies 30 (80) cm in diameter. D: Med. G: branches look like elk's antlers, unite at base, form a compacted structure. Small colonies grow 200+% p.a. Common in areas with strong currents, 5-50+ m. Below: *Porella compressa,* Arctic to Bay of Biscay, 8 cm, 30-300 m.

Pentapora foliacea   Bay of Setúbal, Portugal

Rose Coral
HIPPOPORINIDAE

S: 15 cm high. D: W-Ireland into Med. G: unmistakable; flat, hard, erect, laminate plates, twisted, folded like a coral or a flower head. Largest E-Atl. bryozoan. Orange to dark red to brown. Below: *Hornera frondiculata,* one of many spp with fragile colonies on rock faces. Med., 20-50 m.

Myriapora truncata   Sardinia, Italy

False Coral MYRIAPORIDAE
S: 10+ cm high, 15+ cm in diam. D: Med. G: resembles Red Coral (p. 40). Do not collect living animals (loose colour when drying). Branches end like cut off, tiny polyps hardly visible. Branches of Red Coral end in a point, polyps conspicuous, white. Prefers dark places. In 20+ m. Below: *Smittina cervicornis,* 4 cm, 20+ m, in dark places shallower.

Fragile Bryozoans
BICELLARIIDAE
S: 5 cm. D: temperate NE-Atl.;
Med. G: many similar spp, e.g. *B.
turbinata, B. plumosa*. Others, e.g.
B. neritica, bushy, easily mistaken
for plants. Below: Hornwrack,
Flustra foliacea, very common,
Norway to Bay of Biscay. Dense
beds of greyish clumps, 10+ cm,
with distinctly lemony scent.

Bugula gracilis   Lanzarote, Canary Islands

Sea-mat
MEMBRANIPORIDAE
S: colonies (20+ cm) in layers of
1+ m. D: Norway into Med. G:
on large algae (kelp). After nudibranchs feed on colony, remaining animals develop small spines
that protect from future attacks.
Adjacent colonies do the same!
Below: *Schizomavella cuspidata*, in
thin crusts on rock, dark places.

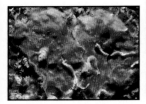

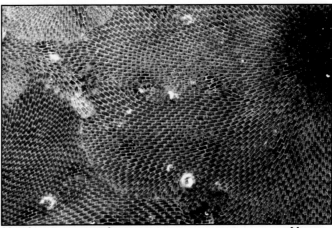

Membranipora membranacea   Norway

S: colonies up to 20 cm long.
D: temp. E-Atl.; Mediterranean.
G: as purple-black thin crust
on rocks, 2-20+ m. Polyps light
grey, when contracted colony
looks darker. Below: the conspicuous encrusting colonies
of *Schizoporella longirostris* can
reach 15 cm in diameter. At
Madeira, where the photo was
taken, they cover large areas
on rocks in 4-20 m depth.

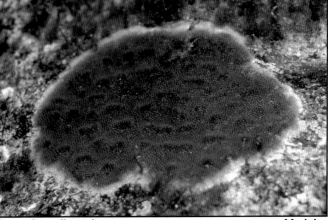

Reptadeonella violacea   Madeira

CANCELLOTHYRITIDAE

S: up to 3.5 cm. D: E-Atl., Med. G: at first sight, lamp-shells resemble bivalves because they possess a shell composed of two hinged valves. However, whereas bivalves have a left and a right valve of equal size, the body of lamp-shells is enclosed by an upper and a lower valve of unequal size. In most species, the lower (larger) valve is attached to the substrate by a short stalk or by cementation. Typical of the lamp-shells are the two spirally coiled arms enclosed by the shell. They bear cilia that create a current from which plankton is collected. *T. retusa*: on current swept rocky substrates in 20-1500 m. Below: *Megerlia truncata*, 1.5 cm, can be found in caves already in 10 m, outside caves deeper down.

Terebratulina retusa　　　Jœsenfjord, Norway

S: 1 cm. D: only Canary and Selvagens Islands. G: this species was originally described from the shell of dead animals. Then author PW found them alive in large numbers in a cave in only 5 m off the island of El Hierro. *Mega-thiris detruncata* (upper small photo) is a Med. species also common in caves at Madeira. The lower small photo of *Novocrania turbinata* was taken at the Cape Verde Islands.

Pajaudina atlantica　　　El Hierro, Canary Islands

Lesser Phoronid
PHORONIDAE

S: 5 cm. D: Med.; Great Britain to S-Africa. W-Atl. G: horseshoe worms have a body consisting of a slender stalk and a crown of filter-feeding tentacles of oval, horseshoe or spiral shape. Stalk surrounded by a chitinous tube. When in danger, the animal can withdraw into the tube. Solitary, but often in groups. Only two genera, *Phoronis* (7 spp), *Phoronopsis* (3 spp). Most of the spp have a world-wide distribution. The lesser phoronid bores into hard bottoms such as crusts of calcareous algae or limestone, in 2+ m. Horseshoe shaped tentacle crown 1 cm wide. Below (Costa del Sol, Spain): *Phoronopsis californica*. The double helix tentacle crown bears about 1500 tentacles. 25 cm. On sand. Med.

Phoronis hippocrepia   Faial Island, Azores

Greater Phoronid

S: 4-6, max 20 cm. D: Med.; Portugal to Cape Verdes and Senegal (not Azores, Madeira where author PW has searched for them extensively). G: lives in the tube wall of large tube anemones (p. 60), in 2-35 m. As it is the only phoronid with this habit, the sp is thus easy to recognize. The animal can move on the tube but never leaves it. The spiral tentacle crown commonly is 2+ cm wide. The photo printed here gives the northernmost record of the species in the Atlantic. Below (São Miguel, Azores): *Phoronopsis harmeri*, 15 m. The tentacles of this species form a double spiral. It is known from sandy bottoms from the Med. and E-Atl. (coast of Spain to Azores), also from the western Atlantic and Indo-Pacific.

Phoronis australis   Bay of Setúbal, Portugal

RED SEA IMMIGRANTS

With the construction of the 160-km-long Suez Canal in 1869, a connection was made between two fauna groups that had evolved separately for millions of years: that of the Red Sea / Indo-Pacific Ocean and that of the Mediterranean Sea / Atlantic Ocean. Through this connection, a slow but steady mixture of the two fauna groups is now taking place. Because there is a slight current from the Red Sea into the Mediterranean Sea, many more Red Sea species are migrating into the Mediterranean Sea than the other way around. Peter Wirtz describes some of them.

The Pearl Oyster *Pinctada radiata* was recorded in the Med only 5 years after the opening of the Suez Canal. (All photos from Cyprus.)

Currently (summer 2003), 59 species of fishes, 45 crustaceans, and 95 mussels and snails from the Red Sea have already been recorded in the Mediterranean Sea! Another 17 decapod crustaceans have already been recorded in the Suez Canal but not (yet) in the eastern Mediterranean Sea. For the

A second reason for the fact that more Red Sea species migrate into the Mediterranean Sea than in the opposite direction is probably that the Red Sea simply contains a larger number of species to start with.

Initially, the water in the Suez Canal was highly saline (70‰, more than twice the normal value of sea water) because two "bitter lakes" were incorporated into the canal during its construction. During this time, the canal was probably a barrier to migration for most marine species. Large numbers of Red Sea animals started to enter the Mediterranean Sea in the 1960s.

Rapidly spreading in the Mediterranean Sea: the Cornetfish *Fistularia commersonii* and...

crabs (Brachyura), the 17 Red Sea species amount to 12% of all the species recorded in the eastern Mediterranean Sea.

The pearl oyster *Pinctada radiata* was recorded from the Mediterranean coast of Egypt in 1878, only five years after the opening of the Suez Canal. It has since spread throughout the eastern Mediterranean Sea and even as far as Sicily and France.

Occasionally, immigrants from the Red Sea start to multiply explosively in the eastern Mediterranean Sea. Some fishes and shrimps from the Red Sea have reached such densities along the Mediterranean coast of Israel that they are now fished commercially. The prawn

...the snail *Ergalatax obscura.*

PHOTOS: PETER WIRTZ

first recorded in the Mediterranean Sea in 1924, now so common that it is commercially fished there: the prawn *Marsupenaeus japonicus*.

Marsupenaeus japonicus shown here is an example. It migrated into the Mediterranean Sea as early as 1924. Females grow up to 27 cm in length, males only to 17 cm.

Less agreeable to man is the recent arrival at the coasts of Israel of the jellyfish *Rhopilema nomadica* because it is a strongly stinging species.

another Red Sea immigrant: the sea cucumber *Synaptula reciprocans*.

New discoveries of Red Sea immigrants are made almost every year. The up to 1.5-m-long predatory Cornetfish *Fistularia commersonii* was spotted along the Mediterranean coast of Israel in the year 2000. It is spreading very rapidly. During a recent holiday on Cyprus, Peter Wirtz found it there in dense populations. Groups of three to five animals are particularly common over seagrass meadows. A pair of the snail *Ergalatax obscura* was clinging to the wall of a cave at a depth of 6 m –

apparently also the first evidence of this species at Cyprus after its first Mediterranean appearance in 1995. In the Red Sea, animals up to 25 mm length have been recorded but in the Mediterranean Sea the "record size" up to now is only 18 mm.

Also very common at Cyprus is another Red Sea immigrant, the synaptid holothurian *Synaptula reciprocans*. The warm waters of the eastern Mediterranean Sea are apparently particularly suitable for Red Sea species arriving through the Suez Canal.

East Atlantic Slate Pen Sea Urchin
CIDARIDAE (this page)
S: spines up to 13 cm. D: Cape Verdes, Gulf of Guinea. G: large primary spines of cidarids are placed at large distance from each other, are surrounded by circles of smaller secondary spines. Species very common on rocky bottoms (Cape Verdes: density 12/100 m^2), also in sea grass. 0-800 m, most common in 10-50 m. Feeds on a great variety of animals/plants: sea grass, algae, sponges (which make up a high proportion of its diet), bryozoans, coral, snails, sea urchins. Leaves shelter at night, moving very slowly. Spines not covered by tissue, hence often overgrown by algae or animals.

Eucidaris tribuloides   **Cape Verde Islands**

Long-spine Slate Pen Sea Urchin
S: with spines up to 20 cm high. D: Mediterranean Sea; Norway to Cape Verdes. G: in cold N-Adriatic much rarer than in other parts of Med. Shell and large spines light grey, ends of spines verging towards green. Small spines greenish. Large spines twice as long as shell diameter. Main function of small spines is to protect the muscular base of the large spines. This is a deep water species, rarely seen in SCUBA diving range. From 50 to 700+ m, can be locally quite common. If you see animals in very shallow water, they have probably been discarded by fishermen cleaning their nets.

Cidaris cidaris   **Tenerife, Canary Islands**

Short-spine Slate Pen Sea Urchin
S: with spines up to 20 cm high. D: Mediterranean. G: similar to preceding sp but spines only slightly longer than shell. Greybrown to pinkish. Sedentary polychaete worms and barnacles may grow on large spines. 30-1000 m, on sand, mud, gravel, into which it may partially dig itself (below).

Stylocidaris affinis   **Cape Palinuro, Italy**

SEA URCHINS

ECHINOIDEA

Brown Long-spined Sea Urchin

DIADEMATIDAE (this page)
S: spines 20 cm. D: Med.; temp.
E-Atl. G: thin long spines and
body usually brown. Lighter and
darker zones alternate on the
spines. However, a black colour
morph looks rather like *Diadema
antillarum* (see below). This black
morph is quite common in the
Azores (small photo). Only *C.
longispinus* has numerous small
purple blobs at the end of small
stalks, rapidly waving around, on
top of its body (large photo).
These blobs are small 3-bladed
valves whose function is to deter
predators and parasites. The
valves have poison sacs, and the
poison is delivered to the terminal fang of each blade. From
about 5 m to at least 200 m.

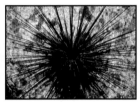

Centrostephanus longispinus   Faial Island, Azores

Black Long-spined Sea Urchin

S: spines 40 cm. D: Madeira to
Gulf of Guinea; W-Atl. G: spines
hollow, easily penetrate human
flesh, then break off, but usually
come out after a day (aid with
lemon juice or vinegar) or simply
dissolve. Disturbed, this sp starts
to rapidly wave its spines. Most
animals black (very dark blue),
some spines or whole animal
also white (photos). During the
day, often in groups with interlocked spines (protection against
e.g. trigger fish). At night, moving
around to feed on algae or small
invertebrates. Where they occur
in high densities, small algae are
unable to grow and rocks may
appear to be quite bare. On
rocky, gravely bottoms and in
seagrass meadows in 2-400+ m.
Not at Azores (see previous sp).

Diadema antillarum   Madeira

Purple Sea Urchin

TOXOPNEUSTIDAE (this page)
S: 13 cm high. D: Med.; E-Atl. G: unmistakably stout with short thick spines, but colour variable. Med.: majority of animals have purple spines with white tips (large photo). E-Atl.: purple or brown, but also different (small photo, Azores). Like *Paracentrotus lividus*, this sp has a tendency to cover itself with algae, stones, shells, or other objects. Despite numerous studies on this behaviour, its function is still not clear. The main predators of this sp are not fish (no fish in Med. or E-Atl. can break the strong shell of this sp) but large sea stars such as *Marthasterias glacialis* (p. 281). 2-120 m. The tiny snail *Vitreolina philippi* (p. 169) may be sitting between its spines.

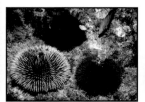

Sphaerechinus granularis   **Malta**

West Indian Sea Egg

Size: up to 15 cm in diameter.
Distribution: West Africa, Ascension Island; western Atlantic: Bermuda, Florida to Brazil.
General: this large sea urchin lives in many different habitats, from seagrass meadows on sand bottoms to wave exposed rock. It has been found from shallow water down to 55 m depth. *Tripneustes ventricosus* feeds on sea grass, other plants, and on detritus.

In Panama, reproductively active individuals can be found throughout the year and spawning appears to occur at random during the lunar cycle.

In the Caribbean, this sea urchin is host to a small cryptically coloured shrimp, *Gnathophylloides mineri*, that lives among the spines near the urchin's mouth and feeds on the epidermis of the spines. It would be well worth searching eastern Atlantic *Tripneustes* for this shrimp or other associates.

Tripneustes ventricosus   **São Tomé**

Black Sea Urchin
ARBACIIDAE

S: 8 cm. D: Med.; temp. E-Atl. G:
one of the most common sea
urchin spp in its range. On rocky
substrate from the water line
downward, usually only in the
first 5 m, max to 50 m. Below:
Arbaciella elegans, a small species,
flattened spines are distinctive. 1-
20+ m. Med., (sub)tropical E-Atl.

Arbacia lixula   Faial Island, Azores

Rock Urchin   ECHINIDAE

S: 8, max 13 cm. D: W-Scotland,
W-Ireland to W-Africa & island
groups; Med. (very common). G:
1-30 m, in S of range to 80 m.
Where the bedrock is soft, it
bores holes into rock (below),
using its fast-growing teeth. Colour variable. Where common, it
severely limits growth of algae
(food). Over-collected, locally
wiped out (human consumption).

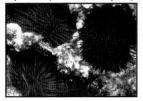

Paracentrotus lividus   Aegean Sea, Greece

Edible Sea Urchin
ECHINIDAE

S: 18 cm high. D: N-Norway to
Atlantic coast of Portugal. G: a
large cold-water sp. Shell pink to
red, rarely light green, spines
short, pinkish. Long thin tube-
feet often extended far beyond
spines. Common in 2-40 m but
recorded to 1200 m. Feeds on a
great variety of plants, encrusting
animals (Bryozoa). Reproduces
in early summer. Its large gonads
are eaten in several countries,
thus its Latin name *"esculentus"*
(= edible). A polychaete worm,
Flabelligera affinis, sometimes lives
among its spines. In the wild, *E.
esculentus* sometimes hybridises
with *E. acutus* (see next page).

Echinus esculentus   Norway

ECHINIDAE

S: 16 cm high. D: Med.; Barents Sea to W-Africa. G: shell has red or brown vertical bands, spines stout, reddish or a dirty white. 20-1000 m, on rock, sand, mud. The closely related *E. melo* (lower small photo) is up to 17 cm high. Shell brownish. Short spines greenish. 25 m to several 100 m in western Med., Adriatic Sea, temperate E-Atl. The Green Urchin *Psammechinus miliaris* (upper small photo, Baltic Sea) belongs to the same family. It has a rather flattened body and reaches a size of only 4 cm. It can be encountered from 4-100 m depth, in the Mediterranean and in the E-Atlantic from S-Norway to coast of Morocco.

Echinus acutus   Sognefjord, Norway

STRONGYLOCENTROTIDAE

S: 8 cm. D: circumpolar species, south to English Channel. G: on hard bottoms to 1200 m. Colour variable. Feeds on algae. Resembles *P. lividus* but lives north of that sp. Caught, eaten in Norway, exported to Japan. Below: *Echinocyamus pusillus* (Fibulariidae, 1 cm). In sand, comes out at night to spawn (photo).

Strongylocentrotus droebachensis   Lofoten Islands

Violet Heart Urchin
SPATANGIDAE
S: 12 cm long. D: Med.; Norway to Morocco. G: all sea urchins on this page live buried in soft sediments. Consequently, their body is not ball-shaped but oval and/or flattened. Their spines are rather soft, short, directed backwards. Colour purple (Latin *"purpureus"*). 5-900 m. In sand or gravel. Feeds on detritus, small invertebrates, including other sea urchins. A small bivalve, *Tellimya ferruginosa,* may occur between the spines of this sp and of *Brissus unicolor* (see p. 261). Nocturnal emergence from the sediment is a common behaviour.

Spatangus purpureus   Costa del Sol, Spain

Grey Heart Urchin
BRISSIDAE
S: 12 cm. D: Azores to Cape Verdes; Med.; W-Atl. G: lives buried in sand. Has many soft grey spines. <u>Photo</u>: the spineless shell of dead animal.
<u>Below</u>: *Meoma ventricosa,* up to 20 cm long, W-Atl. Photo taken during a night dive at São Tiago, Cape Verdes, in 25 m.

Brissus unicolor   Faial Island, Azores

Small Heart Urchin
LOVENIIDAE
S: 5 cm. D: Med.; Norway to S-Africa; W-Atl. G: yellow-white, in sand. 5-200 m. <u>Photo</u>: pufferfish *Sphoeroides marmoratus* has detected it while re-entering the sand. The fish bit out a large piece from the fragile sea urchin.
<u>Below</u>: *Rotula deciesdigitata* (shell; Rotulidae). Lives hidden in sand.

Echinocardium cordatum   Faial Island, Azores

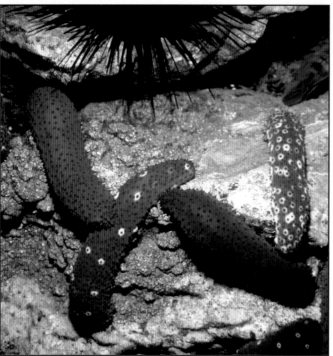

Variable Sea Cucumber

HOLOTHURIIDAE (this page)
S: 25 cm. D: Bay of Biscay to St. Helena, incl. Madeira, Can., CV; Mediterranean. G: most common sea cucumber in the shallows (up to 90/100 m² at the Canaries). Night-active on rocky bottoms, in sea grass down to 80 m. When disturbed it rapidly ejects, out of the rear end, numerous white threads, the so-called "Ductus Cuvieri". These are extremely sticky and adhere to almost any type of surface. They not only entangle and molest potential predators but also secrete poisons that repel most potential predators (harmless for humans). Often confused with *H. forskali* (below). Below: *H. tubulosa*, Med., very common, 30 cm, black, covered with sand.

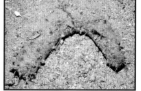

Holothuria sanctori   Madeira

Cotton Spinner

S: up to 25 cm. D: from western Ireland to Senegal; Mediterranean Sea. G: the thick soft skin of this species bears numerous conical papillae with rather pointed tips. The tips of the papillae are often white. Dorsally black to brown, ventrally pale brown to yellowish. Very common throughout range, on rocky substrates from shallow water down to 300+ m. When irritated it rapidly ejects sticky white threads that glue to and entangle potential predators. Feeds like most *Holothuria* spp on detritus, sand, rotting plant material, etc. When this material passes the gut, the organic components and in particular the bacteria in it are digested by the sea cucumber. The photo left shows the typical sandy habitat. Below: Spain.

Holothuria forskali   Croatia, Adriatic Sea

White Sea Cucumber
STICHOPODIDAE

S: 35 cm. D: Great Britain to Sierra Leone; Med.; W-Atl. G: body flattened, sides with large conical papillae. Back white to brown, pink band on belly. 80-300+ m, rarely 40 m. Below: *Parastichopus tremulus*, 20-2000 m, Norway to Portugal and Canaries. To 50 cm.

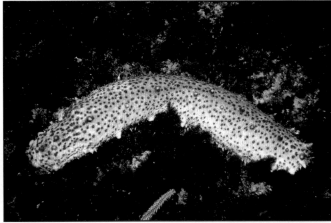

Eostichopus regalis   **Faial Island, Azores**

Tentacle Sea Cucumber
CUCUMARIIDAE

S: 50 cm. D: Norway to Portugal. G: spp of the order Dendrochirotida typically have bushy tentacles, spread to filter-feed for plankton. Body hidden in rock crevices. 5-200 m. Locally common. Below (Portugal): filter feeding feet of *Pawsonia saxicola*, locally common in NE-Atlantic; also in W-Med.

Cucumaria frondosa   **Norway**

Drummond's S. Cucumber

S: up to 25 cm. D: Arctic to Great Britain. G: characterized by the presence of 20 filter-feeding arms in two rings: the ten inner arms being smaller than the ten outer ones. Arms pink to deep red. Body usually hidden in the substrate. From shallow water down to about 1000 m. Below: the same species from eastern Scotland.

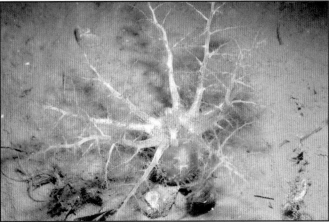

Thyonidium drummondi   **Norway**

Polar Sea Cucumber

Size: up to 20 cm. Distribution: a circumpolar species. In the eastern Atlantic as far south as Great Britain. General: this species has only 10 filter feeding arms, which are all the same length. The colour of *Psolus phantapus* can vary from bright red to red-speckled, to golden-brown to brown. Young animals live as epifauna (sitting on the substrate) but older ones are always buried in the substrate with only the tentacle crown sticking out of the bottom. The species can be encountered in 1 m depth but is more common from 20 m down to about 400 m.

<u>Below</u>: *Aslia lefevri,* Scotland (photo) to Canary Islands, Mediterranean Sea, from shallow water down to c. 25 m.

Psolus phantapus   **Lysefjord, Norway**

East Atlantic Worm Sea Cucumber   SYNAPTIDAE

S: 30-100 cm. D: Canaries, Cape Verdes, São Tomé. W-Atl. G: hidden during the day, emerges to feed at night. Oral tentacles perform alternating, grasping touching movements on the substrate (<u>left</u>), pick up organic particles, molluscs to put them into mouth. Body of all synaptids sticky. Soft body toxic to many fishes. <u>Immediately below</u> (Azores): *Leptosynapta inhaerens,* c. 2 cm, Norway-Equator, Mediterr.

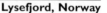

Euapta lappa   **São Tomé**

Mediterranean Feather Star ANTEDONIDAE (this page) S: 15 cm. D: Mediterr. G: feather stars filter plankton with 10 feathery arms, are thus often encountered at exposed sites, facing into current. Cling to substrate with finger-like cirri (size, number specific). This sp has 20-23 cirri. Colour very variable. <u>Small photos:</u> Atlantic Feather Star *A. bifida,* Shetlands to Can.; W-Med. Usually has 12-16 cirri. Eggs brooded on arms of female.

Antedon mediterranea   **Crete Island, Greece**

North Atlantic Feather Star S: 15 cm. D: NE-Atl. south to Irish Sea. G: replaces *A. bifida* in the north and in deeper water. 50-100 cirri. <u>Lower small photo:</u> another individual shows the great colour variation of this species. *Leptometra celtica* (<u>upper small</u>), NE-Atl., Med., grows to 25 cm, can be recognized by its very long cirri (compare <u>large photo</u>). Only rarely encountered shallower than 60 m depth.

Antedon petasus   **Western Scotland**

SEALOCHS

The west coast of Scotland has an extraordinary coastline, dissected by more than 80 long, narrow arms of the sea, called sealochs.

The UW-photographer and biologist Sue Scott discloses why they are very special places.

Loch Carron, a fjordic sealoch, showing currents in the narrows. There is a distinct line or 'front' between brackish surface 'sealoch' water (bottom and bottom right) and more saline and mixed open coast water (left).

The sealochs are glacial features, formed by the flooding of ice-cut basins after the last ice ages. Fjordic sealochs have basins up to 200 m deep, scoured out by large glaciers moving down from high mountains, while fjardic sealochs have much shallower basins, formed by ice sheets moving horizontally across the land. Now the sealochs are home to a very varied assemblage of marine creatures. Many of these are special to sealochs,

This seabed is covered with a rich assortment of animals and plants only because hundreds of Flame Shells *Limaria hians* stabilise the seabed beneath. They live completely hidden in felt-lined nests.

and can be seen by divers nowhere else. Sealochs are great places to dive when it's too rough on the open coast!

Most sealochs are connected to the open coast by a narrow and shallow channel or 'sill', a partial barrier which makes sealochs quite different in structure to non-glaciated inlets further south (which are drowned valleys, with depths gradually decreasing inside). This profoundly affects water movement and quality inside the lochs, which in turn determines the marine creatures inhabiting them.

Strong tidal currents pour through the narrows as the

Living Flame or File Shell *Limaria hians*.

tide rises and falls, bringing 'fast food' for filter-feeding animals. Dense beds of Horse Mussels *Modiolus modiolus* and Flame Shells *Limaria hians* stabilise loose seabeds by binding together shells and stones with tough byssus threads, forming 'biogenic' reefs. Sea firs (Hydrozoa), soft corals

Bed of maerl or calcified seaweed, *Phymatolithon calcareum,* with sunstars, soft coral and brittle stars.

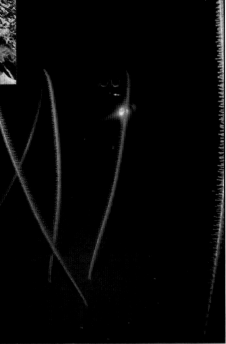

(Alcyonaria) and many other animals live on and in these highly complex and diverse reefs, which are important nursery and feeding grounds for commercial fish and shellfish. Sadly, many areas of biogenic reef have been destroyed by mobile fishing gear, especially heavy scallop dredgers.

Pink beds of maerl (calcified seaweed) also thrive in fast currents, its hard branched nodules protecting tiny urchins, worms, crabs and many other small creatures. Beneath the thin layer of live maerl, in the gravel made from dead maerl fragments accumulated over thousands of years, are many bivalves, sea cucumbers and the big burrowing purple urchin *Spatangus purpureus*.

Inside the deep, sheltered basins, conditions are quite different. Here the strong currents dissipate rapidly, leaving still water where even

Forest of Giant Seapens *Funiculina quadrangularis*.

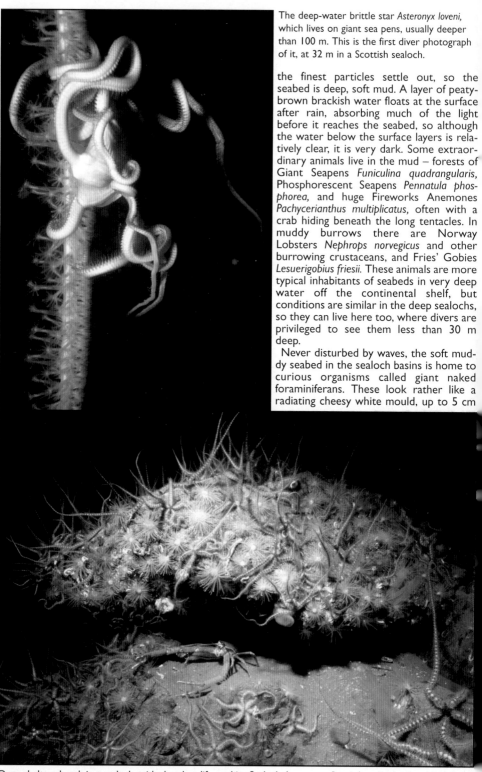

The deep-water brittle star *Asteronyx loveni*, which lives on giant sea pens, usually deeper than 100 m. This is the first diver photograph of it, at 32 m in a Scottish sealoch.

the finest particles settle out, so the seabed is deep, soft mud. A layer of peaty-brown brackish water floats at the surface after rain, absorbing much of the light before it reaches the seabed, so although the water below the surface layers is relatively clear, it is very dark. Some extraordinary animals live in the mud – forests of Giant Seapens *Funiculina quadrangularis*, Phosphorescent Seapens *Pennatula phosphorea,* and huge Fireworks Anemones *Pachycerianthus multiplicatus*, often with a crab hiding beneath the long tentacles. In muddy burrows there are Norway Lobsters *Nephrops norvegicus* and other burrowing crustaceans, and Fries' Gobies *Lesuerigobius friesii.* These animals are more typical inhabitants of seabeds in very deep water off the continental shelf, but conditions are similar in the deep sealochs, so they can live here too, where divers are privileged to see them less than 30 m deep.

Never disturbed by waves, the soft muddy seabed in the sealoch basins is home to curious organisms called giant naked foraminiferans. These look rather like a radiating cheesy white mould, up to 5 cm

Deep sheltered rock in a sealoch, with abundant life – white Sealoch Anemones *Protanthea simplex*, brachiopods (small brown 'limpets' in foreground), brittle stars *Ophiothrix fragilis*, and Long-clawed Squat Lobster *Munida rugosa*.

Norway Lobster
Nephrops norvegicus
beside its mud burrow.

across and partly cov-
ered by an organised
network of sand
grains.

Deep rock in the
very sheltered sealoch
basins also has special
communities of ani-
mals. Typically, the
ghostly white Sealoch
Anemone *Protanthea
simplex* is most
conspicuous, often
together with big
bunches of the
Peacock Fan Worm
Sabella pavonina, and
solitary sea squirts
Ciona intestinalis and *Ascidia mentula.* Also abundant,
but very inconspicuous and often hidden under a

Sealoch Anemones *Protanthea
simplex* and the blue sponge
Hymedesmia paupertas.

layer of silt, are little shells
only a centimetre across that
look like small limpets, but
are actually a different class
of shelled animals called
brachiopods (*Neocrania ano-
mala*). You may also be lucky
enough to see small patches
of a brilliant blue sponge
called *Hymedesmia paupertas*
by scientists.

Where rock walls are sheltered from waves, but sub-
ject to gentle tidal currents,
dense sea squirts *Ciona
intestinalis* are often accompanied by featherstars *Antedon bifida* and *A. petasus,* with
occasional crabs and big
Dahlia Anemones nestling
amongst them. The bright
red cushion star *Porania
pulvillus* can often be found
feeding on sea squirts.

Rock wall covered with ascidians *Ciona intestinalis,* feather stars *Antedon bifida,*
and the occasional crab nestling amongst them.

Common Brittle Star
OPHIOTRICIDAE

S: 15 cm. D: Med.; N-Norway &
Iceland to South Africa. G: very
common, typical are numerous
thin spines on body and arms.
The long thin arms break apart
easily. Colour very variable, see
preceding page and below. The
planktonic larvae like to settle
on the surface of sponges.

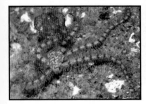

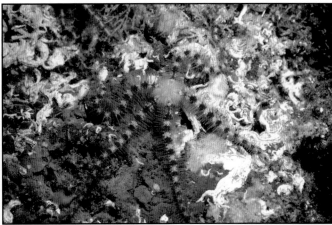

Ophiothrix fragilis   **Faial Island, Azores**

Black Brittle Star
OPHIOCOMIDAE

S: 15, max 25 cm. D: Med.; Norway to W-Africa. G: central disc
relatively large (compare to *O.
fragilis!*), arms decrease markedly
in diameter along their length.
Hides below stones, in crevices,
often hundreds of individuals sit
close together waiting for night-
fall. When disturbed by light,
they quickly try to flee to dark
places. While brittle stars do not
have eyes, they have light-sensitive patches of cells all over the
disk (see "Invertebrate Vision").
Found on rocky bottoms down
to about 400 m. Feeds on a
great variety of organic material:
detritus, algae, and small animals.

Ophiocomina nigra   **Madeira**

S: 15, max 20 cm. D: Mediterranean Sea. G: usually buried in
sandy or muddy bottoms. Holds
2 or 3 arms out of the bottom
to capture food (any small
organic item). Locally common.
From about 3 m downwards.
Below: one of the many colour
patterns of *Ophioderma longicauda:* here disk and arms are differently coloured. See also the
first section on the next page.

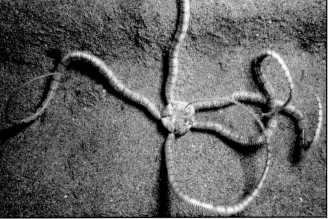

Ophiopsila aranea   **Costa del Sol, Spain**

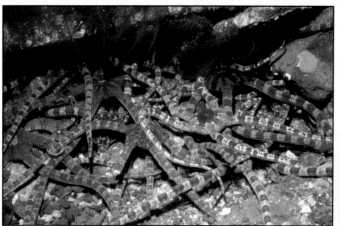

Annulated Brittle Star
OPHIOCOMIDAE
S: 22 cm. D: Med. G: one of the most common brittle star spp in Med. and temp. E-Atl. 3-80+ m. On rocky and on sandy bottoms rich in organic material; seagrass meadows. Most common colour brown-green (large photo), also brown, red. See also small photo on bottom of preceding page.

Ophioderma longicauda   Cyprus

Crevice Brittle Star
OPHIACTIDAE
S: 20 cm. D: circumpolar, S-limit in E-Atl.: English Channel. G: 10-1800 m, feeds on detritus. Often buried in gravel or in crevices, with only arm tips visible. Small photo (Norway): Light Brittle Star, *Ophiura albida*. Distinct, light double lines at base of each arm. Norway to Med., 10-200 m.

Ophiopholis aculeata   North Sea

Gorgon's Head
GORGONOCEPHALIDAE
S: disc 9 cm; arms 50+ cm. D: Norway to Ireland. G: *Astrospartus mediterraneus* is similar, Med. Both have frequently branched arms. *G. c.* can have 5000+ arm tips! 25-1200 m. Arms either folded against body (below) or spread out for feeding. Likes to sit in areas with a slight current.

Gorgonocephalus caputmedusae   Norway

APPETISING

If you are a vegetarian turn the page now! But if you like all the various kinds of delicious seafood as much as Peter Wirtz does, why not try a few unusual but easy recipes?

Usable sea anemones are, for instance, the Snakelocks Anemone *Anemonia viridis*, which can grow in fields of many thousands of individuals, or the Beadlet Anemone *Actinia equina*. Wash them in running water to remove all grit. Then they may simply be incorporated in a bouillabaisse. Or use them in an omelette. Or how about "sea anemone fritters"? Just prepare batter in the usual way, dip the sea anemones in it, put them in the pan and fry for 10 minutes. A word of warning when handling sea anemones: make sure you do not touch your eyes or lips before you have washed your hands thoroughly. While the cnidocells cannot penetrate the thick skin of your hands, they can cause considerable damage in other areas. Cooking the anemones does, of course, destroy the stinging action of the cnidocells so that the dish will not be very "hot" unless you have put a lot of pepper into it.

Giant barnacles *(Megabalanus azoricus)* are served in many restaurants of the Azores. Like lobster, they are simply boiled in salt water. The taste is quite similar, just a bit saltier perhaps. To extract them from their shells, you will be provided with a special hook, which is usually made from a simple nail.

The inhabitants of the Macaronesian Islands also share the habit of being very fond of limpets. Quickly heated in special little frying pans and sprinkled with lemon juice, limpets are a true delicacy. The photo left shows Prof. Steven Hawkins, one of the

Above: highly scientific research on limpets.
Below right: Peter Wirtz enjoying giant barnacles.

world experts on limpet biology. Prehistoric rubbish dumps on the coast of England, for instance, show that our ancestors also ate limpets. However, if you should try to cook northern species of limpets in Macaronesian style you would experience a – literally – bitter disappointment: they taste terribly. Northern limpets eat brown algae that contain bitter substances called tannines and they taste accordingly.

Dried sea cucumber (trepang, bêche-de-mer) is considered a delicacy in the Far East. One of the many species used is the Mediterranean and eastern Atlantic *Holothuria tubulosa*. Croatia exported more than 15.000 kg (i.e. more than 120.000 animals!) from the Split area in the Adriatic Sea in 1998. Here is how to prepare them: the dried sea cucumber is washed, soaked for several hours, boiled for about an hour, salted and spiced or cut into noodles and stewed for some time. Another word of warning, however: trepang is supposed to have aphrodisiac qualities, so be careful whom you invite for a meal!

BEATE MÜLLER

Red Comb-star
ASTROPECTINIDAE
S: 55 cm. D: Spain to Angola; Med. G: on sand, 5-180 m. By day hidden in sand, to emerge at night. Unlike most sea stars, the tube feet of this species do not end in little suckers but have pointed tips. Large photo: the spawning position of this (and many other) sea star species.

Astropecten aranciacus   Madeira

ASTROPECTINIDAE
S: up to 18 cm. D: Med. G: like all members of this genus, this is a rather stiff-armed species. It is locally common and lives down to a depth of c. 50 m. Below: Sand Star *A. irregularis*, 18 cm, Norway to Morocco, Cape Verdes to South Africa, 5-1000 m. *Acholoe squamosa (A. astericola* is similar, p. 102) can be found in its arm grooves.

Astropecten bispinosus   Crete Island, Greece

Long-armed Sea Star
CHAETASTERIDAE
S: 20 cm. D: Med.; Bay of Biscay to Ascension. G: on rocks, 40-1100 m. Recognized by yellow colour, body is so small that the animal appears to consist of long arms only. Small photo: *Astropecten africanus* (Astropectinidae). 13 cm, Cape Verdes (photo) to Angola, down to 100 m depth.

Chaetaster longipes   Faial Island, Azores

North Atlantic Cushion Sea Star

GONIASTERIDAE (this page)
S: 8 cm Ø. D: E-Atl.: Greenland and Faroe Islands to the Skagerrak; In the western Atlantic from Newfoundland to Long Island. G: this beautiful orange sea star can be found on a wide range of bottoms, from 30-1300 m depth. The upper surface of the Rigid cushion star *Hippasteria phrygiana* (small photo) is covered with rounded knob-like spines. It grows to 30 cm in diameter and lives from the Arctic to north Ireland (E-Atlantic) and to Cape Cod (W-Atlantic), in 20-850 m depth. The species can have green spots which are due to the presence of symbiotic unicellular algae.

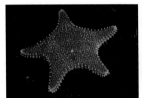

Ceramaster granularis   **Norway**

Placenta Cushion Sea Star

Size: up to 15 cm in diameter but usually less than 10 cm. Distribution: Mediterranean Sea; from Iceland and Norway to the Equator and in the western Atlantic from Cape Cod to the Caribbean. General: this species is frequently called *Sphaerodiscus placenta*. It can be found from 10-1000 m depth.

The small photo below shows *Goniaster tesselatus*. The photo is from São Tomé Island, and the first record of the species from there. It lives on soft bottoms, from 2-90 m depth, from Morocco to São Tomé including the Cape Verde Islands. It reaches 15 cm in diameter.

Peltaster placenta   **Eolian archipelago, Italy**

Seven-armed Sea Star
LUIDIIDAE
S: 60 cm. D: Med.; S-Norway to
Madeira. G: 7 arms, rarely 6 or 8.
Active at night. Soft bottoms, 5-
400 m. Yellow to light orange in
N, vivid orange in Portugal, red-
brown at Mad. Preys on bivalves,
snails, echinoderms. Below: *L.
sarsi*, to 40 cm, 5 arms, on mud
in 20+ m, Norway to SA; Med.

Luidia ciliaris   **Madeira**

Purple Sea Star
OPHIDIASTERIDAE
S: 40 cm. D: Azores to St. Helena, incl. island groups; W-Med.
G: locally common, on rocky
substrates, 3-100 m (rare below
20 m). Usually has 5 arms, also
6. Colour varies from bright
orange to dark purple; may also
be spotted. In contrast to most
sea star spp, it is not a predator
but grazes the organic layer on
the bottom. It is therefore comparatively easy to keep in an
aquarium. At the Azores,
author PW has detected a
caprellid living on this sea star
(now described as *Caprella stella*,
p. 113). Such associations could
also exist in other places.

Ophidiaster ophidianus   **Faial Island, Azores**

Bouvier's Sea Star
OPHIDIASTERIDAE
S: 12 cm. D: Cape Verdes (common, up to 18/100 m²), Gulf of
Guinea. G: from tide pools to
20 m, on rock, rocky sand. Below:
L. guildingi, trop. Atl., 3-300 m. 4-7
arms, 30 cm. Often reproduces
asexually by voluntarily detaching
one arm that then grows a new
set of arms. Thus comet-shaped
individuals can be common.

Linckia bouvieri   **Cape Verde Islands**

Smooth Sea Star
OPHIDIASTERIDAE

S: up to 20 cm in diameter.
D: Med.; E-Atl.: Azores to the
Gulf of Guinea. G: usually lives
on rocky bottoms below 20 m
depth, down to about 150 m.
The spotted appearance of the
body surface is typical of the
species. The small photo is
from the Azores.

Hacelia attenuata   Crete Island, Greece

Canary Sea Star
OPHIDIASTERIDAE

S: 20 cm. D: Canaries to the
Equator. G: brightly red, easy to
recognize because of the typical
triangular shape of the arms. 15-
150 m, on soft bottoms. Below:
Copidaster lymani, span to 30 cm,
is known from Guinea, the Cape
Verde Islands (photo), Annobon
Island, and the tropical W-Atl.

Narcissia canariensis   Lanzarote, Canary Islands

Red Cushion Star
PORANIIDAE

Size: up to 12 cm across.
Distribution: from Norway to
the Atlantic coast of Spain.
General: this species is often
found on moderately exposed
rocks, sometimes apparently
eating *Alcyonium digitatum* (p.
35) but it also lives in more
sheltered places, from 5-500 m
depth. The many white or
transparent "papulae" projecting from the red or orange
dorsal side are withdrawn
when touched. They can also
be greenish in colour and then
probably contain symbiotic
unicellular algae.

Porania pulvillus   Isle of Man

Variable Cushion Star
ASTERINIDAE
S: 6 cm. D: Med.; from English Channel south. G: flat, 5 short arms. Colour variable. Male first, changes sex after 4 years. Eggs glued to rock, tiny yellow sea stars hatch from them directly, no larval phase. <u>Below</u>: Goose Foot Sea Star *Anseropoda placenta*, Faroe Is. to Sierra Leone, 22 cm, 10-500 m.

Asterina gibbosa   **Tenerife, Canary Islands**

Pimple Sea Star
OREASTERIDAE
S: 22 cm. D: Cape Verdes, Senegal to Gulf of Guinea. G: on rocky bottoms, 2-20 m. Red to brown. *O. reticulatus* (W-Atl.) also at CV; recognized by a reticulate pattern of the plates forming its dorsal surface. Whereas the <u>large photo</u> shows an individual of about 5 cm in diameter, the <u>small photo</u> (CV) shows one of about 15 cm.

Oreaster clavatus   **Cape Verde Islands**

Ice Sea Star
PTERASTERIDAE
S: span up to 15 cm. D: circum-polar all around the Arctic, E-Atl.: as far south as Skagerrak. G: this sturdy species lives on hard bottoms, from 10-1100 m. It is yellow to yellow-red in colour. The small photo (São Tomé) probably also shows *Oreaster clavatus* (see text of the section above). The animal had a diameter of about 5 cm.

Pteraster militaris   **Norway**

Common Sunstar
SOLASTERIDAE

S: 35 cm. D: Norway to N-Brittany; NW-Atl. G: 8-14 arms, usually 11-13. Its colour is quite variable, from dark red through dirty purple to brown, with or without concentric rings of white. Its surface is rather spiny. It lives on hard bottoms from about 10 m down to 900 m. The main prey of this sp are other sea stars, incl. smaller individuals of the same sp but especially *Asterias rubens,* and holothurians and mussels. <u>Below</u>: Purple Sunstar *Solaster endeca,* 40 cm, 7-13 arms (usually 9-10). Arms much thicker than in Common sunstar. Lives around the world in subarctic waters, E-Atl.: S to Kattegat. Arm tips frequently curled upwards. On a wide range of bottoms, from about 30-450 m.

Crossaster papposus   North Sea

Red Sea Star
ECHINASTERIDAE

S: 32 cm. D: Roscoff (France) to Ghana, incl. island groups except Azores; Med. G: common, can be confused with the common red *Ophidiaster ophidianus.* However, *O. ophidianus* has much rounder arms, is much harder. *E. sepositus* has a softer, crinkled surface. 2-250 m, on hard and soft bottoms, including seagrass meadows. It is not a predator but grazes the organic layer on the bottom. No planktonic larval stage: small sea stars hatch from the eggs, the sp can therefore be reproduced in the aquarium. <u>Below</u> (Ireland): Bloody Henry *Henricia oculata,* very common in NE-Atl., colour variable, sometimes impossible to distinguish from *H. sanguinolenta* without close examination. Up to 17 cm.

Echinaster sepositus   Malta

Asterias rubens   Norway

Asterias rubens   Isle of Man

Common Sea Star
ASTERIIDAE (both pages)

S: up to 32 cm in diameter.
D: E-Atl.: Arctic to S-Portugal;
W-Atl.: Labrador to Florida.
G: this is the commonest sea
star in a large part of the NE-
Atlantic. It has five (very rarely
4-8) blunt-tipped arms and is
covered with small, scattered
white spines, which form a line
along the top of the arms.
Small animals are quite stiff but
larger ones are rather soft and
flaccid. Body colour is a pale
orange to brown, sometimes
blue or purple.

The Common sea star lives
from shallow water (tide
pools) down to about 900 m
depth on a great variety of
bottoms, especially in mussel
beds *(Mytilus edulis)*. Mussels
react to the smell of this sea
star species by reducing their
growth rate and instead forming stronger adductor muscles
which keep the shells closed
against the pull of a sea star
attempting to open the mussel
and to insert its evertible
stomach into the bivalve shell.
Asterias rubens is one of the
few sea star species which can
tolerate brackish conditions. It
produces planktonic larvae in
summer and these can be so
plentiful that they dominate
any plankton sample. A caprellid amphipod (see page 113),
Pariambus typicus, is often
attached to the spines of this
sea star species.

Blue Sea Star
S: 27 cm. D: Med.; Bay of Biscay to Gulf of Guinea, incl. I.
groups; St. Helena; W-Atl. G:
often reproduces by dividing
into two parts, each half
regenerating new arms, hence
often with short & long arms.
7, also 4, 6, 8, 9 arms. Arms
with 5 spine rows. Brown to
greenish, also blue (below).

Coscinasterias tenuispina   Madeira

Spiny Sea Star

Size: up to 80 cm in diameter.
Distribution: Mediterranean
Sea; in the eastern Atlantic
from Iceland and Norway to
South Africa.
General: this is the largest sea
star of E-Atl. and the Med. It
usually has five arms, rarely
eight. It is quite variable in
colour, from almost pure white
to green and brown, but easy
to recognize by its strong
spines forming three longitudinal lines along the arms. It can
be found in a wide range of
habitats and preys on bivalves,
snails, sea urchins (the small
photo shows an individual
attempting to eat a large
Sphaerechinus granularis) and
even other sea stars species. It
lives from shallow water down
to about 180 m depth.

Marthasterias glacialis   Faial Island, Azores

Marthasterias glacialis   Cape Verde Islands

Linear Sea Star

Size: up to 30 cm in diameter.
Distribution: in the eastern
Atlantic from the Lofoten
islands to the Bay of Biscay
(but rare south of Ireland)
General: this yellow to orange
sea star has 5 long, stiff, slender, tapering arms with a regu-
lar linear pattern of rounded
plates on the dorsal surface. It
lives from 5 to about 370 m
depth, on hard and soft bottoms and can be locally quite
common. In Norway, it produces planktonic larvae in the
months of August and September.

Stichastrella rosea   Norway

GIANT SINGLE CELLS

The animal and plant species that consist of a single cell usually are not visible to the naked eye. However, there are exceptions. Peter Wirtz portraits some of them.

The foraminiferan *Miniacina miniacea* is common on the lower side of stones and on the walls of caves.

Some single-celled species are indeed large enough to be seen and others occur in such quantities that they cannot be overlooked. Most foraminiferans build a shell from organic material or calcite. Some species are sessile, others free-living. Both forms can reach surprising dimensions. One of the largest and most common species in the Mediterranean Sea and in the eastern Atlantic is *Miniacina miniacea*. Because of its size, it was first thought to be a hydrocoral (like *Millepora*) or a bryozoan. The conspicuous red shell grows to almost a centimetre in size. Minute, transparent protoplasm arms reach out from tiny holes in the calcareous shell. *Miniacina miniacea* is common on the lower side of stones and on the walls of caves, and has been found down to 1000 m depth.

This photo of *Zoothamnium niveum* was taken at Lanzarote, Canary Islands. It is the first record of the species from the Eastern Atlantic.

The soft muddy seabed of sheltered sealoch basins on the western coasts of Scotland is home to giant naked foraminiferans, recently named *Toxosarcon alba*. These look rather like a radiating cheesy white mould, up to 5 cm across. In the laboratory this species has been seen to change into a blob and crawl up out of the sediment!

The ciliate *Zoothamnium niveum* is up to 1.5 cm long. The large size is possible because this is actually more than one cell: it is a colony of cells on a stalk. The whole

The giant naked foraminiferan *Toxosarcon alba,* also a single-celled organism, reaches 5 cm in diameter!

Red tide at the coast of western Scotland. Millions of single-celled organisms (the dinoflagellate *Noctiluca scintil-lans*) cause the red colour of the water, as well as spectacular phosphorescence at night.

feather-like structure contracts every 5 to 30 seconds with a rather "nervous looking" twitching movement. The white colour of the species, indicated in the name *"niveum"* (i.e. "snowy"), is due to a coat of bacteria all over the surface of the ciliate. *Zoothamnium niveum* lives only in places where sulfidic water seeps from mangrove peat or from cracks in the rock. The bacteria metabolise the sulphide and the ciliate feeds on the bacteria! The species has so far been recorded from the Caribbean and from the Red Sea. In May 2001, Peter Wirtz also found it in a cave on the coast of Cyprus. There it might be another newcomer from the Red Sea or – much more likely – the species is common in many places around the world but has been overlooked in the past. Look for it: it is likely to occur in other areas.

Some dinoflagellates, especially the genera *Gymnodinium* and *Gonyaulax,* can multiply explosively and reach densities of 6 million cells per litre. At high densities of these single-celled organisms, the water is coloured red, which has given the name "red tides" to such spectacular plankton blooms. These dinoflagellates produce a toxin called "Saxitoxin". Whilst many red tides appear to cause little negative influence, others result in catastrophic mortalities of coastal organisms including fish. Accumulated by mussels and scallops, the toxin can cause paralytic shell-fish poisoning in man.

Despite its size (stalk 3 cm high and umbrella 1 cm wide), the plant *Acetabularia acetabulum* also consist of only a single cell!

Rectangular Ascidian
ASCIDIIDAE (this page)
S: 9 cm. D: Norway to Med. G: ascidians are like a sack with two openings: an inhalant on top and an exhalant on the side. Inside the body, a net filters plankton out of the water current. *A. virginea* is rectangular, usually red-spotted, also dark red, light pink. On hard bottoms, 10-3000 m.

Ascidia virginea   **Jœsenfjord, Norway**

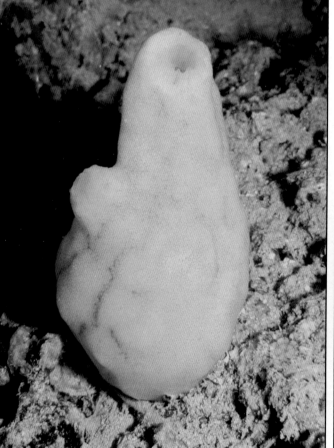

White Sea-squirt

S: up to 15 (rarely 20) cm high. D: SW-Britain and Ireland to Madeira; Med. G: unmistakable. The thick, milky-white body wall is covered in large, rounded bumps. It can be found from shallow water down to 180 m. It grows on rock or stones, in sheltered places, often close to clay or muddy bottoms. A small golden-spotted shrimp, *Pontonia flavomaculata*, sometimes lives in it (p. 130); it is closely related to those living in bivalves (see the story "My Shell Is My Castle"). The small photo (Adriatic Sea) shows the closely related *P. fumigata*, unmistakable because of its form and colour. Its surface is much smoother than that of *P. mammilata*. Up to 15 cm high.

Phallusia mammillata   **Madeira**

Tube Sea-squirt CIONIDAE

S: 12 cm. D: in all oceans; Med.
G: one of the most common
tunicate species in North Sea
and Baltic Sea. Colour variable,
but can always be recognized
by the small, brilliantly yellow
or red spots on the rim of the
inhalant and exhalant opening.
5-500 m. Common on harbour
walls, piers, where it can reach
densities of 2000/m^2.

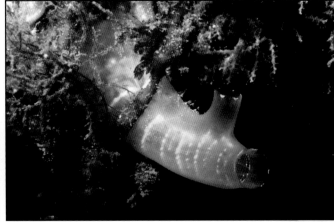

Ciona intestinalis   **Norway**

Football Sea-squirt
CIONIDAE

S: individual 5 cm; colony 40 cm.
D: W-Scotland to Med. G: forms
gelatinous colonies, young ones
ball-shaped, older ones flattened.
Individuals are separate distally
but embedded in a common
basal mass. On rocks, 20-200 m,
in strong currents. Forms a hard
globular resting stage in winter.

Diazona violacea   **North Sea**

Parallel Sea-squirt
CORELLIDAE

S: up to 5 cm high. D: from N-
Norway into Med. G: a solitary
ascidian with an oval or squarish
body, laterally compressed.
There are many different colour
forms of this species, from white
to yellow to bright crimson.
Often a series of parallel lines
can be seen on the body, which
explains the name *"parallelogramma"*. The species lives from shallow water down to about
200 m. It is usually attached to
stones, or shells, sometimes on
large kelp. It appears to prefer
more offshore, clearer waters.
The branchial basket and the gut
are often visible through the
transparent body.

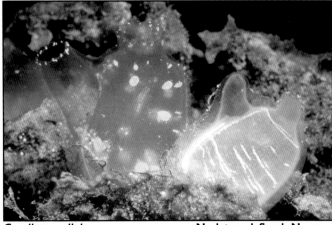

Corella parallelogramma   **Nedstrandsfjord, Norway**

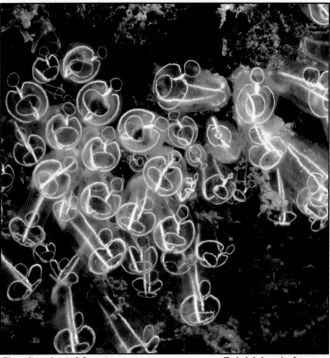

Light-bulb Ascidian
CLAVELINIDAE (this page)
S: 3 cm. D: Norway to Canaries;
W-Med. G: a colonial species
that on first glance resembles
Diazona violacea but individuals
are more transparent, much
softer, and not embedded basally
in common mass. A yellow-
white rim around the openings
distinguishes this sp from several
similar ones. Animals may be
transparent-white or yellowish.
Yellow forms appear to be more
common in the N-part of the
distribution. Probably transported to Azores by boats. See
"Long Distance". The yellow
Clavelina from Madeira (below)
may be a different sp. It differs in
habitat preference from white
form (also present at Madeira): it
appears to be restricted to dark
places such as caves, overhangs.

Clavelina lepadiformis   **Faial Island, Azores**

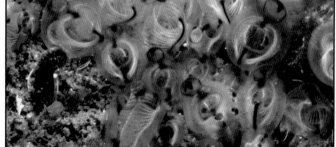

Blue Ascidian
S: up to 6 cm. D: Med.; Strait of
Gibraltar; Madeira. G: its blue
colour is distinctive. At Madeira,
it is locally common from low
water spring tide level down to
at least 6 m depth. Below: *C.
oblonga,* very common on Faial
Island, Azores, where it can
cover large areas. It is, however,
a species from the W-Atl. (Ber-
mudas-Brazil) apparently transported to the Azores by yachts.
See the story "Long Distance".

Clavelina dellavallei   **Madeira**

White Ascidian
CLAVELINIDAE

S: individuals up to 5 mm high, colonies to 10 cm in diameter. D: W-Mediterranean; Madeira. G: this species was considered a Mediterranean endemic (i.e. only occurring in the Mediterranean Sea) until author PW found it at Madeira. There it is common from shallow water down to at least 45 m depth.

Pycnoclavella taureanensis   Madeira

Small Neon Sea-squirt
CLAVELINIDAE

S: up to 6 mm high. D: from Great Britain into the Med.? G: this brightly yellow ascidian forms colonies. The genus *Pycnoclavella* needs revision. The yellow forms from Britain, the Med., or the Canary Islands (<u>below</u>: Lanzarote) probably belong to different species.

Pycnoclavella aurilucens   Crete Island, Greece

DIDEMNIDAE look like sponges, cannot be identified from photos.

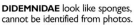

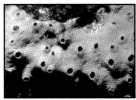

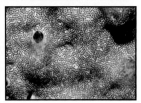

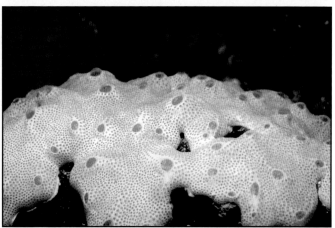

Didemnum species   Crete Island, Greece

Orange Ascidian
POLYCITORIDAE

S: rosette 1.5 cm, cluster 40 cm. D: Faial, Azores; W-Atl. G: very common at Faial where it covers vertical walls in shallow water. Described from Azores, only later found to be a W-Atl. sp (see "Long ...")! 8-20 individuals each have their own mouth but share a common central exhalent opening. Upper small ph.: resting stage, no openings. Lower: Cystodytes delle-chiajei, all seas, looks like sponge.

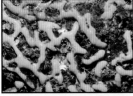

Distaplia corolla   **Faial Island, Azores**

Blotched Ball Synascidian
POLYCLINIDAE

S: 20 cm. D: Adriatic, W-Med.; temp. E-Atl. G: colony cone/cush-ion-shaped, orange to white, firm, fleshy in texture. Tiny, dark inhal-ant openings of individuals group-ed around a larger, common exha-lant one. 5-50 m, on rock. Below (Portugal): Pillow Synascidian *Aplidium proliferum*, gelatinous thick sheets to 20 cm long, SW-England to Med. Round openings with ten-dency to form sinuous lines.

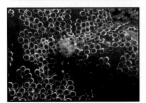

Aplidium conicum   **Croatia, Adriatic Sea**

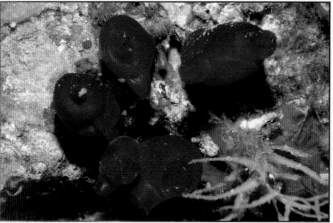

Blood-red Ascidian
PYURIDAE

S: 10 cm. D: Med.; temp. E-Atl. (not Az.; Mad.). G: openings surrounded by fine bristles that seem to have a sensory function. When touched, opening closes. Avoids bright places, 2-100 m. Simultan. hermaphrodite. <u>Below</u> (Barents S.): *H. pyriformis,* closely related, Arctic-Norway (where *H. papillosa* does not exist), to 10 cm high.

Halocynthia papillosa   **Crete Island, Greece**

Rock Violet   PYURIDAE

S: 8 cm. D: Med.; Portug. Atl. G: *Microcosmus* (Greek: small world) spp are frequently overgrown by a large number of many different animal species. *M. polymorphus* has somewhat "quadrangular" siphonal openings. Hard bottoms down to about 50 m. <u>Below</u>: Sea Fig *M. sabatieri,* easily recognized by the 8 stripes in the openings. 25 cm, 5-200 m, only in Med.

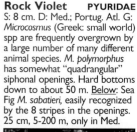

Microcosmus polymorphus   **Crete Island, Greece**

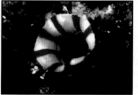

Star Squirt   STYELIDAE

S: colony 2-4 cm. D: Med.; Spitsbergen to Canaries. G: 4-16 individuals in star-shaped pattern, share a common exhalant opening (but each with small inhalant one). Grow to build flat colony, which encrusts stones or algae. Colour variable. <u>Below</u>: *Stolonica socialis,* in clusters of individuals connected by basal tubes (usually sand-coated). 2 cm, 5-35 m.

Botryllus schlosseri   **Norway**

LONG DISTANCE

Some marine animals and plants show very curious areas of distribution. Transport by humans appears to be the only explanation. The transfer and dispersal of marine species, usually in the ballast tanks of bulk cargo vessels, can have unforeseen consequences.

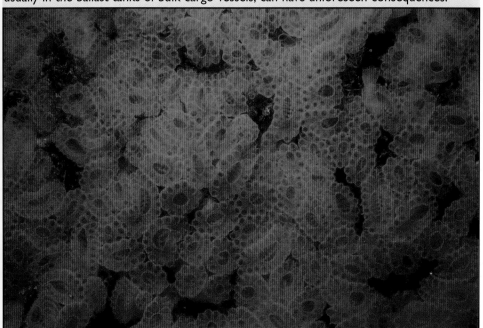

The colonial ascidian *Distaplia corolla,* originally described from the Azores, is actually a Caribbean species that has travelled a long distance (Faial, Azores).

Divers at the island of Faial in the Azores are surprised by the colourful splendour of the rock faces. Bright orange, dark lilac and brilliantly white carpets cover the rock. The orange and lilac areas are two different colour morphs of the colonial ascidian *Distaplia corolla.* This species was recorded off the island of Faial by the French tunicate experts Francoise and Claude Monniot. Imagine their surprise when, several years later, they found that the species is quite common in the Caribbean. The white species also is an "American". It is the tunicate *Clavelina oblonga,* which lives along the western Atlantic coasts from Brazil to Bermuda.

Because the two American tunicates are found only at Faial and not at the other Azorean islands, human transport is the most likely explanation for their occurrence there. The harbour of Horta, the capital of Faial, is a famous stopover place for yachts crossing the Atlantic. *Distaplia corolla* and *Clavelina oblonga* have come to the Azores as stowaways on one of them.

The Spiral Fan Worm *Sabella spallanzanii* is a common Mediterranean species. However, one can also see it at the following places: the Azores, the Canary Islands, Brazil, Java and Australia. This more than strange area of distribution apparently follows the routes to South America and Asia taken by the old commercial sailing ships.

Nowadays the European Shore Crab *Carcinus maenas* can be found along the coasts of eastern and western North America, South Africa, and Australia. At California, they are responsible for dramatic declines in the abundance of native clams in mudflat habitats; these declines may well translate into declines among wintering populations of migratory shore birds that depend on these clams for food.

The appearance and mass development of the western (!) Atlantic comb jelly *Mnemiopsis leidyi* in the Black Sea at the end of the 1980s caused a collapse in commercial fishery catches because this species feeds on eggs and larvae of fish.

The Eurasian Zebra Mussel *Dreissena polymorpha* appeared in the Great Lakes of North America in 1988. There it is now causing large economic damage by clogging pipes. A recent genetic study, comparing populations from many different areas, has shown that the Zebra Mussel must have invaded the Great Lakes repeatedly. Those in Lake Superior apparently come from the Rhine River, while those in Lake Ontario are more closely related to Zebra Mussels from Poland.

The common north European moss animal *Membranipora membranacea* is now covering kelp in subtidal rocky reefs in the Gulf of Maine, USA. It was first observed in 1987 and then increased

The Spiral Fan Worm Sabella spallan-zanii was spread all over the world by the old commercial sailing ships (Crete, Mediterranean Sea).

dramatically. However, in contrast to European kelp, the American species are not adapted to being covered by this moss animal: they grow brittle and break off.

Some species, formerly living in comparatively small areas, have already reached an almost world-wide distribution. The red alga Asparagopsis armata, originally from

The red alga Asparagopsis armata, originally from New Zealand, has reached an almost world-wide distribution (Crete).

The East Asian "Ship-worm" Teredo navalis has now also reached a worldwide distribution. The photo shows a piece of wood destroyed by the bore holes of this mussel. The white calcareous layers inside have been secreted by the mussels (Madeira).

The moss animal *Membranipora membranacea* from northern Europe is now growing on kelp in the Gulf of Maine, USA. The kelp is not adapted to this new settler and breaks (North Sea).

SUE DALY

The Slipper Limpet *Crepidula fornicata* was introduced to Europe together with American oysters and recorded from Britain already in 1870 (Scotland).

The Chinese Mitten Crab *Eriocheir sinensis* originally comes from China and was accidentally introduced to northern Germany in 1912 (Oosterschelde, Netherlands).

New Zealand is an example. The first record of this species from the Mediterranean Sea is from 1925. The Chinese Mitten Crab *Eriocheir sinensis* originally comes from China, as the name indicates. Accidentally introduced into the river Aller, a tributary of the river Weser, in northern Germany in 1912, it then spread along the coasts of Germany, Holland, Belgium, France, Finland, Sweden, Poland and Russia. Reproducing populations were recorded from southern Norway in 1977, from the mouth of the river Thames in 1995. A few years ago, this crab appeared in California and first records of it now begin to appear all over the USA.

The eastern Atlantic Royal Spiny Lobster *Panulirus regius* "escaped" from aquaculture into the north-western Mediterranean Sea (Costa Calida, Spain).

How did the South American coral *Oculina patagonica* come to the coast of southeastern Spain and Italy? How did *Asparagopsis, Carcinus, Membranipora, Mnemiopsis,* the Chinese Mitten Crab and many other species travel such large distances? The most likely answer is: in ballast water. To compensate for unloaded cargo and to stabilise the ship, cargo vessels flood tanks with seawater, modern freighters taking up to 1000 tons of water that contains larval stages of animals and plants. Some of those that survive the transport manage to establish new populations in distant areas. The ballast water of one ship contained 367 different species! The five most common groups were crustaceans, polychaetes, turbellarian flatworms, cnidarians, and molluscs. Because ships are becoming faster and faster, the danger of accidental introductions is even increasing: a larger proportion of larvae is surviving the trip.

The Shipworm *(Teredo navalis)* is not a worm but a mussel that bores into wood, producing long holes and weakening the wood structure. This East Asian species has now also reached a worldwide distribution. It was the bane of the merchant fleets and navies of ancient times. Many a ship and many a seemingly strong wooden pier, structurally weakened by burrowing Shipworms, broke apart in a strong sea.

Almost invariably, exotic species kept in aquaculture in floating cages in the sea escape from their holding tanks into the wild. One of countless examples is the Royal Spiny Lobster *Panulirus regius*. This eastern Atlantic species has repeatedly been recorded in the northwestern Mediterranean Sea.

The American Oyster *Crassostrea virginica* has been imported many times and put out on beds of the native European Oyster *Ostrea edulis* to supplement the larger summer demand. The American Oyster never became established in Europe but, nevertheless, a large number of animals associated with it were accidentally introduced and spread. The most famous of these is the Slipper Limpet *Crepidula fornicata,* recorded from the coast of Great Britain already in 1870. The Slipper Limpet then extended its range along the coasts of Sweden, Denmark, Germany, the Netherlands, Belgium and France. By the mid 1970s it had its southern limit in the Arcachon area. In 1989 it was also found in the Mediterranean lagoon of Salses-Leucate (France).

The European Shore Crab *Carcinus maenas* can nowadays be found in America, Africa, and Australia (North Sea).

Great Salp

Size: colony up to 40 m long.
Distribution: Mediterranean
Sea and (sub)tropical Atlantic
Ocean.
General: salps are planktonic
tunicates, usually in colonies of
many individuals, forming
chains or rings, or other structures. They are creatures of
the open ocean. Once carried
by currents near the shore,
they are usually doomed to
death. Salps have such delicate
bodies that they are soon bat-
tered to pieces on a rocky
shore. Like almost all animals
of the plankton, they usually
are more or less transparent.
Like their sessile relatives, the
ascidians, they are filter-feed-
ers.
     A larva starts the colony by
growing and by budding genetically identical individuals.
When the colony becomes
sexually mature it produces
sperm or eggs and new little
larvae are created.
     The individual elements of
Salpa maxima are rather large,
up to 10 cm long. The long
chains of this species may have
given rise to some of the stories about sea serpents.

Salpa maxima   Madeira

S: individual elements in the
chain are up to 6 cm long.
D: Mediterranean Sea, in the
Atlantic from 56°N to 23°S.
G: only about 50 species of
salps are known. Most salps
are live-bearing: the large egg
is fertilized inside the body of
the female and develops there.
A well-advanced embryo is
released into the water. Salps
hold the world-record in
growth rate among the multi-
celled animals: under ideal
conditions, the body can grow
in length 10% per hour and
the weight can double every
day. *Cyclosalpa* species have 10
light organs inside the body,
which harbour the luminescent
bacteria.

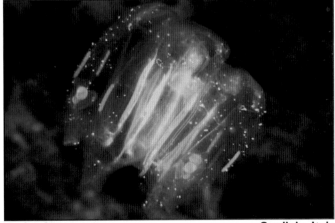

Cyclosalpa pinnata   Sardinia, Italy

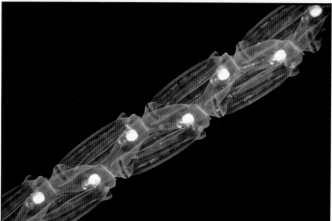

Jasis zonaria   **Faial Island, Azores**

Banded Salp

Size: individual elements in the chain are up to 5 cm long.
Distribution: Mediterranean Sea; in the Atlantic Ocean from Greenland to about 40 degrees south.
General: each individual in the colony essentially corresponds to a transparent tube, which is open at both ends. With pumping movements of the body and the action of minute cilia on the gills, a water current is drawn through the body and small organisms (phytoplankton, mainly) are filtered from it.

Fire Roller

S: 3 m. D: Med.; Atl. G: body stout, almost cartilaginous. Because of many protuberances, older individuals feel a bit spiky when touched. Nevertheless, when currents carry a fire roller near the shore, fish nibble it to death. It is composed of many 1000s of tiny individuals (upper small photo) forming a tube closed at one end. Each one filters water for plankton. The incurrent openings are on the outside, the excurrent openings discharge into the interior of the tube. As the water pressed into the tube by the colony members is ejected through the end of the tube, a jet is created that slowly propels the colony through the sea. "Pyrosoma" (literally "fire-body") refers to the strong yellow-green bioluminescence (bacteria), visible only at night.

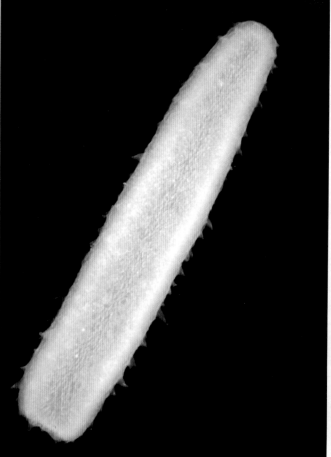

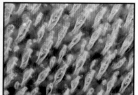

Pyrosoma atlanticum   **Madeira**

MEDITERRANEAN DEEP SEA

In contrast to the inhabitants of the near-surface layers of the oceans we have very limited knowledge of deep sea dwellers, including aspects of their species diversity, geographic and vertical distribution, ecology and special modifications. In the spring of 1999 the German research vessel *Meteor* carried out a 36-day deep-sea research cruise in the Mediterranean from Haifa, Israel to Malaga, Spain. As a biologist from the University of Greifswald specialised in cephalopods of the pelagic realm, Volker Miske was on board to examine the fascinating deep water cephalopods that they encountered.

R/V *Meteor* operating in the Mediterranean Sea.

Deep sea in the Mediterranean? Yes! The Mediterranean Sea is much deeper than most people believe: the greatest depth measured is 5092 m. Vast areas lie below 2000 m. According to some definitions, the "deep sea" begins at about 1000 m water depth, but many biologists see the upper limit at 200 to 400 m, because at this depth you can find the first distinct changes in appearance, physiology and behaviour of the animals inhabiting the pelagic zone. Due to the special geological and hydrological history of this sea there are no "true" bathypelagic species as found in the open ocean. They died out. The ancestors of today's members of the Mediterranean deep water fauna immigrated from the upper layer of the deep sea, the mesopelagic zone (about 200 to 1000 m depth), into the bathypelagic realm relatively recently in geological terms. The objective of the *Meteor* and its international staff of scientists was to catch such strange animals and to determine the environmental conditions in which they live.

Beside our working group (marine zoology; 6 scientists, 2 technical assistants and 2 students), the expedition also included microbiologists dealing with bacteria, biogeochemists determining fluxes of substances in the deep water using sediment trap systems, oceanographers examining the structure of the water column and meteorologists. They hailed from Germany, Italy, Greece and Israel. The work on board the vessel was very exciting, because nearly every tow we did

The 10-m²-MOCNESS back on the surface. All nets are closed.

In general we sampled the deep sea with net systems called MOC-NESS ("multiple opening and closing net and environmental sampling system") during daytime and at night. The larger one has 6 nets with openings of

Some of the cephalopods came up alive despite the long trawling time. Most of the specimens caught belong to the Bobtail Squid *Heteroteuthis dispar* (family Sepiolidae). These reddish, big-eyed animals possess very large light organs (photophores) on their underside.

10 m², the smaller one is equipped with 20 nets with openings of 1 m² each. To probe the fauna near and directly on the sea floor we used a big, so-called bottom sleigh with a closing net system on it.

The most exciting haul from a very great depth with a 10-m²-MOCNESS was made in the Ierapetra Deep, a deep sea depression southeast of Crete. The system caught animals in 4250 m only 10 m off the sea floor without touching the bottom. The trawl cable had a length of 8250 m, meaning the nets were more than 7 km behind the ship. This is about 72 times the length of the *Meteor* (97.5 m)! The MOC-NESS has instruments to measure its depth (via pressure), its distance from the seafloor (with echo sounding) and the inclination angle of its frame, which send their data through the conducting trawl cable to the computer in our control lab. Using these and other data (trawling speed, winch speed) the net operator is able to hold it at a certain depth with surprising accuracy by giving commands to the winch operator to speed up, slow down, stop winching or unreel the cable. One MOCNESS deep sea haul costs about 10,000 Euro; the whole high technology system used on this cruise is worth about 68,000 Euro. So it was critical that near-bottom trawls be operated with the highest concentration. It takes about two hours to lower the MOCNESS to a depth of 2500 m. After this the net system is towed at a trawling speed of about 2 knots. During trawling the nets are opened and closed one net after another in different depth horizons for a defined period of time. So one entire haul takes around 6 hours.

Five *Heteroteuthis dispar* were captured in one 10-m²-MOCNESS

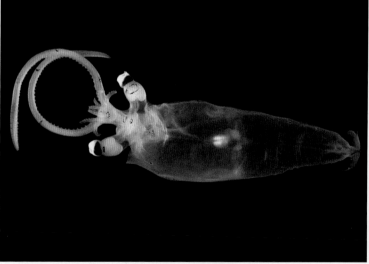

An almost transparent Glass Squid (family Cranchiidae). Members of this family possess a large chamber containing a solution of ammonium chloride, which serves as a buoyancy device. Within the Cranchiidae there are about 60 species, many of which remain undescribed. Members of this family live in the water column from the surface to unknown depths of over 2000 m.

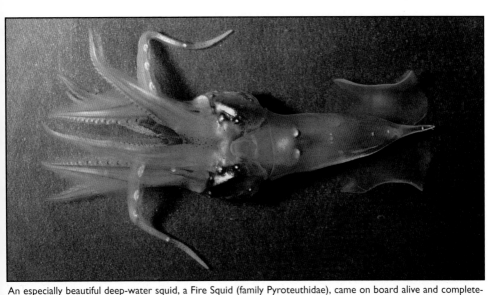

An especially beautiful deep-water squid, a Fire Squid (family Pyroteuthidae), came on board alive and completely undamaged. I transferred it immediately to an on-board aquarium. On the underside of the body you can find light organs with filters in different colours. I don't think that I've seen such a beautiful animal live before! It was caught in the depth between 0 and 750 m. While the adults of the Pyroteuthidae live in mesopelagic depths, the juveniles occupy the upper 200 m; probably all members of this family undergo extensive vertical migrations.

tow southeast of Crete (total depth about 3200 m) at depths between 150 m and 250 m shortly after midnight. Other specimens were caught with the 1-m²-double-MOCNESS: one individual southeast of Crete (total depth about 2500 m) in 450-500 m in the morning, one east of Crete (total depth about 1600 m) in 300-350 m in the afternoon, and one southeast of Crete (total depth about 2500 m) in 200-250 m in the evening. The remaining *Heteroteuthis* specimen was captured southwest of Cyprus (total depth about 2500 m). It came from an integrated haul (0-1850 m) providing no precise information on capture depth.

This small bobtail squid belongs in a subfamily (Heteroteuthinae) which lives free-swimming worldwide in tropical to temperate waters. They contrast with the other subfamilies (Rossiinae and Sepiolinae) which live on the seafloor (are benthic). *Heteroteuthis dispar* is a small (20 to 40 mm body length), semi-deepwater sepiolid which has the lower part of the short, rounded mantle extended to form a "shield" with special optical properties. It covers a large bacterial light organ which is found in the mantle cavity. *Heteroteuthis* is able to produce brilliant luminescence from this large light organ. The luminous liquid of the organ can be ejected together with the ink. These sepiolids normally swim at an angle of around 30-45 degrees with the mantle raised higher than the head.

Heteroteuthis dispar is one of the most common pelagic cephalopod species in the Mediterranean. It seems to migrate towards the surface at night. *Heteroteuthis* is preyed upon by a range of predators, including other cephalopods, sharks, swordfishes and dolphins.

View of the underside of *Abraliopsis* (family Enoploteuthidae) caught from depths between 0 and 450 m showing hundreds of small light organs. Members of this genus possess two to four large light organs on tips of the lower arms, which can be "switched off" by covering them with flaps of black tissue.

INDEX OF SCIENTIFIC SPECIES AND GENERA NAMES

BIBLIOGRAPHY

Bergbauer, M. & B. Humberg (1999) Was lebt im Mittelmeer? Stuttgart.
Bianchi, C.N., G. Dore & C. Morri (1995) Guida del subaqueo naturalista mediterraneo e tropici. Sassari.
Cattaneo-Vietti, R., R. Chemello & R. Gianuzzi-Savelli (1990) Atlas of Mediterranean Nudibranchs. Rome.
Costello, M., C. Emblow & R. White (2001) European Register of Marine Species. Paris.
Daly, S. (1998) Marine Life of the Channel Islands. Waterlooville.
Debelius, H. (1998) Nudibranchs and sea snails - Indo-Pacific field guide. Frankfurt.
Debelius, H. (1999) Crustacea guide of the world. Frankfurt.
Erwin, D. & B. Picton (1987) Guide to inshore marine life. London.
Fischer, W., M. Schreiber & M.L. Bauchot (1987) Fiches FAO d' identification des espèces pour les besoins de la pêche. Méditerranée et mer noire. Vol. I. Rome.
Gibson, R., B. Hextall & A. Rogers (2001) Photographic guide to the sea & shore life of Britain & north-west Europe. Oxford.
Göthel, H. (1992) Farbatlas Mittelmeerfauna. Stuttgart.
González Pérez, J.A. (1995) Catálogo de los crustáceos decápodos de las islas Canarias. Santa Cruz de Tenerife.
Guerreiro, A. & F. Reiner (2000) Moluscos marinhos de ilha de S. Vicente. Oeiras.
Hayward, P.J. & J.S. Ryland (1995) Handbook of the marine fauna of north-west Europe. Oxford.
Humann, P. (1992) Reef creature identification. Jacksonville.
Humann, P. (1999) Niedere Tiere Karibik. Hamburg.
Irving, R. (1998) Sussex marine life. Burgess Hill.
Kästner, A. (1969 ff) Lehrbuch der Speziellen Zoologie. Stuttgart.
Luther, W. & K. Fiedler (1961) Die Unterwasserfauna der Mittelmeerküsten. Hamburg.
Maître-Allain, T. & P. Louisy (2000) Animaux du bord de mer. Saint-Amand-Montrond.
Manning, R.B. & L.B. Holthuis (1981) West African Brachyuran Crabs. Smithsonian Contributions to Zoology 306. 379 pp.
Mebs, D. (2000) Gifttiere. Stuttgart.
Moen, F.E. & E. Svensen (2000) Dyreliv i havet. Handbok i norsk marin fauna. Kristiansund.
Mojetta, A. & A. Ghisotti (1997) Tiere und Pflanzen des Mittelmeeres. Augsburg.
Moosleitner, H. & R. Patzner (1995) Unterwasserführer Mittelmeer Niedere Tiere. Stuttgart.
Norman, M. (2000) Cephalopods. A world guide. Conchbooks.
Ocaña Martín, A., L. Sánchez Tocino, S. López González, J.E. Viciana Martín (2000) Guía submarina de invertebrados no artrópodos. Granada.
Picton, B. (1993) A field guide to the shallow-water echinoderms of the British Isles. London
Picton, B. & C.C. Morrow (1994) A field guide to the nudibranchs of the British Isles. London.
Poppe, G.T. & Y. Goto (1991) European Seashells. Vol I. Wiesbaden.
Riedl, R. (1983) Fauna und Flora des Mittelmeeres. Hamburg.
Rodrígues, R.G. & J.M.P. Sánches (1997) Moluscos Bivalvos de Canarias. Ediciones del Cabildo Insular de Gran Canaria, 425 pp.
Roper, C.F.E., M.J. Sweeney & C.E. Nauen (1984) Cephalopods of the World. FAO Species Catalogue Vol. 3.
Schick, K.L. (1998) Atlas submarino de la costa del sul. Malaga.
van Soest, R.W.M., B. Picton & C. Morrow (2000) Sponges of the North East Atlantic. CD-ROM. Heidelberg.
Tebble, N. (1975) British Bivalve Seashells. Edinburgh.
Weinberg, S. (1992) Découvrir la Méditeranée. Paris.
Weinberg, S. (1994) Découvrir l'Atlantique, la Manche et la mer du Nord. Paris.
Westheide, W. & R. Rieger (1996) Spezielle Zoologie. Teil I: Einzeller und Wirbellose Tiere. Stuttgart.
Wirtz, P. (1995) Madeira Kanaren Azoren Niedere Tiere. Stuttgart.
Wirtz, P. (2001) Madeira Marine Life. Funchal.

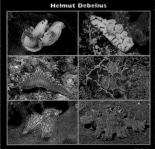